INSTRUCTOR'S SOLUTIONS MANUAL

BASIC COLLEGE MATHEMATICS

ESSENTIAL MATHEMATICS

INSTRUCTOR'S
SOLUTIONS MANUAL

BASIC COLLEGE MATHEMATICS
SIXTH EDITION

ESSENTIAL MATHEMATICS

Margaret L. Lial
American River College

Stanley A. Salzman
American River College

Diana L. Hestwood
Minneapolis Community and Technical College

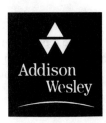

Addison
Wesley

Boston San Francisco New York
London Toronto Sydney Tokyo Singapore Madrid
Mexico City Munich Paris Cape Town Hong Kong Montreal

Reproduced by Addison-Wesley from camera-ready copy supplied by Laurel Technical Services.

Copyright © 2002 Pearson Education, Inc.

ISBN   0-321-09060-8

1 2 3 4 5 6 7 8 9 10 VG 05 04 03 02 01

CONTENTS

CHAPTER 8   GEOMETRY

CHAPTER 9   BASIC ALGEBRA

CHAPTER 10   STATISTICS

APPENDIX

Chapter 1

WHOLE NUMBERS

1.1 Reading and Writing Whole Numbers

2. 5139; thousands: 5; ones: 9

4. 75,229; ten thousands: 7; ones: 9

6. 1,700,225,016; billions: 1; millions: 0

8. 28,785,203; millions: 28; thousands: 785; ones: 203

10. 100,258,100,006; billions: 100; millions: 258; hundreds: 100; ones: 6

12. No doubt there is a relationship here. One answer might be that people could count using their fingers and toes and, therefore, thought of them as numbers or digits.

14. 37,886 is thirty-seven thousand, eight hundred eighty-six.

16. 218,033 is two hundred eighteen thousand, thirty-three.

18. 999,993,000 is nine hundred ninety-nine million, nine hundred ninety-three thousand.

20. Ninety-five thousand, one hundred eleven is 95,111.

22. One hundred million, two hundred is 100,000,200.

24. Two hundred eighty million, four hundred eighty-nine thousand in digits is 280,489,000.

26. Four hundred seventy-three thousand is 473,000.

28. Twenty billion, five hundred twenty-eight million, four hundred ninety-one thousand dollars in digits is $20,528,491,000.

30. 70,306,735,002,102 is seventy trillion, three hundred six billion, seven hundred thirty-five million, two thousand, one hundred two.

32. From the table, "drive alone" is the method of transportation most used. 84,215,298 written out is eighty-four million, two hundred fifteen thousand, two hundred ninety-eight.

34. From the table, the number of people who carpool is 15,377,634. Written out, 15,377,634 is fifteen million; three hundred seventy-seven thousand, six hundred thirty-four.

1.2 Adding Whole Numbers

2.
$$\begin{array}{r} 14 \\ +\ 13 \\ \hline 27 \end{array}$$

4.
$$\begin{array}{r} 83 \\ +\ 15 \\ \hline 98 \end{array}$$

6.
$$\begin{array}{r} 738 \\ +\ 261 \\ \hline 999 \end{array}$$

8.
$$\begin{array}{r} 135 \\ 253 \\ +\ 410 \\ \hline 798 \end{array}$$

10.
$$\begin{array}{r} 121 \\ 5705 \\ +\ 3163 \\ \hline 8989 \end{array}$$

12. Line up:
$$\begin{array}{r} 517 \\ 131 \\ +\ 250 \\ \hline 898 \end{array}$$

14. Line up:
$$\begin{array}{r} 3241 \\ 1513 \\ +\ 2014 \\ \hline 6768 \end{array}$$

16. Line up:
$$\begin{array}{r} 41,124 \\ 12,302 \\ +\ 23,500 \\ \hline 76,926 \end{array}$$

18. Line up:
```
    6344
 +  1655
    7999
```

20. Line up:
```
   63,251
 + 36,305
   99,556
```

22.
```
   1
   91
 + 29
  120
```

24.
```
   1
   37
 + 85
  122
```

26.
```
   1
   79
 + 79
  158
```

28.
```
   1
   96
 + 47
  143
```

30.
```
   1
   68
 + 37
  105
```

32.
```
    1
   621
 + 359
   980
```

34.
```
   11
   798
 + 206
  1004
```

36.
```
    1
   172
 + 156
   328
```

38.
```
   11
   686
 + 726
  1412
```

40.
```
   11
   116
 + 897
  1013
```

42.
```
   111
   1768
 + 8275
  10,043
```

44.
```
     1
   9382
 + 7 586
  16,968
```

46.
```
   1  1
   5718
   5 623
 + 7 436
  18,777
```

48.
```
   1  1
   4022
    709
   8621
 +   37
  13,389
```

50.
```
   211
   1708
    321
     61
 + 8 926
  11,016
```

52.
```
    12
   6506
    173
   7044
 +  168
  13,891
```

54.
```
   212
   7631
   5983
      7
     36
 +  505
  14,162
```

56.
```
  1 1 3
    322
   6508
     93
    745
     18
 + 2005
   9691
```

58.
```
  2 2 3
   3187
    810
    527
     76
   2665
 +  317
   7582
```

60.
```
  3 3 2
    576
   7934
     60
    781
   5968
 +  317
 15,690
```

62.
```
   1857
    852
    679
 +  326
   1857  correct
```

64.
```
   1120
     17
    296
    713
 +   94
   1220
```
incorrect; should be 1120

66.
```
 11,583
   3628
     72
    564
 + 7319
 11,583  correct
```

68.
```
 11,212
    516
   8760
     24
    189
 + 1723
 11,212  correct
```

70.
```
 16,709
   6715
    283
   9617
     13
 +   81
 16,719
```
incorrect; should be 16,709

72. Grouping the addition of numbers in any order does not change the sum. You can add numbers in any order. For example, you can add pair of numbers that add to 10.

74. The shortest distance from Elk Hill to Oakton is through Thomasville.
```
  18   Elk Hill to Thomasville
 + 17   Thomasville to Oakton
  35   miles
```

76. The shortest distance from Murphy to Thomasville is through Austin and Rena.
```
  11   Murphy to Austin
  15   Austin to Rena
 + 12   Rena to Thomasville
  38   miles
```

78.
```
   35
 + 73
  108
```
Jean ordered 108 gallons.

80.
```
  1 1
   283
 + 218
   501
```
There are 501 employees in the two departments.

82.
```
  1 1
  5924
 + 7284
 13,208
```
The new altitude is 13,208 feet.

84. To find the perimeter add the 4 sides in any order.

```
    48
    32
    48
 +  32
   160  feet
```

86. To find the perimeter add the 4 sides in any order.

```
    65
    73
    98
 +  73
   309  meters
```

1.3 Subtracting Whole Numbers

2.
```
    19      Check:   12
 - 12             +  7
    7                19
```

4.
```
    78      Check:   35
 - 35             + 43
   43                78
```

6.
```
    95      Check:   71
 - 71             + 24
   24                95
```

8.
```
   602      Check:   301
 - 301            + 301
   301               602
```

10.
```
   888      Check:   215
 - 215            + 673
   673               888
```

12.
```
  4420      Check:  4110
 - 310            + 310
  4110              4420
```

14.
```
  1875      Check:  1362
 - 1362           + 513
   513              1875
```

16.
```
  9654      Check:  4323
 - 4323           + 5331
  5331              9654
```

18.
```
  57,921    Check:   23,120
 - 34,801          + 34,801
  23,120             57,921
```

20.
```
  75,904    Check:  72,202
 - 3 702           + 3 702
  72,202            75,904
```

22.
```
   76      Check:   43
 - 43            + 33
   33              76  correct
```

24.
```
   47      Check:   13
 - 35            + 35
   13              48  incorrect

   47
 - 35
   12  is the correct answer.
```

26.
```
   754     Check:   342
 - 342           + 412
   412             754  correct
```

28.
```
  5217     Check:   1132
 - 4105          + 4105
  1132             5237  incorrect

  5217
 - 4105
  1112  is the correct answer.
```

30.
```
  9428     Check:   6324
 - 3124          + 3124
  6324             9448  incorrect

  9428
 - 3124
  6304  is the correct answer.
```

32.
```
    7 16
    8 6
  - 2 8
    5 8
```

34.
```
    8 18
    9 8
  - 6 9
    2 9
```

36.
```
    7 13
    8 3
  - 5 5
    2 8
```

38.
$$\begin{array}{r} {}^{8\,10\,16} \\ \cancel{9}\,\cancel{1}\,\cancel{6} \\ -\ 6\ 1\ 8 \\ \hline 2\ 9\ 8 \end{array}$$

40.
$$\begin{array}{r} {}^{8\,16\,13} \\ \cancel{9}\,\cancel{7}\,\cancel{3} \\ -\ 7\ 8\ 8 \\ \hline 1\ 8\ 5 \end{array}$$

42.
$$\begin{array}{r} {}^{5\,10\,16\,11} \\ \cancel{6}\,\cancel{1}\,\cancel{7}\,\cancel{1} \\ -\ 1\ 1\ 8\ 2 \\ \hline 4\ 9\ 8\ 9 \end{array}$$

44.
$$\begin{array}{r} {}^{2\,15\,6\,16} \\ \cancel{3}\,\cancel{5}\,\cancel{7}\,\cancel{6} \\ -\ 1\ 6\ 5\ 8 \\ \hline 1\ 9\ 1\ 8 \end{array}$$

46.
$$\begin{array}{r} {}^{5\,10\,12\,6\,18} \\ \cancel{6}\,1,\cancel{2}\,\cancel{7}\,\cancel{8} \\ -\ \ \ 3\ 5\ 5\ 9 \\ \hline 5\ 7,7\ 1\ 9 \end{array}$$

48.
$$\begin{array}{r} {}^{7\,10} \\ \cancel{8}\,\cancel{0} \\ -\ 7\ 3 \\ \hline 7 \end{array}$$

50.
$$\begin{array}{r} {}^{6\,10} \\ \cancel{7}\,\cancel{0} \\ -\ 2\ 7 \\ \hline 4\ 3 \end{array}$$

52.
$$\begin{array}{r} {}^{5\,10\,10} \\ \cancel{6}\,\cancel{0}\,\cancel{0} \\ -\ 5\ 9\ 9 \\ \hline 1 \end{array}$$

54.
$$\begin{array}{r} {}^{5\,10\,12} \\ 4\,\cancel{0}\,\cancel{0}\,\cancel{2} \\ -\ 2\ 0\ 6\ 3 \\ \hline 2\ 5\ 3\ 9 \end{array}$$

56.
$$\begin{array}{r} {}^{0\,11\,10} \\ 7\,\cancel{1}\,\cancel{2}\,\cancel{0} \\ -\ \ 6\ 0\ 3\ 3 \\ \hline 1\ 0\ 8\ 7 \end{array}$$

58.
$$\begin{array}{r} {}^{2\,10} \\ \cancel{3}\,\cancel{0}\,6\,8 \\ -\ 2\ 1\ 0\ 5 \\ \hline 9\ 6\ 3 \end{array}$$

60.
$$\begin{array}{r} {}^{7\,11\,10\,13} \\ \cancel{8}\,\cancel{2}\,\cancel{0}\,\cancel{3} \\ -\ 5\ 3\ 6\ 5 \\ \hline 2\ 8\ 3\ 8 \end{array}$$

62.
$$\begin{array}{r} {}^{4\,10} \\ 7\,0\,\cancel{5}\,\cancel{0} \\ -\ 6\ 0\ 4\ 5 \\ \hline 1\ 0\ 0\ 5 \end{array}$$

64.
$$\begin{array}{r} {}^{5\,10\,10\,14} \\ 1\cancel{6},\cancel{0}\,\cancel{0}\,\cancel{4} \\ -\ \ 5\ 0\ 8\ 7 \\ \hline 1\ 0,9\ 1\ 7 \end{array}$$

66.
$$\begin{array}{r} {}^{7\,10\,10\,10\,10} \\ \cancel{8}\,\cancel{1},\cancel{0}\,\cancel{0}\,\cancel{0} \\ -\ 5\ 5\ 4\ 5\ 6 \\ \hline 2\ 5,5\ 4\ 4 \end{array}$$

68.
$$\begin{array}{r} {}^{6\,10\,10\,10} \\ 7\,\cancel{7},\cancel{0}\,\cancel{0}\,\cancel{0} \\ -\ 6\ 5,3\ 0\ 8 \\ \hline 1\ 1,6\ 9\ 2 \end{array}$$

70.
$$\begin{array}{r} {}^{7\,10\,10\,10\,14\,16} \\ \cancel{8}\,\cancel{0},\cancel{0}\,\cancel{3}\,\cancel{6} \\ -\ 2\ 3,8\ 6\ 9 \\ \hline 5\ 6,1\ 8\ 7 \end{array}$$

72.
$$\begin{array}{cc} 1671 & 1325 \\ -\ 1325 & +\ 1346 \\ \hline 1346 & 2671 \ \text{incorrect} \end{array}$$

Rework.
$$\begin{array}{r} {}^{6\,11} \\ 16\cancel{7}\,\cancel{1} \\ -\ 1\ 3\ 2\ 5 \\ \hline 3\ 4\ 6 \ \text{ is the correct answer.} \end{array}$$

74.
$$\begin{array}{cc} 5274 & 4144 \\ -\ 1130 & +\ 1130 \\ \hline 4144 & 5274 \ \text{correct} \end{array}$$

76.
$$\begin{array}{cc} 82{,}357 & 68{,}961 \\ -\ 14{,}396 & +\ 14{,}396 \\ \hline 68{,}961 & 83{,}357 \ \text{incorrect} \end{array}$$
$$\begin{array}{r} {}^{7\,11\,12\,15} \\ 8\,2,\cancel{3}\,\cancel{5}\,7 \\ -\ 1\ 4,3\ 9\ 6 \\ \hline 6\ 7,9\ 6\ 1 \ \text{ is the correct answer.} \end{array}$$

78.
$$\begin{array}{r} 34,821 \\ -\ 17,735 \\ \hline 17,735 \end{array} \qquad \begin{array}{r} 17,735 \\ +\ 17,735 \\ \hline 35,470 \end{array} \text{ incorrect}$$

Rework.

$$\begin{array}{r} {}^{2\,14\,7\,11\,11} \\ \cancel{3\,4,8\,2\,1} \\ -\ 1\,7,7\,3\,5 \\ \hline 1\,7,0\,8\,6 \end{array} \text{ is the correct answer.}$$

80. No, you cannot. Numbers must be subtracted in the order given. The difference found in subtracting is the result of subtracting the subtrahend from the minuend. Changing the order of the minuend and subtrahend does change the answer.

82.
$$\begin{array}{r} {}^{6\,12} \\ \$7\,\cancel{2}\,9 \\ -\ 2\,4\,9 \\ \hline \$4\,8\,0 \end{array}$$

$480 remains in the account.

84.
$$\begin{array}{r} {}^{7\,10} \\ 5\,\cancel{8}\,\cancel{0} \\ -\ 2\,1\,7 \\ \hline 3\,6\,3 \end{array}$$

The plane travels 363 miles per hour faster than the falcon.

86.
$$\begin{array}{r} 7994 \\ -\ 5822 \\ \hline 2172 \end{array}$$

On Friday, 2172 more people went to the game.

88.
$$\begin{array}{r} \$24,870 \\ -\ 2\,500 \\ \hline \$22,370 \end{array} \quad \begin{array}{l} \text{price of 2000 Mustang} \\ \text{price of 1964 Mustang} \\ \text{increase in price} \end{array}$$

90.
$$\begin{array}{r} 23,156 \\ -\ 14,679 \\ \hline 8\,477 \end{array}$$

In the district 8477 students have not received eye exams.

92.
$$\begin{array}{r} \$1568 \\ -\ 1479 \\ \hline \$89 \end{array}$$

The monthly increase is $89.

94.
$$\begin{array}{r} \$2671 \\ -\ 2382 \\ \hline \$289 \end{array}$$

Alice earned $289 last month.

96.
$$\begin{array}{r} 24,000,000 \\ -\ 7\,000 \\ \hline 23,993,000 \end{array}$$

There are 23,993,000 small and midsize businesses.

98.
$$\begin{array}{r} 147 \\ -\ 126 \\ \hline 21 \end{array} \quad \begin{array}{l} \text{Deliveries made on Friday} \\ \text{Deliveries made on Tuesday} \\ \text{More deliveries made on Friday} \end{array}$$

Diana made 21 more deliveries on Friday than on Tuesday.

100.
$$\begin{array}{r} 119 \\ +\ 89 \\ \hline 208 \end{array} \quad \begin{array}{l} \text{Deliveries made on Wednesday} \\ \text{Deliveries made on Thursday} \\ \text{Total deliveries on the two slowest days} \end{array}$$

208 deliveries were made on the two slowest days.

1.4 Multiplying Whole Numbers

2. $3 \times 5 \times 3$
$(3 \times 5) \times 3 = 15 \times 3 = 45$

4. $2 \times 4 \times 5$
$(2 \times 4) \times 5 = 8 \times 5 = 40$
or
$2 \times (4 \times 5) = 2 \times 20 = 40$

6. $9 \cdot 0 \cdot 5$
$(9 \cdot 0) \cdot 5 = 0 \cdot 5 = 0$

8. $1 \cdot 5 \cdot 7$
$(1 \cdot 5) \cdot 7 = 5 \cdot 7 = 35$
or
$1 \cdot (5 \cdot 7) = 1 \cdot 35 = 35$

10. $(4)(1)(9)$
$(4)(1)(9) = 4 \cdot 9 = 36$

12. $(0)(9)(4)$
$(0)(9)(4) = (0)(4) = 0$
The product of any number and 0 is 0.

14. You may group the multiplication of numbers in any order. Just as in addition, the different grouping results in the same answer.

16.
$$\begin{array}{r} 62 \\ \times\ 8 \\ \hline 496 \end{array}$$
$8 \cdot 2 = 16$ Write 6, carry 1
$8 \cdot 6 = 48$ Add 1 to get 49
          Write 49

18.   76
$\times$ 5
———
380
$5 \cdot 6 = 30$ Write 0, carry 3
$5 \cdot 7 = 35$ Add 3 to get 38
          Write 38

20. $\overset{2}{4}$72
$\times$ 4
———
1888

22. $\overset{31}{8}$52
$\times$ 7
———
5964

24. $\overset{12}{1}$137
$\times$ 3
———
3411

26. $\overset{111}{2}$544
$\times$ 3
———
7632

28. $\overset{113}{7}$326
$\times$ 5
———
36,630
$6 \cdot 5 = 30$ Write 0, carry 3
$5 \cdot 2 = 10$ Add 3 to get 13
          Write 3, carry 1
$5 \cdot 3 = 15$ Add 1 to get 16
          Write 6, carry 1
$5 \cdot 7 = 35$ Add 1 to get 36
          Write 36

30. $\overset{3\ \ \ 2}{2}$8,116
$\times$ 4
———
112,464
$4 \cdot 6 = 24$ Write 4, carry 2
$4 \cdot 1 = 4$ Add 2 to get 6
          Write 6
$4 \cdot 1 = 4$ Write 4
$4 \cdot 8 = 32$ Write 2, carry 3
$4 \cdot 2 = 8$ Add 3 to get 11
          Write 11

32.   20 1 zero   2   20
$\times$ 7 $\times$ 7 $\times$ 7
                   —— ——
                   14 140 Attach 0

34.   70 1 zero   7   70
$\times$ 5 $\times$ 5 $\times$ 5
                   —— ——
                   35 350 Attach 0

36.   200 2 zeros   2   200
$\times$ 7 $\times$ 7 $\times$ 7
                   —— ———
                   14 1400 Attach 00

38. $\overset{4}{8}$6
$\times$ 7
———
602
$7 \cdot 6 = 42$ Write 2, carry 4
$7 \cdot 8 = 56$ Add 4 to get 60
          Write 60

40.   246   246   246
$\times$ 50 1 zero $\times$ 5 $\times$ 50
———   ——— ———
                     1230 12,300 Attach 0

42.   8522   8 522
$\times$ 50 $\times$ 5
—————— ———
          42,610
          8 522
$\times$ 50
——————
426,100   Attach 1 zero

44.   400   4   400
$\times$ 700 $\times$ 7 $\times$ 700
————   —— ———
                    28 280,000 Attach 4 zeros

46.   11,000   11   11,000
$\times$ 9 000 $\times$ 9 $\times$ 9 000
———————   —— ——————
                99 99,000,000 Attach 6 zeros

48. $730 \cdot 40$ 73
                   $\times$ 4
                   ———
                   292
$730 \cdot 40 = 29,200$ Attach 2 zeros

50. $850 \cdot 700$ 85
                   $\times$ 7
                   ———
                   595
$850 \cdot 700 = 595,000$
Attach 3 zeros

52. $10,050 \cdot 300$
$1005 \cdot 3 = 3015$
$10,050 \cdot 300 = 3,015,000$
Attach 3 zeros

54.   18
$\times$ 47
———
126
72
———
846

56.
```
      82
  ×   32
     164
     246
    2624
```

58. (62)(31)
```
      62
  ×   31
      62
     186
    1922
```

60. (82)(67)
```
      82
  ×   67
     574
     492
    5494
```

62. (26)(33)
```
      26
  ×   33
      78
      78
     858
```

64. (58)(312)
```
     312
  ×   58
   2 496
   15 60
  18,096
```

66. (681)(47)
```
     681
  ×   47
   4 767
   27 24
  32,007
```

68.
```
     286
  ×  574
   1 144
   20 02
   143 0
 164,164
```

70.
```
     621
  ×  415
   3 105
   6 21
   248 4
 257,715
```

72.
```
      3228
  ×    751
     3 228
    161 40
   2 259 6
 2,424,228
```

74.
```
      528
  ×   106
    3 168
    52 80
   55,968
```

76.
```
      218
  ×   106
    1 308
    21 80
   23,108
```

78.
```
      3706
  ×    208
    29 648
    741 20
   770,848
```

80.
```
       3533
  ×    5001
      3 533
   17 665 00
 17,668,533
```

82.
```
       1502
  ×    2009
     13 518
   3 004 00
  3,017,518
```

84.
```
      291        291
  ×   307    ×   307
    2 037      2 037
    0 00       87 30
    87 3      89,337
   89,337
```

86.
```
      500  2 zeros
  ×    30  1 zero
   15,000
```

15,000 tablets are in the medical supply house.

88.   65   times per second
 × 30   seconds
 1950   times

The hummingbird's wings beat 1950 times in 30 seconds.

90.   27   fishing boats
 × 40   tons of squid
 1080   tons

The total catch for the night was 1080 tons.

92. 38 employees at $64 per day:

$$
\begin{array}{r}
64 \\
\times\ 38 \\
\hline
512 \\
192 \\
\hline
2432
\end{array}
$$

The total cost is $2432.

94. 76 flats of flowers at $22:

$$
\begin{array}{r}
76 \\
\times\ 22 \\
\hline
152 \\
152 \\
\hline
1672
\end{array}
$$

The total cost is $1672.

96. 520 printers at $219 per printer:

$$
\begin{array}{r}
520 \\
\times\ 219 \\
\hline
4\ 680 \\
5\ 20 \\
104\ 0 \\
\hline
\$113{,}880
\end{array}
$$

The total cost is $113,880.

98. (600)(8)(75)(40)

$$
\begin{array}{rrr}
600 & 4800 & 360{,}000 \\
\times\ \ 8 & \times\ \ 75 & \times\ \ \ \ \ 40 \\
\hline
4800 & 24\ 000 & 14{,}400{,}000 \\
 & 336\ 00 & \\
\cline{2-2}
 & 360{,}000 &
\end{array}
$$

100.
$$
\begin{array}{r}
15{,}225 \\
\times\ \ 28 \\
\hline
121\ 800 \\
304\ 50 \\
\hline
426{,}300
\end{array}
$$

The blue whale weighs 426,300 pounds.

102. $1,100,000   received by Florida
 − 505,551   received by Vermont
 $594,449   more received by Florida

Florida will receive $594,449 more.

1.5 Dividing Whole Numbers

2. $20 \div 5 = 4:\ 5\overline{)20}{}^{\,4}\ ;\ \dfrac{20}{5} = 4$

4. $\dfrac{56}{8} = 7:\ 8\overline{)56}{}^{\,7}\ ;\ 56 \div 8 = 7$

6. $8\overline{)48}{}^{\,6}:\ 48 \div 8 = 6\ ;\ \dfrac{48}{8} = 6$

8. $42 \div 6 = 7$

10. $\dfrac{8}{0}:$ undefined

12. $6 \div 6 = 1$

14. $\dfrac{12}{1} = 12$

16. $\dfrac{0}{7} = 0$

18. $\dfrac{2}{0}$ undefined

20. $\dfrac{0}{0}$ undefined

22. $\dfrac{0}{5} = 0$

24. $4\overline{)84}{}^{\,21}$

Check: $4 \times 21 = 84$

26. $6\overline{)16^{4}8}{}^{\,28}$

Check: $6 \times 28 = 168$

28. $5\overline{)23^{3}05}{}^{\,461}$

Check: $5 \times 461 = 2305$

30. $8\overline{)13^53^55}$ 166 R7

Check: $8 \times 166 + 7 = 1328 + 7 = 1335$

32. $9\overline{)83^271}$ 930 R1

Check: $9 \times 930 + 1 = 8370 + 1 = 8371$

34. $8\overline{)85^56}$ 107

Check: $8 \times 107 = 856$

36. $4\overline{)801^12}$ 2003

Check: $4 \times 2003 = 8012$

38. $8\overline{)32,009}$ 4 001 R1

Check: $8 \times 4001 + 1 = 32,008 + 1 = 32,009$

40. $7\overline{)59^39^43}$ 856 R1

Check: $7 \times 856 + 1 = 5992 + 1 = 5993$

42. $9\overline{)33,^62^88^75}$ 3 698 R3

Check: $9 \times 3698 + 3 = 33,282 + 3 = 33,285$

44. $6\overline{)17,^59^53^57}$ 2 989 R3

Check: $6 \times 2989 + 3 = 17,934 + 3 = 17,937$

46. $7\overline{)46,^45^36^10}$ 6 651 R3

Check: $7 \times 6651 + 3 = 46,557 + 3 = 46,560$

48. $9\overline{)8199}$ 911

Check: $9 \times 911 = 8199$

50. $5\overline{)7^22,^2 54^43}$ 1 4, 50 8 R3

Check: $5 \times 14,508 + 3 = 72,540 + 3 = 72,543$

52. $3\overline{)7^17,^2 6^22^11}$ 2 5, 8 7 3 R2

Check: $3 \times 25,873 + 2 = 77,619 + 2 = 77,621$

54. $4\overline{)17^12,2^25^15}$ 4 3,0 6 3 R3

Check: $4 \times 43,063 + 3 = 172,252 + 3 = 172,255$

56. $3\overline{)1282}$ 427 R1

Check: $3 \times 427 + 1 = 1281 + 1 = 1282$ correct

58. $5\overline{)2158}$ 432 R3

Check: $5 \times 432 + 3 = 2160 + 3 = 2163$ incorrect
Rework.

$5\overline{)21^158}$ 431 R3

Check: $5 \times 431 + 3 = 2155 + 3 = 2158$ correct

60. $9\overline{)5974}$ 663 R5

Check: $9 \times 663 + 5 = 5967 + 5 = 5972$ incorrect
Rework.

$9\overline{)59^57^34}$ 6 6 3 R7

Check: $9 \times 663 + 7 = 5967 + 7 = 5974$ correct

62. $6\overline{)3192}$ 532

Check: $6 \times 532 = 3192$ correct

64. $8\overline{)33,664}$ 4 208

Check: $8 \times 4208 = 33,664$ correct

66. $3\overline{)82,598}$ 27,532 R1

Check:
$3 \times 27,532 + 1 = 82,596 + 1 = 82,597$ incorrect
Rework.

$3\overline{)8^22,^1 598}$ 2 7, 532 R2

Check:
$3 \times 27,532 + 2 = 82,596 + 2 = 82,598$ correct

68. $7\overline{)50{,}809}$ 7 258 R4

Check:

$7 \times 7258 + 4 = 50{,}806 + 4 = 50{,}810$ incorrect

Rework.

$7\overline{)50{,}^18^40^59}$ 7 2 5 8 R3

Check:

$7 \times 7258 + 3 = 50{,}806 + 3 = 50{,}809$ correct

70. $4\overline{)311{,}216}$ 77,804

Check:

$4 \times 77{,}804 = 311{,}216$ correct

72. Three choices might be:

1. A number is divisible by 2 if it ends in a 0, 2, 4, 6, or 8.
2. A number is divisible by 5 if it ends in 0 or 5.
3. A number is divisible by 10 if it ends in 0.

74. $12\overline{)16^42^60}$ 1 3 5

Check: $12 \times 135 = 1620$

Each school will receive 135 books.

76. $9\overline{)34^78^63}$ 3 8 7

They need 387 gallons.

78. $5\overline{)8^37^250}$ 1 7 50

1750 bags of rice can be filled.

80. Each home needs 21 squares. Divide to find the number of homes that can be roofed.

$21\overline{)22^16^168}$ 1 0 8

108 homes can be roofed.

82. $117{,}000{,}000 \div 9 = 13{,}000{,}000$

Check: $9 \times \$13{,}000{,}000 = \$117{,}000{,}000$
His pay for one year is \$13,000,000.

84. $8\overline{)168}$ 21

21 light diffusers can be assembled in 1 hour.

  21   light diffusers can be assembled in 1 hour.
$\times\ 3$ hours
  63   light diffusers in 3 hours.

86. 35 does not end in a 0, 2, 4, 6, or 8, so it is not divisible by 2. $3 + 5 = 8$ which is not divisible by 3, so 35 is not divisible by 3. 35 ends in 5, so it is divisible by 5. 35 does not end in a 0, so it is not divisible by 10.

88. 96 ends in 6 so it is divisible by 2.

$9 + 6 = 15$, 15 is divisible by 3, so 96 is dibisible by 3.

96 does not end in 5 or 0, so it is not divisible by 5 or 10.

90. 897 does not end in 0, 2, 4, 6, or 8, so it is not divisible by 2.

$8 + 9 + 7 = 24$, 24 is divisible by 3, so 897 is divisible by 3.

897 does not end in 0 or 5, so it is not divisible by 5 or 10.

92. 500 ends in 0, so it is divisible by 2, 5, and 10.

$5 + 0 + 0 = 5$ which is not divisible by 3, so 500 is not divisible by 3.

94. 8302 ends in 2, so it is divisible by 2.

$8 + 3 + 0 + 2 = 13$, 13 is not divisible by 3, so 8302 is not divisible by 3.

8302 does not end in 0 or 5, so it is not divisible by 5 or 10.

96. 32,472 ends in 2, so it is divisible by 2.

$3 + 2 + 4 + 7 + 2 = 18$, 18 is divisible by 3, so 32,472 is divisible by 3.

32,472 does not end in 0 or 5, so it is not divisible by 5 or 10.

1.6 Long Division

2. $14\overline{)476}$
3; 34; 304
$14\overline{)476}$ 3

3 goes over the 7, because $\frac{47}{14}$ is about 3. The answer must then be a two-digit number or 34.

4. $42 \overline{)7560}$

18; 180; 1800

$\dfrac{1}{42 \overline{)7560}}$

1 goes over the 5, because $\frac{75}{42}$ is about 1. The answer must then be a three-digit number or 180.

6. $46 \overline{)24,026}$

5; 52; 522 R14

$\dfrac{5}{46 \overline{)24,026}}$

5 goes over the 0, because $\frac{240}{42}$ is about 5. The answer must then be a three-digit number or 522 R14.

8. $12 \overline{)116,953}$

974 R2; 9746 R1; 97,460

$\dfrac{9}{12 \overline{)116,953}}$

9 goes over the 6, because $\frac{116}{12}$ is about 9. The answer must then be a four-digit number or 9746 R1.

10. $64 \overline{)208,138}$

325 R2; 3252 R10; 32,521

$\dfrac{3}{64 \overline{)208,138}}$

3 goes over the 8, because $\frac{208}{64}$ is about 3. The answer must then be a four-digit number or 3252 R10.

12. $230 \overline{)253,230}$

11; 110; 1101

$\dfrac{1}{230 \overline{)253,230}}$

1 goes over the 3, because $\frac{253}{230}$ is about 1. The answer must be a four-digit number or 1101.

14.
```
        63
29)1827      Check:    63
   174              ×  29
    87                567
    87                126
     0               1827
```

16.
```
      478 R18
83)39,692      Check:    478
   33 2               ×  83
    6 49              1 434
    5 81              38 24
    682               39,674
    664               +   18
     18               39,692
```

18.
```
     3 008 R25
28)84,249           3008
   84             ×   28
   249            24,064
   224            60 16
    25            84,224
                  +   25
                  84,249
```

20.
```
       785
238)186,948 R118  Check:    785
    166 6                ×  238
     20 34               6 280
     19 04               23 55
      1 308              157 0
      1 190              186,830
        118              +   118
                         186,948
```

22.
```
       87
308)26,796   Check:    308
    24 64            ×  87
     2 156           2 156
     2 156           24 64
         0           26,796
```

24.
```
       170
900)153,000  Check:    170
    90 0            ×  900
    63 00           153,000
    63 00
       00
       00
        0
```

26. $64\overline{)2712}$ 42 R26

Check: $\begin{array}{r} 64 \\ \times\ 42 \\ \hline 128 \\ 256 \\ \hline 2688 \\ +\ 26 \\ \hline 2714 \end{array}$ incorrect

Rework: $64\overline{)2712}$ 42 R24

$\begin{array}{r} 256 \\ \hline 152 \\ 128 \\ \hline 24 \end{array}$

Check: $\begin{array}{r} 64 \\ \times\ 42 \\ \hline 128 \\ 256 \\ \hline 2688 \\ +\ 24 \\ \hline 2712 \end{array}$

The correct answer is 42 R24.

28. $145\overline{)34,776}$ 239 R121

Check: $\begin{array}{r} 239 \\ \times\ 145 \\ \hline 1\ 195 \\ 9\ 56 \\ 23\ 9 \\ \hline 34,655 \\ +\ 121 \\ \hline 34,776 \end{array}$ correct

30. $557\overline{)97,286}$ 174 R368

Check:

$\begin{array}{r} 174 \\ \times\ 557 \\ \hline 1\ 218 \\ 8\ 70 \\ 87\ 0 \\ \hline 96,918 \\ +\ 368 \\ \hline 97,286 \end{array}$ correct

32. Multiply the quotient and the divisor and add any remainder. One example is $18 \div 5 = 3$ R3.
Check: $(3 \times 5) + 3 = 15 + 3 = 18$

34. Divide to find the weight of the ink used each day.

$200\overline{)255,000}$ 1 275

$\begin{array}{r} 200 \\ \hline 55\ 0 \\ 40\ 0 \\ \hline 15\ 00 \\ 14\ 00 \\ \hline 1\ 000 \\ 1\ 000 \\ \hline 0 \end{array}$

Each day 1275 pounds of the ink are used.

36. $\begin{array}{r} \$3718 \\ -\ 1880 \\ \hline \$1838 \end{array}$ education costs
amount one parent paid

The other parent paid $1838.

38. $225\overline{)13,050}$ 58

$\begin{array}{r} 11\ 25 \\ \hline 1\ 800 \\ 1\ 800 \\ \hline 0 \end{array}$

The consultant charged $58 per hour.

40. $\begin{array}{r} 240 \\ \times\ 8 \\ \hline 1920 \\ \times\ 2 \\ \hline 3480 \end{array}$ sacks
hours
sacks in one line
sacks in two lines

The total number of sacks packaged by the two lines is 3840.

42. $120\overline{)4080}$ 34   Check: $\begin{array}{r} 120 \\ \times\ 34 \\ \hline 480 \\ 360 \\ \hline 4080 \end{array}$

$\begin{array}{r} 360 \\ \hline 480 \\ 480 \\ \hline 0 \end{array}$

Each restaurant employs 34 people.

1.7   Rounding Whole Numbers

2. 307 rounded to the nearest ten: 310

3_0_7 Next digit is 5 or more.

Tens place changes $(0 + 1 = 1)$. The digit to the right of the underlined place changes to zero.

4. 826 rounded to the nearest ten: 830

8<u>2</u>6   Next digit is 5 or more.

Tens place changes $(2+1=3)$. The digit to the right of the underlined place changes to zero.

6. 5847 rounded to the nearest hundred: 580

5<u>8</u>47   Next digit is 4 or less.

Hundreds place does not change. All digits to the right of the underlined place change to zeros.

8. 17,211 rounded to the nearest hundred: 17,200

17,<u>2</u>11 Next digit is 4 or less.

Hundreds place does not change. All digits to the right of the underlined place change to 0.

10. 18,273 rounded to the nearest hundred: 18,300

18,<u>2</u>73 Next digit is 5 or more.

Hundreds place changes $(2+1=3)$. All digits to the right of the underlined place change to 0.

12. 4452 rounded to the nearest hundred: 4500

4<u>4</u>52 Next digit is 5 or more.

Hundreds place changes $(4+1=5)$. All digits to the right of the underlined place change to zeros.

14. 28,465 rounded to the nearest thousand: 28,000

2<u>8</u>,465 Next digit is 4 or less.

Thousands place does not change. All digits to the right of the underlined place change to 0.

16. 14,314 rounded to the nearest thousand: 14,000

1<u>4</u>,314 Next digit is 4 or less.

Thousands place does not change. All digits to the right of the underlined place change to 0.

18. 49,706 rounded to the nearest thousand: 50,000

4<u>9</u>,706 Next digit is 5 or more.

Thousands place changes $(9+1=10)$. Write 0, carry 1. All digits to the right of the underlined place change to 0.

20. 6599 rounded to the nearest ten thousand: 10,000

<u> </u>6599 Next digit is 5 or more.

Ten thousands place changes $(0+1=1)$. All digits to the right of the underlined place change to zeros.

22. 725,182 rounded to the nearest ten thousand: 730,000

72<u>5</u>,182 Next digit is 5 or more.

Ten thousands place changes $(2+1=3)$. All digits to the right of the underlined place change to 0.

24. 13,713,409 rounded to the nearest million: 14,000,000

1<u>3</u>,713,409 Next digit is 5 or more.

Millions place changes $(3+1=4)$. All digits to the right of the underlined place change to 0.

26. to the nearest ten:

64<u>8</u>3 Next digit is 4 or less. All digits to the right of the underlined place are changed to zero. Leave 8 as 8.

6480

28. to the nearest hundred:

6<u>4</u>83   Next digit is 5 or more. All digits to the right of the underlined place are changed to zero.
Add 1 to 4.

6500

to the nearest thousand:

<u>6</u>483   Next digit is 4 or less. All digits to the right of the underlined place are changed to zero.
Leave 6 as 6.

6000

30. to the nearest ten:

70<u>6</u>5   Next digit is 5 or more. All digits to the right of the underlined place are changed to zero.
Add 1 to 6.

7070

to the nearest hundred:

7<u>0</u>65   Next digit is 5 or more. All digits to the right of the underlined place are changed to zero.
Add 1 to 0.

7100

to the nearest thousand:

<u>7</u>065   Next digit is 4 or less. All digits to the right of the underlined place are changed to zero.
Leave 7 as 7.

7000

32. to the nearest ten:

    7456   Next digit is 5 or more. All digits to the right of the underlined place are changed to zero.
Add 1 to 5.

    7460

to the nearest hundred:

    7456   Next digit is 5 or more. All digits to the right of the underlined place are changed to zero.
Add 1 to 4.

    7500

to the nearest thousand:

    7456   Next digit is 4 or less. All digits to the right of the underlined place are changed to zero.
Leave 7 as 7.

    7000

34. to the nearest ten:

    59,806   Next digit is 5 or more. All digits to the right of the underlined place are changed to zero.
Add 1 to 0.

    59,810

to the nearest hundred:

    59,806   Next digit is 4 or less. All digits to the right of the underlined place are changed to zero.
Leave 7 as 7.

    59,800

to the nearest thousand:

    59,806   Next digit is 5 or more. All digits to the right of the underlined place are changed to zero.
Add 1 to 9.

    60,000

36. to the nearest ten:

    78,519   Next digit is 5 or more. All digits to the right of the underlined place are changed to zero.
Add 1 to 1.

    78,520

to the nearest hundred:

    78,519   Next digit is 4 or less. All digits to the right of the underlined place are changed to zero.
Leave 5 as 5.

    78,500

to the nearest thousand:

    78,519   Next digit is 5 or more. All digits to the right of the underlined place are changed to zero.
Add 1 to 8.

    79,000

38. to the nearest ten:

    84,639   Next digit is 5 or more. All digits to the right of the underlined place are changed to zero.
Add 1 to 3.

    84,640

to the nearest hundred:

    84,639   Next digit is 4 or less. All digits to the right of the underlined place are changed to zero.
Leave 6 as 6.

    84,600

to the nearest thousand:

    84,639   Next digit is 5 or more. All digits to the right of the underlined place are changed to zero.
Add 1 to 4.

    85,000

40. *Step* 1 Locate the place to be rounded and underline it.

Step 2 Look only at the next digit to the right. If this digit is 4 or less, do not change the underlined digit.

Step 3 Change all digits to the right of the underlined place to zeros.

42.

estimate	exact
60	56
20	24
90	85
+ 70	+ 71
240	236

44.

estimate	exact
60	57
− 20	− 24
40	33

46.

estimate	exact
50	53
× 80	× 75
4000	265
	371
	3975

48.

estimate	exact
600	623
400	362
200	189
+ 700	+ 736
1900	1910

50.

estimate	exact
600	614
− 300	− 276
300	338

52.

estimate	exact
800	845
× 400	× 396
320,000	5 070
	76 05
	253 5
	334,620

54.

estimate	exact
3000	2 685
70	73
600	592
+ 7000	+ 7 183
10,670	10,533

56.

estimate	exact
500	543
−200	−174
300	369

58.

estimate	exact
900	864
× 70	× 74
63,000	3 456
	60 48
	63,936

60. Rounding numbers usually allows for faster calculation and results in an estimated answer prior to getting an exact answer.

One example is:

estimate	exact
400	432
− 200	− 209
200	223

62. 59 rounded to the nearest ten: 60

5̲9 Next digit is 5 or more.

Tens place changes $(5 + 1 = 6)$.
Digit to the right of the underlined place is changed to zero.

38 rounded to the nearest ten: 40

3̲8 Next digit is 5 or more.

Tens place changes $(3 + 1 = 4)$.
Digit to the right of the underlined place is changed to zero.

64. 23 rounded to the nearest ten: 20

2̲3 Next digit is 4 or less.
Tens place doesn't change.
Digit to the right of the underlined place is changed to zero.

35 rounded to the nearest ten: 40

3̲5 Next digit is 5 or more.
Tens place changes $(3 + 1 = 4)$.
Digit to the right of the underlined place is changed to zero.

66. 621,999,652 to the nearest thousand: 622,000,000

621,99̲9,652 Next digit is 5 or more.
All digits to the right of the underlined place are changed to zeros.
Add 1 to 9.

To the nearest ten thousand: 622,000,000

621,9̲99,652 Next digit is 5 or more.
All digits to the right of the underlined place are changed to zeros.
Add 1 to 9.

To the nearest hundred thousand: 622,000,000

621,9̲99,652 Next digit is 5 or more.
All digits to the right of the underlined place are changed to zeros.
Add 1 to 9.

68. To the nearest hundred thousand:

Next digit is 5 or more. Hundred thousands place changes $(7+1=8)$. Digits to the right of the underlined place are changed to zero.

$18,915,800,000

To the nearest hundred million:

$18,915,762,568 Next digit is 4 or less. Hundred millions place doesn't change. All digits to the right of the underlined place are changed to zero.

$18,900,000,000

To the nearest ten billion:

$18,915,762,568 Next digit is 5 or more. Ten billion place changes $(1+1=2)$. Digits to the right of the underlined place are changed to zero.

$20,000,000,000

1.8 Exponents, Roots, and Order of Operations

2. Exponent is 3, base is 2.
$$2^3 = 2 \cdot 2 \cdot 2 = 8$$

4. Exponent is 2, base is 3.
$$3^2 = 3 \cdot 3 = 9$$

6. Exponent is 3, base is 10.
$$10^3 = 10 \cdot 10 \cdot 10 = 1000$$

8. Exponent is 3, base is 11.
$$11^3 = 11 \cdot 11 \cdot 11 = 1331$$

10. From the table,
$$5^2 = 25, \text{ so } \sqrt{25} = 5.$$

12. From the table,
$$6^2 = 36, \text{ so } \sqrt{36} = 6.$$

14. From the table,
$$11^2 = 121, \text{ so } \sqrt{121} = 11.$$

16. From the table,
$$15^2 = 225, \text{ so } \sqrt{225} = 15.$$

18. $9^2 = 9 \cdot 9 = 81$, so $\sqrt{81} = \sqrt{9 \cdot 9} = 9$.

20. $30^2 = 30 \cdot 30 = 900$, so $\sqrt{900} = \sqrt{30 \cdot 30} = 30$.

22. $38^2 = 38 \cdot 38 = 1444$, so $\sqrt{1444} = \sqrt{38 \cdot 38} = 38$.

24. $50^2 = 50 \cdot 50 = 2500$, so
$$\sqrt{2500} = \sqrt{50 \cdot 50} = 50.$$

26. $60^2 = 60 \cdot 60 = 3600$, so
$$\sqrt{3600} = \sqrt{60 \cdot 60} = 60.$$

28. (1) Do all operations inside parentheses.

(2) Simplify expressions with exponents and square roots.

(3) Multiply or divide from left to right.

(4) Add or subtract from left to right.

30. $\begin{array}{ll} 6^2 + 4 - 5 & \textit{Exponent} \\ 36 + 4 - 5 & \textit{Add} \\ 40 - 5 = 35 & \textit{Subtract} \end{array}$

32. $\begin{array}{ll} 5 \cdot 7 - 7 & \textit{Multiply} \\ 35 - 7 = 28 & \textit{Subtract} \end{array}$

34. $\begin{array}{ll} 6 \cdot 8 \div 8 & \textit{Multiply} \\ 48 \div 8 = 6 & \textit{Divide} \end{array}$

36. $\begin{array}{ll} 36 \div 18(7 - 3) & \textit{Parentheses} \\ 36 \div 18 \cdot 4 & \textit{Divide} \\ 2 \cdot 4 = 8 & \textit{Multiply} \end{array}$

38. $\begin{array}{ll} 8 \cdot 3^2 - \dfrac{10}{2} & \textit{Exponent} \\[2mm] 8 \cdot 9 - \dfrac{10}{2} & \textit{Multiply} \\[2mm] 72 - \dfrac{10}{2} & \textit{Divide} \\[2mm] 72 - 5 = 67 & \textit{Subtract} \end{array}$

40. $\begin{array}{ll} 3 \cdot 2 + 7(3 + 1) + 5 & \textit{Parentheses} \\ 3 \cdot 2 + 7 \cdot 4 + 5 & \textit{Multiply from} \\ 6 + 7 \cdot 4 + 5 & \textit{left to right} \\ 6 + 28 + 5 & \textit{Add from left} \\ 34 + 5 = 39 & \textit{to right} \end{array}$

42. $\begin{array}{ll} 4^2 \cdot 5^2 + (20 - 9) \cdot 3 & \textit{Parentheses} \\ 4^2 \cdot 5^2 + 11 \cdot 3 & \textit{Exponents} \\ 16 \cdot 25 + 11 \cdot 3 & \textit{Multiply} \\ 400 + 33 = 433 & \textit{Add} \end{array}$

44. $\begin{array}{ll} 2 \cdot \sqrt{100} - 3 \cdot 4 & \textit{Square root} \\ 2 \cdot 10 - 3 \cdot 4 & \textit{Multiply} \\ 20 - 12 = 8 & \textit{Subtract} \end{array}$

46. $\begin{array}{ll} 10 \cdot 3 + 6 \cdot 5 - 20 & \textit{Multiply} \\ 30 + 30 - 20 & \textit{Add} \\ 60 - 20 = 40 & \textit{Subtract} \end{array}$

48. $3^2 \cdot 4^2 + (15 - 6) \cdot 2$ *Parentheses*

$3^2 \cdot 4^2 + 9 \cdot 2$ *Exponents*

$9 \cdot 16 + 9 \cdot 2$ *Multiply*

$144 + 18 = 162$ *Add*

50. $6 + 8 \div 2 + \dfrac{0}{8}$ *Divide*

$6 + 4 + \dfrac{0}{8}$

$6 + 4 + 0 = 10$ *Add*

52. $4^2 + 5^2 + (25 - 9) \cdot 3$ *Parentheses*

$4^2 + 5^2 + 16 \cdot 3$ *Exponents*

$16 + 25 + 16 \cdot 3$ *Multiply*

$16 + 25 + 48$ *Add from*

$41 + 48 = 89$ *left to right*

54. $6 \cdot \sqrt{64} - 6 \cdot 5$ *Square root*

$6 \cdot 8 - 6 \cdot 5$ *Multiply*

$48 - 30 = 18$ *Subtract*

56. $5 \cdot 2 + 3(5 + 3) - 6$ *Parentheses*

$5 \cdot 2 + 3 \cdot 8 - 6$ *Multiply from*

$10 + 3 \cdot 8 - 6$ *left to right*

$10 + 24 - 6$ *Add*

$34 - 6 = 28$ *Subtract*

58. $3 \cdot \sqrt{25} - 6(3 - 1)$ *Parentheses*

$3 \cdot \sqrt{25} - 6 \cdot 2$ *Square root*

$3 \cdot 5 - 6 \cdot 2$ *Multiply from*

$15 - 6 \cdot 2$ *left to right*

$15 - 12 = 3$ *Subtract*

60. $5 \cdot (4 - 3) + \sqrt{9}$ *Parentheses*

$5 \cdot 1 + \sqrt{9}$ *Square root*

$5 \cdot 1 + 3$ *Multiply*

$5 + 3 = 8$ *Add*

62. $3^2 - 2^2 + 3 - 2$ *Exponents*

$9 - 4 + 3 - 2$ *Subtract*

$5 + 3 - 2$ *Add*

$8 - 2 = 6$ *Subtract*

64. $5^2 \cdot 3^2 + (30 - 20) \cdot 2$ *Parentheses*

$5^2 \cdot 3^2 + 10 \cdot 2$ *Exponents*

$25 \cdot 9 + 10 \cdot 2$ *Multiply from*

$225 + 10 \cdot 2$ *left to right*

$225 + 20 = 245$ *Add*

66. $8 + 3 \div 3 + 6 \cdot 3$ *Divide*

$8 + 1 + 6 \cdot 3$ *Multiply*

$8 + 1 + 18$ *Add from*

$9 + 18 = 27$ *left to right*

68. $8 \cdot \sqrt{49} - 6(5 + 3)$ *Parentheses*

$8 \cdot \sqrt{49} - 6 \cdot 8$ *Square root*

$8 \cdot 7 - 6 \cdot 8$ *Multiply*

$56 - 48 = 8$ *Subtract*

70. $6^2 + 4^2 - 8 \cdot 4$ *Exponents*

$36 + 16 - 8 \cdot 4$ *Multiply*

$36 + 16 - 32$ *Add*

$52 - 32 = 20$ *Subtract*

72. $2 + 12 \div 6 + 5 + \dfrac{0}{5}$ *Divide from*

$2 + 2 + 5 + \dfrac{0}{5}$ *left to right*

$2 + 2 + 5 + 0$ *Add from*

$4 + 5 + 0$ *left to right*

$9 + 0 = 9$

74. $8 \cdot \sqrt{36} - 4 \cdot 6$ *Square root*

$8 \cdot 6 - 4 \cdot 6$ *Multiply from*

$48 - 4 \cdot 6$ *left to right*

$48 - 24 = 24$ *Subtract*

76. $6 \cdot \sqrt{81} - 3 \cdot \sqrt{49}$ *Square root*

$6 \cdot 9 - 3 \cdot 7$ *Multiply*

$54 - 21 = 33$ *Subtract*

78. $12 \div 4 \cdot 5 \cdot 4 \div (15 - 13)$ *Parentheses*

$12 \div 4 \cdot 5 \cdot 4 \div 2$ *Multiply*

$3 \cdot 5 \cdot 4 \div 2$ *and divide*

$15 \cdot 4 \div 2$ *from left*

$60 \div 2 = 30$ *to right*

80. $9 \div 1 \cdot 4 \cdot 2 \div (11 - 5)$ *Parentheses*

$9 \div 1 \cdot 4 \cdot 2 \div 6$ *Multiply and*

$9 \cdot 4 \cdot 2 \div 6$ *divide from*

$36 \cdot 2 \div 6$ *left to*

$72 \div 6 = 12$ *right*

82. $10 \cdot \sqrt{49} - 4 \cdot \sqrt{64}$ *Square root*

$10 \cdot 7 - 4 \cdot 8$ *Multiply from*

$70 - 4 \cdot 8$ *left to right*

$70 - 32 = 38$ *Subtract*

84. $15 \div 3 \cdot 8 \cdot 9 \div (12 - 8)$ *Parentheses*

$15 \div 3 \cdot 8 \cdot 9 \div 4$ *Multiply*

$5 \cdot 8 \cdot 9 \div 4$ *and divide*

$40 \cdot 9 \div 4$ *from left*

$360 \div 4 = 90$ *to right*

86. $3 - 2 + 5 \cdot 4 \cdot \sqrt{144} \div \sqrt{36}$ *Square roots*
$3 - 2 + 5 \cdot 4 \cdot 12 \div 6$ *Multiply and*
$3 - 2 + 20 \cdot 12 \div 6$ *divide from*
$3 - 2 + 240 \div 6$ *left to right*
$3 - 2 + 40$ *Subtract*
$1 + 40 = 41$ *Add*

88. $6 - 4 + 2 \cdot 9 - 3 \cdot \sqrt{225} \div \sqrt{25}$
$6 - 4 + 2 \cdot 9 - 3 \cdot 15 \div 5$
$6 - 4 + 18 - 3 \cdot 15 \div 5$
$6 - 4 + 18 - 45 \div 5$
$6 - 4 + 18 - 9$
$2 + 18 - 9$
$20 - 9 = 11$

90. $9 \cdot \sqrt{36} \cdot \sqrt{81} \div 2 + 6 - 3 - 5$
$9 \cdot 6 \cdot 9 \div 2 + 6 - 3 - 5$
$54 \cdot 9 \div 2 + 6 - 3 - 5$
$486 \div 2 + 6 - 3 - 5$
$243 + 6 - 3 - 5$
$249 - 3 - 5$
$246 - 5 = 241$

1.9 Reading Pictographs, Bar Graphs, and Line Graphs

2. According to the pictograph, there are 20 thousand video rental outlets in China.

4. According to the pictograph, India, Bulgaria, and Japan have the least number of video rental outlets.

6. $\begin{array}{r} 20,000 \\ - 10,000 \\ \hline 10,000 \end{array}$ *China*
Bulgaria

China has 10,000 more video rental outlets than Bulgaria.

8. From the bar graph 18 people out of 100 found their careers because they studied for the career in school.

10. (a) From the bar graph, the least number of people found their career by being promoted from within.

   (b) From the bar graph, 6 people out of 100 found their career as a result of being promoted from within.

12. From the bar graph, 27 people out of 100 found their career as a result of either "Studied in School" or "Trained for a Job."

14. From the line graph, 1997 and 2001 were the two years with the least number of home sales. There were 2500 home sales in each of these years.

16. $\begin{array}{r} 4000 \\ - 2500 \\ \hline 1500 \end{array}$ home sales 2000
   home sales 2001
   decrease in home sales

The decrease in the number of home sales from 2000 to 2001 is 1500.

18. Possible answers are:
   1. many qualified buyers
   2. high employment
   3. good economy
   4. availability of loans at favorable interest rates

1.10 Solving Application Problems

2. *Step* 1 Find the total pounds of coffee sold.

   Step 2 "Total" indicates addition.

   Step 3 Estimate: $\begin{array}{r} 300 \\ 80 \\ 100 \\ 500 \\ + \ 100 \\ \hline 1080 \end{array}$

   Step 4 $\begin{array}{r} 325 \\ 75 \\ 137 \\ 495 \\ + \ 105 \\ \hline 1137 \end{array}$

During the week, 1137 pounds of coffee are sold.

4. *Step* 1 Find how much more money there is in the large machines.

   Step 2 "How much more" indicates subtraction.

   Step 3 Estimate: $\begin{array}{r} \$300,000 \\ - \ 20,000 \\ \hline \$280,000 \end{array}$

   Step 4 Exact: $\begin{array}{r} \$250,000 \\ - \ 15,000 \\ \hline \$235,000 \end{array}$

The large machines have $235,000 more than the small machines.

6. *Step* 1 Find the number of tickets sold in a 12-day period.

Step 2 The number of tickets sold in one day is given. To find "how many in a 12-day period," multiply.

Step 3 About 10 times 500 gives an estimate of 5000 tickets.

Step 4
```
    450
  ×  12
    900
    450
   5400
```

In a 12-day period 5400 tickets are sold.

8. *Step* 1 Find the amount each employee will receive.

Step 2 "Divide evenly" indicates division.

Step 3 $700,000 ÷ 1000 gives an estimate of $700.

Step 4
```
            680
   1000)680,000
        600 0
         80 00
         80 00
            00
            00
             0
```

Check:
```
        680
     × 1000
    680,000
```

Each employee will receive $680.

10. *Step* 1 Find the amount of money that needs to be collected.

Step 2 Since the amount collected is less than the amount needed, subtract.

Step 3 $80,000 − $50,000 gives an estimate of $30,000.

Step 4
```
     $75,650
    − 52,882
     $22,768
```

The community needs to raise $22,768.

12. *Step* 1 The cost of tuition for 1 quarter is given. Find the amount needed for 5 quarters.

Step 2 Multiply to find the total amount.

Step 3 Estimate $800 × 5 = $4000 is needed.

Step 4
```
    785
  ×   5
   3925
```

$3925 is needed for 5 quarters.

14. *Step* 1 Find how much more an accountant makes than a journalist.

Step 2 "How much more" indicates subtraction.

Step 3 Estimate:
```
   $30,000
  − 20,000
   $10,000
```

Step 4
```
   $29,800   Accountant
  + 21,700   Journalist
    $8 100
```

An accountant earns $8100 more than a journalist.

16. (a) *Step* 1 Find the total earnings.

Step 2 "Total" indicates addition.

Step 3 Estimate:
$20,000 + $20,000 = $40,000 Gonsalves
$20,000 + $20,000 = $40,000 Horton

Step 4
```
   $22,000   Dental hygienist
  + 16,400   Secretary
   $38,400   Gonsalves
```

```
   $16,500   Flight attendant
  + 24,000   State police officer
   $40,500   Horton
```

The Hortons had higher earnings.

(b) *Step* 1 Find the difference in the couples' earnings.

Step 2 "Difference" indicates subtraction.

Step 3 $40,000 − $40,000 = $0 is a reasonable estimate.

Step 4
```
   $40,500   Horton
  − 38,400   Gonsalves
    $2 100   difference in earnings
```

The difference between the Horton's earnings and the Gonsalves' earnings is $2100.

18. *Step* 1 Find the amount remaining in the checking account.

Step 2 Add to find the total amount of the checks written. Subtract that total from the balance in the account.

Step 3 $300 + $600 + $800 = $1700 was spent. His balance is about $3000 − $1700 = $1300.

Step 4
```
   $308    $2874
    580   − 1666
  + 778    $1208
   $1666
```

$1208 remains in the account.

20. *Step* 1 Find the number of gallons polluted in a year.

Step 2 Multiply by 365 to find the amount polluted each day.

Step 3 $200,000 \times 400$ gives an estimate of 80,000,000 gallons.

Step 4
$$
\begin{array}{r}
209,670 \\
\times \quad 365 \\
\hline
1\ 048\ 350 \\
12\ 580\ 20 \\
62\ 901\ 0 \\
\hline
76,529,550
\end{array}
$$

Each year 76,529,550 gallons are polluted.

22. *Step* 1 The total cost of all Convenience and Comfort items must be found.

Step 2 "Find the total" indicates addition.

Step 3 Estimate the total.
$600 + $200 + $900 + $300 + $300 = $2300

Step 4
$$
\begin{array}{r}
\$595 \\
215 \\
860 \\
340 \\
+ \quad 280 \\
\hline
\$2290
\end{array}
$$

The total cost is $2290.

24. *Step* 1 Find the difference between the total for the options purchased separately and the dealer's group of options.

Step 2 First, add to find the total of the items purchased separately.

Step 3 Estimate.
$400 + $600 + $100 + $300 + $900 + $200 = $2500

$$
\begin{array}{r}
\$2500 \\
- \quad 1800 \\
\hline
\$700
\end{array}
$$

Step 4
Child seats	$375	$2480
Antilock brakes	$565	− $1750
Full size spare	$125	$730
Power windows	$340	
Air conditioning	$860	
Roof rack	$215	
	$2480	

The amount saved is $730.

26. *Step* 1 Find the total cost.

Step 2 To find the cost of the computers use multiplication. The cost of the printers must also be found using multiplication. Finally, the two totals must be added.

Step 3 Estimate:
$(\$500 \times 20) + (\$500 \times 10) = \$15,000$

Step 4
$$
\begin{array}{rrr}
506 & 482 & 8\ 602 \\
\times \quad 17 & \times \quad 13 & + \ 6\ 266 \\
\hline
3542 & 1446 & 14,868 \\
506 & 482 & \\
\hline
8602 & 6266 &
\end{array}
$$

The total cost is $14,868.

28. (1) Read the problem carefully.

(2) Work out a plan.

(3) Estimate a reasonable answer.

(4) Solve the problem.

(5) State the answer.

(6) Check your work.

30. estimate: $7000 + 6000 + 2000 = 15,000$

exact: $7438 + 6493 + 2390 = 16,321$

The answers vary by more than 1000 as a result of the rounding. However, the estimated answer and the exact answer are close enough to give some assurance that the answer is reasonable.

32. *Step* 1 Find the combined income of Brian and Maria.

Step 2 To find the earnings multiply the rate per hour by the number of hours worked. Do this for each person and add the two totals.

Step 3 Estimate 40 hours at $8 per hour and 40 hours at $9 per hour:

$40 \cdot \$8 + 40 \cdot \$9 = \$320 + \$360 = \$680$

Step 4
$$
\begin{array}{rrr}
38 & 39 & \$351 \\
\times \quad 8 & \times \quad 9 & + \ 304 \\
\hline
304 & 351 & \$655
\end{array}
$$

Their combined earnings are $655.

34. *Step* 1 Find the balance in the preschool operating account.

Step 2 Subtract the expenses and add the amount raised by the parents to the account balance.

Step 3 Estimate the answer:
$2300 − $700 + $600 = $2200

Step 4
$$
\begin{array}{rr}
\$2324 & \$1590 \\
-\ 734 & +\ 568 \\
\hline
\$1590 & \$2158 \\
\end{array}
$$

The balance in the account is $2158.

36. *Step* 1 Find the difference between a four-night stay at the Ritz-Carlton and a four-night stay at Motel 6.

Step 2 Multiply the cost per night by the length of the stay at each hotel and subtract the totals.

Step 3 Estimate:
($380 × 4) − ($30 × 4) = $1400

Step 4
$$
\begin{array}{rrrr}
375 & \$32 & \$1500 & \text{Check:} \quad \$128 \\
\times\ 4 & \times\ 4 & -\ 128 & \qquad +\ 1372 \\
\hline
\$1500 & \$128 & \$1372 & \qquad \$1500 \\
\end{array}
$$

38. *Step* 1 Find the total number of flats needed.

Step 2 Add the eggs collected in the morning to the eggs collected in the afternoon and divide the total by the number of eggs in each flat.

Step 3 Estimate:

$$
\begin{array}{r}
200 \\
30\overline{)6000} \\
\underline{60} \\
0 \\
\underline{0} \\
00 \\
\underline{0} \\
0 \\
\end{array}
$$

200 flats is a reasonable estimate.

Step 4
$$
\begin{array}{rl}
3545 & \text{morning} \\
+\ 2575 & \text{afternoon} \\
\hline
6120 & \text{total} \\
\end{array}
$$

$$
\begin{array}{r}
204 \\
30\overline{)6120} \\
\underline{60} \\
12 \\
\underline{0} \\
120 \\
\underline{120} \\
0 \\
\end{array}
$$

240 flats are needed for packing.

40. *Step* 1 Find the number of boxes each store will receive.

Step 2 Use multiplication to find the total number of grapevine wreaths made per year. Use division to find the number of boxes per year and the number of boxes each store receives.

Step 3 Estimate:

24 × 40 = 960 wreaths per year
960 ÷ 6 = 160 boxes per year
160 ÷ 5 = 32 boxes per store

Step 4 In this case, the estimate is the same as the exact amount. Each storre will receive 32 boxes.

Chapter 2

MULTIPLYING AND DIVIDING FRACTIONS

2.1 Basics of Fractions

2. The figure has 8 equal parts.
Five parts are shaded: $\frac{5}{8}$

Three parts are unshaded: $\frac{3}{8}$

4. An area equal to 5 of the $\frac{1}{3}$ parts is shaded.

$$\frac{5}{3}$$

One part is unshaded: $\frac{1}{3}$.

6. An area equal to 11 of the $\frac{1}{6}$ parts is shaded.

$$\frac{11}{6}$$

An area equal to 1 of the $\frac{1}{6}$ parts is unshaded.

$$\frac{1}{6}$$

8. There are 8 recording stars; 7 are men.

$$\frac{7}{8}$$

10. There are 98 bicycles of which 67 are mountain bikes (98 − 67 = 31 are not mountain bikes).

$$\frac{31}{98}$$

12. There are 12 cheerleaders.
12 − 5 = 7 are freshmen.

$$\frac{7}{12}$$

14. $\frac{5}{6}$ $\leftarrow$ numerator
$\leftarrow$ denominator

16. $\frac{7}{5}$ $\leftarrow$ numerator
$\leftarrow$ denominator

18. Proper fractions:

$$\frac{1}{3}, \frac{3}{8}, \frac{3}{4}$$

Improper fractions:

$$\frac{16}{12}, \frac{10}{8}, \frac{6}{6}$$

20. Proper fractions: none
Improper fractions:

$$\frac{12}{12}, \frac{15}{11}, \frac{13}{12}, \frac{11}{8}, \frac{17}{17}, \frac{19}{12}$$

22. An example of a proper fraction is

$$\frac{1}{2}.$$

An example of an improper fraction is

$$\frac{3}{2}.$$

In a proper fraction the numerator is *smaller* than the denominator.

In an improper fraction the numerator is *greater* than or equal to the denominator.

$\frac{1}{2}$ $\qquad$ $\frac{3}{2}$

Proper fraction $\qquad$ Improper fraction

24. The fraction $\frac{15}{16}$ represents *15* of the *16* equal parts into which a whole is divided.

26. The fraction $\frac{7}{64}$ represents *7* of the *64* equal parts into which a whole is divided.

2.2 Mixed Numbers

2. $2\frac{1}{3}$ $\quad 2 \cdot 3 = 6$
$6 + 1 = 7$

$$2\frac{1}{3} = \frac{7}{3}$$

4. $4\frac{3}{4}$ $\quad 4 \cdot 4 = 16$
$16 + 3 = 19$

$$4\frac{3}{4} = \frac{19}{4}$$

6. $5\frac{3}{5}$ $\quad 5 \cdot 5 = 25$
$25 + 3 = 28$

$$5\frac{3}{5} = \frac{28}{5}$$

8. $8\frac{1}{2}$ $8 \cdot 2 = 16$

$16 + 1 = 17$

$8\frac{1}{2} = \frac{17}{2}$

10. $4\frac{3}{7}$ $4 \cdot 7 = 28$

$28 + 3 = 31$

$4\frac{3}{7} = \frac{31}{7}$

12. $8\frac{2}{3}$ $8 \cdot 3 = 24$

$24 + 2 = 26$

$8\frac{2}{3} = \frac{26}{3}$

14. $12\frac{2}{3}$ $12 \cdot 3 = 36$

$36 + 2 = 38$

$12\frac{2}{3} = \frac{38}{3}$

16. $5\frac{4}{5}$ $5 \cdot 5 = 25$

$25 + 4 = 29$

$5\frac{4}{5} = \frac{29}{5}$

18. $2\frac{8}{9}$ $2 \cdot 9 = 18$

$18 + 8 = 26$

$2\frac{8}{9} = \frac{26}{9}$

20. $3\frac{4}{7}$ $3 \cdot 7 = 21$

$21 + 4 = 25$

$3\frac{4}{7} = \frac{25}{7}$

22. $12\frac{3}{8}$ $12 \cdot 8 = 96$

$96 + 3 = 99$

$12\frac{3}{8} = \frac{99}{8}$

24. $15\frac{3}{10}$ $15 \cdot 10 = 150$

$150 + 3 = 153$

$15\frac{3}{10} = \frac{153}{10}$

26. $19\frac{8}{11}$ $19 \cdot 11 = 209$

$209 + 8 = 217$

$19\frac{8}{11} = \frac{217}{11}$

28. $7\frac{3}{16}$ $7 \cdot 16 = 112$

$112 + 3 = 115$

$7\frac{3}{16} = \frac{115}{16}$

30. $9\frac{7}{12}$ $12 \cdot 9 = 108$

$108 + 7 = 115$

$9\frac{7}{12} = \frac{115}{12}$

32. $\frac{8}{5}$

$\begin{array}{r} 1 \\ 5\overline{)8} \\ 5 \\ \overline{3} \end{array}$ $\leftarrow$ *whole number*

$\leftarrow$ *remainder*

$\frac{8}{5} = 1\frac{3}{5}$

34. $\frac{13}{3}$

$\begin{array}{r} 4 \\ 3\overline{)13} \\ 12 \\ \overline{1} \end{array}$ $\leftarrow$ *whole number*

$\leftarrow$ *remainder*

$\frac{13}{3} = 4\frac{1}{3}$

36. $\frac{64}{8}$

$\begin{array}{r} 8 \\ 8\overline{)64} \\ 64 \\ \overline{0} \end{array}$ $\leftarrow$ *whole number*

$\leftarrow$ *remainder*

$\frac{64}{8} = 8$

38. $\frac{33}{7}$

$\begin{array}{r} 4 \\ 7\overline{)33} \\ 28 \\ \overline{5} \end{array}$ $\leftarrow$ *whole number*

$\leftarrow$ *remainder*

$\frac{33}{7} = 4\frac{5}{7}$

40. $\frac{40}{9}$

$\begin{array}{r} 4 \\ 9\overline{)40} \\ 36 \\ \overline{4} \end{array}$ $\leftarrow$ *whole number*

$\leftarrow$ *remainder*

$\frac{40}{9} = 4\frac{4}{9}$

42. $\dfrac{78}{6}$

$$\begin{array}{r} 13 \leftarrow \textit{whole number} \\ 6\overline{)78} \\ \underline{6} \\ 18 \\ \underline{18} \\ 0 \leftarrow \textit{remainder} \end{array}$$

$$\dfrac{78}{6} = 13$$

44. $\dfrac{19}{5}$

$$\begin{array}{r} 3 \leftarrow \textit{whole number} \\ 5\overline{)19} \\ \underline{15} \\ 4 \leftarrow \textit{remainder} \end{array}$$

$$\dfrac{19}{5} = 3\dfrac{4}{5}$$

46. $\dfrac{65}{9}$

$$\begin{array}{r} 7 \leftarrow \textit{whole number} \\ 9\overline{)65} \\ \underline{63} \\ 2 \leftarrow \textit{remainder} \end{array}$$

$$\dfrac{65}{9} = 7\dfrac{2}{9}$$

48. $\dfrac{37}{6}$

$$\begin{array}{r} 6 \leftarrow \textit{whole number} \\ 6\overline{)37} \\ \underline{36} \\ 1 \leftarrow \textit{remainder} \end{array}$$

$$\dfrac{37}{6} = 6\dfrac{1}{6}$$

50. $\dfrac{92}{3}$

$$\begin{array}{r} 30 \qquad \leftarrow \textit{whole number} \\ 3\overline{)92} \\ \underline{9} \\ 2 \\ \underline{0} \\ 2 \leftarrow \textit{remainder} \end{array}$$

$$\dfrac{92}{3} = 30\dfrac{2}{3}$$

52. $\dfrac{149}{8}$

$$\begin{array}{r} 18 \leftarrow \textit{whole number} \\ 8\overline{)149} \\ \underline{8} \\ 69 \\ \underline{64} \\ 5 \leftarrow \textit{remainder} \end{array}$$

$$\dfrac{149}{8} = 18\dfrac{5}{8}$$

54. $\dfrac{212}{11}$

$$\begin{array}{r} 19 \leftarrow \textit{whole number} \\ 11\overline{)212} \\ \underline{11} \\ 102 \\ \underline{99} \\ 3 \leftarrow \textit{remainder} \end{array}$$

$$\dfrac{212}{11} = 19\dfrac{3}{11}$$

56. Divide the numerator by the denominator. The quotient is the whole number of the mixed number and the remainder is the numerator of the fraction part. The denominator is unchanged.

$$\dfrac{5}{2} \qquad 2\overline{)5}\;^{2}\;\text{R1} \qquad 2\dfrac{1}{2}$$

58. $218\dfrac{3}{5}$ $\qquad 218 \cdot 5 = 1090$
$$1090 + 3 = 1093$$

$$218\dfrac{3}{5} = \dfrac{1093}{5}$$

60. $401\dfrac{1}{2}$ $\qquad 401 \cdot 2 = 802$
$$802 + 1 = 803$$

$$401\dfrac{1}{2} = \dfrac{803}{2}$$

62. $622\dfrac{1}{4}$ $\qquad 622 \cdot 4 = 2488$
$$2488 + 1 = 2489$$

$$622\dfrac{1}{4} = \dfrac{2489}{4}$$

64. $\dfrac{219}{4}$

$$\begin{array}{r} 54 \leftarrow \textit{whole number} \\ 4\overline{)219} \\ \underline{20} \\ 19 \\ \underline{16} \\ 3 \leftarrow \textit{remainder} \end{array}$$

$$\dfrac{219}{4} = 54\dfrac{3}{4}$$

66. The commands used to solve will vary by calculator. The following is a screen shot of a TI-83:

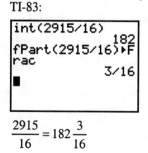

$$\dfrac{2915}{16} = 182\dfrac{3}{16}$$

68. The commands used to solve will vary by calculator. The following is a screenshot of a TI-83:

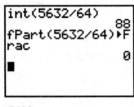

```
int(5632/64)
              88
fPart(5632/64)▸F
rac
               0
■
```

$$\frac{5632}{64} = 88$$

2.3 Factors

2. Factorizations of 15:

$1 \cdot 15 = 15 \qquad 3 \cdot 5 = 15$

The factors are 1, 3, 5, and 15.

4. Factorizations of 28:

$1 \cdot 28 = 28 \qquad 2 \cdot 14 = 28 \qquad 4 \cdot 7 = 28$

The factors are 1, 2, 4, 7, 14, and 28.

6. Factorizations of 30:

$1 \cdot 30 = 30 \qquad 2 \cdot 15 = 30$
$3 \cdot 10 = 30 \qquad 5 \cdot 6 = 30$

The factors are 1, 2, 3, 5, 6, 10, 15, and 30.

8. Factorizations of 20:

$1 \cdot 20 = 20 \qquad 2 \cdot 10 = 20 \qquad 4 \cdot 5 = 20$

The factors are 1, 2, 4, 5, 10, and 20.

10. Factorizations of 60:

$1 \cdot 60 = 60 \qquad 2 \cdot 30 = 60$
$3 \cdot 20 = 60 \qquad 4 \cdot 15 = 60$
$5 \cdot 12 = 60 \qquad 6 \cdot 10 = 60$

The factors are 1, 2, 3, 4, 5, 6, 10, 12, 15, 20, 30, and 60.

12. Factorizations of 84:

$1 \cdot 84 = 84 \qquad 2 \cdot 42 = 84$
$3 \cdot 28 = 84 \qquad 4 \cdot 21 = 84$
$6 \cdot 14 = 84 \qquad 7 \cdot 12 = 84$

The factors are 1, 2, 3, 4, 6, 7, 12, 14, 21, 28, 42, and 84.

14. 6 has factors of 2 and 3 so it is composite.

16. 7 has no factor other than itself and 1 so it is prime.

18. 9 has a factor of 3 so it is composite.

20. 65 has factors of 5 and 13 so it is composite.

22. 17 has no factor other than itself and 1 so it is prime.

24. 26 has factors of 2 and 13 so it is composite.

26. 47 has no factor other than itself and 1 so it is prime.

28. 53 has no factor other than itself and 1 so it is prime.

30. 15

$$3\overline{)15} \;\; 5$$
$$5\overline{)5} \;\; 1$$
$$15 = 3 \cdot 5$$

32. 40

$$2\overline{)40} \;\; 20$$
$$2\overline{)20} \;\; 10$$
$$2\overline{)10} \;\; 5$$
$$5\overline{)5} \;\; 1$$
$$40 = 2 \cdot 2 \cdot 2 \cdot 5 = 2^3 \cdot 5$$

34. 18

$$2\overline{)18} \;\; 9$$
$$3\overline{)9} \;\; 3$$
$$3\overline{)3} \;\; 1$$
$$18 = 2 \cdot 3 \cdot 3 = 2 \cdot 3^2$$

36. 56

$$2\overline{)56} \;\; 28$$
$$2\overline{)28} \;\; 14$$
$$2\overline{)14} \;\; 7$$
$$56 = 2 \cdot 2 \cdot 2 \cdot 7 = 2^3 \cdot 7$$

38. 70

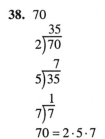

$$70 = 2 \cdot 5 \cdot 7$$

40.

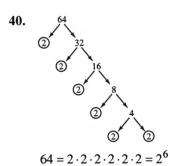

$$64 = 2 \cdot 2 \cdot 2 \cdot 2 \cdot 2 \cdot 2 = 2^6$$

42.

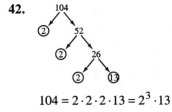

$$104 = 2 \cdot 2 \cdot 2 \cdot 13 = 2^3 \cdot 13$$

44.

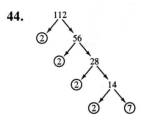

$$112 = 2 \cdot 2 \cdot 2 \cdot 2 \cdot 7 = 2^4 \cdot 7$$

46.

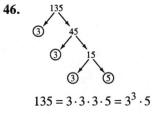

$$135 = 3 \cdot 3 \cdot 3 \cdot 5 = 3^3 \cdot 5$$

48.

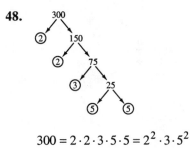

$$300 = 2 \cdot 2 \cdot 3 \cdot 5 \cdot 5 = 2^2 \cdot 3 \cdot 5^2$$

50.

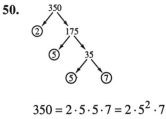

$$350 = 2 \cdot 5 \cdot 5 \cdot 7 = 2 \cdot 5^2 \cdot 7$$

52.

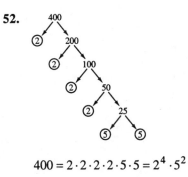

$$400 = 2 \cdot 2 \cdot 2 \cdot 2 \cdot 5 \cdot 5 = 2^4 \cdot 5^2$$

54. No even number other than 2 is prime because all even numbers have 2 as a factor. Many odd numbers are multiples of prime numbers and are not prime. For example, 9, 21, 33, and 45 are all multiples of 3.

56. No. The order of division does not matter. As long as you use only prime numbers, your answers will be correct. However, it does seem easier to always start with the smallest prime number and then use progressively larger prime numbers. The prime factorization of 36 is

$$2 \cdot 2 \cdot 3 \cdot 3.$$

58. 640

$$640 = 2 \cdot 2 \cdot 2 \cdot 2 \cdot 2 \cdot 2 \cdot 2 \cdot 5 = 2^7 \cdot 5$$

60. 1125

$$3\overline{)1125} \quad \frac{375}{}$$

$$3\overline{)375} \quad \frac{125}{}$$

$$5\overline{)125} \quad \frac{25}{}$$

$$5\overline{)25} \quad \frac{5}{}$$

$$5\overline{)5} \quad \frac{1}{}$$

$$1125 = 3 \cdot 3 \cdot 5 \cdot 5 \cdot 5 = 3^2 \cdot 5^3$$

62. 2000

$$2\overline{)2000} \quad \frac{1000}{}$$

$$2\overline{)1000} \quad \frac{500}{}$$

$$2\overline{)500} \quad \frac{250}{}$$

$$2\overline{)250} \quad \frac{125}{}$$

$$5\overline{)125} \quad \frac{25}{}$$

$$5\overline{)25} \quad \frac{5}{}$$

$$5\overline{)5} \quad \frac{1}{}$$

$$2000 = 2 \cdot 2 \cdot 2 \cdot 2 \cdot 5 \cdot 5 \cdot 5 = 2^4 \cdot 5^3$$

64.

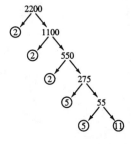

$$2200 = 2 \cdot 2 \cdot 2 \cdot 5 \cdot 5 \cdot 11 = 2^3 \cdot 5^2 \cdot 11$$

2.4 Writing a Fraction in Lowest Terms

		2	3	5	10
2.	60	✓	✓	✓	✓
4.	36	✓	✓	X	X
6.	175	X	X	✓	X
8.	120	✓	✓	✓	✓

10. $\dfrac{5}{10} = \dfrac{5 \div 5}{10 \div 5} = \dfrac{1}{2}$

12. $\dfrac{4}{12} = \dfrac{4 \div 4}{12 \div 4} = \dfrac{1}{3}$

14. $\dfrac{32}{48} = \dfrac{32 \div 16}{48 \div 16} = \dfrac{2}{3}$

16. $\dfrac{22}{33} = \dfrac{22 \div 11}{33 \div 11} = \dfrac{2}{3}$

18. $\dfrac{21}{35} = \dfrac{21 \div 7}{35 \div 7} = \dfrac{3}{5}$

20. $\dfrac{72}{80} = \dfrac{72 \div 8}{80 \div 8} = \dfrac{9}{10}$

22. $\dfrac{73}{146} = \dfrac{73 \div 73}{146 \div 73} = \dfrac{1}{2}$

24. $\dfrac{8}{400} = \dfrac{8 \div 8}{400 \div 8} = \dfrac{1}{50}$

26. $\dfrac{165}{180} = \dfrac{165 \div 15}{180 \div 15} = \dfrac{11}{12}$

28. $\dfrac{112}{128} = \dfrac{112 \div 16}{128 \div 16} = \dfrac{7}{8}$

30. $\dfrac{16}{64} = \dfrac{\overset{1}{\cancel{2}} \cdot \overset{1}{\cancel{2}} \cdot \overset{1}{\cancel{2}} \cdot \overset{1}{\cancel{2}}}{\underset{1}{\cancel{2}} \cdot \underset{1}{\cancel{2}} \cdot \underset{1}{\cancel{2}} \cdot \underset{1}{\cancel{2}} \cdot 2 \cdot 2} = \dfrac{1}{4}$

32. $\dfrac{20}{32} = \dfrac{\overset{1}{\cancel{2}} \cdot \overset{1}{\cancel{2}} \cdot 5}{\underset{1}{\cancel{2}} \cdot \underset{1}{\cancel{2}} \cdot 2 \cdot 2 \cdot 2} = \dfrac{5}{8}$

34. $\dfrac{36}{48} = \dfrac{\overset{1}{\cancel{2}} \cdot \overset{1}{\cancel{2}} \cdot \overset{1}{\cancel{3}} \cdot 3}{\underset{1}{\cancel{2}} \cdot \underset{1}{\cancel{2}} \cdot 2 \cdot 2 \cdot \underset{1}{\cancel{3}}} = \dfrac{3}{4}$

36. $\dfrac{192}{48} = \dfrac{\cancel{2}\cdot\cancel{2}\cdot\cancel{2}\cdot\cancel{2}\cdot 2\cdot 2\cdot\cancel{3}}{\cancel{2}\cdot\cancel{2}\cdot\cancel{2}\cdot\cancel{2}\cdot\cancel{3}} = 4$

38. $\dfrac{65}{234} = \dfrac{5\cdot\cancel{13}}{2\cdot 3\cdot 3\cdot\cancel{13}} = \dfrac{5}{18}$

40. $\dfrac{4}{10}$ and $\dfrac{20}{50}$

$\dfrac{4}{10} = \dfrac{\cancel{2}\cdot 2}{\cancel{2}\cdot 5} = \dfrac{2}{5}$

$\dfrac{20}{50} = \dfrac{\cancel{2}\cdot 2\cdot\cancel{5}}{\cancel{2}\cdot\cancel{5}\cdot 5} = \dfrac{2}{5}$

The fractions are equivalent $\left(\dfrac{2}{5} = \dfrac{2}{5}\right)$.

42. $\dfrac{22}{32}$ and $\dfrac{32}{48}$

$\dfrac{22}{32} = \dfrac{\cancel{2}\cdot 11}{\cancel{2}\cdot 2\cdot 2\cdot 2\cdot 2} = \dfrac{11}{16}$

$\dfrac{32}{48} = \dfrac{\cancel{2}\cdot\cancel{2}\cdot\cancel{2}\cdot\cancel{2}\cdot 2}{\cancel{2}\cdot\cancel{2}\cdot\cancel{2}\cdot\cancel{2}\cdot 3} = \dfrac{2}{3}$

The fractions are not equivalent $\left(\dfrac{11}{16} \neq \dfrac{2}{3}\right)$.

44. $\dfrac{21}{33}$ and $\dfrac{9}{12}$

$\dfrac{21}{33} = \dfrac{\cancel{3}\cdot 7}{\cancel{3}\cdot 11} = \dfrac{7}{11}$

$\dfrac{9}{12} = \dfrac{3\cdot\cancel{3}}{2\cdot 2\cdot\cancel{3}} = \dfrac{3}{4}$

The fractions are not equivalent $\left(\dfrac{7}{11} \neq \dfrac{3}{4}\right)$.

46. $\dfrac{27}{90}$ and $\dfrac{24}{80}$

$\dfrac{27}{90} = \dfrac{\cancel{3}\cdot\cancel{3}\cdot 3}{\cancel{3}\cdot\cancel{3}\cdot 2\cdot 5} = \dfrac{3}{10}$

$\dfrac{24}{80} = \dfrac{\cancel{2}\cdot\cancel{2}\cdot\cancel{2}\cdot 3}{\cancel{2}\cdot\cancel{2}\cdot\cancel{2}\cdot 2\cdot 5} = \dfrac{3}{10}$

The fractions are equivalent $\left(\dfrac{3}{10} = \dfrac{3}{10}\right)$.

48. $\dfrac{45}{15}$ and $\dfrac{96}{32}$

$\dfrac{45}{15} = \dfrac{\cancel{3}\cdot 3\cdot\cancel{5}}{\cancel{3}\cdot\cancel{5}} = 3$

$\dfrac{96}{32} = \dfrac{\cancel{2}\cdot\cancel{2}\cdot\cancel{2}\cdot\cancel{2}\cdot\cancel{2}\cdot 3}{\cancel{2}\cdot\cancel{2}\cdot\cancel{2}\cdot\cancel{2}\cdot\cancel{2}} = 3$

The fractions are equivalent (3 = 3).

50. $\dfrac{24}{72}$ and $\dfrac{30}{90}$

$\dfrac{24}{72} = \dfrac{\cancel{2}\cdot\cancel{2}\cdot\cancel{2}\cdot\cancel{3}}{\cancel{2}\cdot\cancel{2}\cdot\cancel{2}\cdot\cancel{3}\cdot 3} = \dfrac{1}{3}$

$\dfrac{30}{90} = \dfrac{\cancel{2}\cdot\cancel{3}\cdot\cancel{5}}{\cancel{2}\cdot\cancel{3}\cdot 3\cdot\cancel{5}} = \dfrac{1}{3}$

The fractions are equivalent $\left(\dfrac{1}{3} = \dfrac{1}{3}\right)$.

52. Two fractions are equivalent when they are of equal value.

The fractions $\dfrac{10}{15}$ and $\dfrac{8}{12}$ are equivalent.

$\dfrac{10}{15} = \dfrac{2\cdot\cancel{5}}{3\cdot\cancel{5}} = \dfrac{2\cdot 1}{3\cdot 1} = \dfrac{2}{3}$

$\dfrac{8}{12} = \dfrac{\cancel{2}\cdot\cancel{2}\cdot 2}{\cancel{2}\cdot\cancel{2}\cdot 3} = \dfrac{1\cdot 1\cdot 2}{1\cdot 1\cdot 3} = \dfrac{2}{3}$

The fractions are equivalent $\left(\dfrac{2}{3} = \dfrac{2}{3}\right)$.

54. $\dfrac{363}{528} = \dfrac{363 \div 33}{528 \div 33} = \dfrac{11}{16}$

56. $\dfrac{525}{105} = \dfrac{\overset{1}{\cancel{3}} \cdot \overset{1}{\cancel{5}} \cdot 5 \cdot \overset{1}{\cancel{7}}}{\underset{1}{\cancel{3}} \cdot \underset{1}{\cancel{5}} \cdot \underset{1}{\cancel{7}}} = \dfrac{5}{1} = 5$

2.5 Multiplying Fractions

2. $\dfrac{1}{2} \cdot \dfrac{2}{3} = \dfrac{1}{\underset{1}{\cancel{2}}} \cdot \dfrac{\overset{1}{\cancel{2}}}{3} = \dfrac{1 \cdot 1}{1 \cdot 3} = \dfrac{1}{3}$

4. $\dfrac{2}{5} \cdot \dfrac{3}{4} = \dfrac{2}{5} \cdot \dfrac{3}{\underset{2}{\cancel{4}}} = \dfrac{1 \cdot 3}{5 \cdot 2} = \dfrac{3}{10}$

6. $\dfrac{4}{9} \cdot \dfrac{12}{7} = \dfrac{4}{\underset{3}{\cancel{9}}} \cdot \dfrac{\overset{4}{\cancel{12}}}{7} = \dfrac{4 \cdot 4}{3 \cdot 7} = \dfrac{16}{21}$

8. $\dfrac{7}{8} \cdot \dfrac{16}{21} \cdot \dfrac{1}{2} = \dfrac{\overset{1}{\cancel{7}}}{\underset{1}{\cancel{8}}} \cdot \dfrac{\overset{\overset{1}{\cancel{2}}}{\cancel{16}}}{\underset{3}{\cancel{21}}} \cdot \dfrac{1}{\cancel{2}} = \dfrac{1 \cdot 1 \cdot 1}{1 \cdot 3 \cdot 1} = \dfrac{1}{3}$

10. $\dfrac{2}{5} \cdot \dfrac{3}{8} \cdot \dfrac{2}{3} = \dfrac{\overset{1}{\cancel{2}}}{5} \cdot \dfrac{\overset{1}{\cancel{3}}}{\underset{\underset{2}{\cancel{4}}}{\cancel{8}}} \cdot \dfrac{\overset{1}{\cancel{2}}}{\underset{1}{\cancel{3}}} = \dfrac{1 \cdot 1 \cdot 1}{5 \cdot 2 \cdot 1} = \dfrac{1}{10}$

12. $\dfrac{5}{12} \cdot \dfrac{7}{10} = \dfrac{\overset{1}{\cancel{5}}}{12} \cdot \dfrac{7}{\underset{2}{\cancel{10}}} = \dfrac{1 \cdot 7}{12 \cdot 2} = \dfrac{7}{24}$

14. $\dfrac{6}{11} \cdot \dfrac{22}{15} = \dfrac{\overset{2}{\cancel{6}}}{\underset{1}{\cancel{11}}} \cdot \dfrac{\overset{2}{\cancel{22}}}{\underset{5}{\cancel{15}}} = \dfrac{2 \cdot 2}{1 \cdot 5} = \dfrac{4}{5}$

16. $\dfrac{35}{64} \cdot \dfrac{32}{15} \cdot \dfrac{27}{72} = \dfrac{\overset{7}{\cancel{35}}}{\underset{2}{\cancel{64}}} \cdot \dfrac{\overset{1}{\cancel{32}}}{\underset{3}{\cancel{15}}} \cdot \dfrac{\overset{\overset{1}{\cancel{3}}}{\cancel{27}}}{\underset{8}{\cancel{72}}} = \dfrac{7 \cdot 1 \cdot 1}{2 \cdot 1 \cdot 8} = \dfrac{7}{16}$

18. $\dfrac{39}{42} \cdot \dfrac{7}{13} \cdot \dfrac{7}{24} = \dfrac{\overset{\overset{1}{\cancel{3}}}{\cancel{39}}}{\underset{\underset{2}{\cancel{6}}}{\cancel{42}}} \cdot \dfrac{\overset{1}{\cancel{7}}}{\underset{1}{\cancel{13}}} \cdot \dfrac{7}{24} = \dfrac{1 \cdot 1 \cdot 7}{2 \cdot 1 \cdot 24} = \dfrac{7}{48}$

20. $40 \cdot \dfrac{3}{4} = \dfrac{\overset{10}{\cancel{40}}}{1} \cdot \dfrac{3}{\underset{1}{\cancel{4}}} = \dfrac{30}{1} = 30$

22. $\dfrac{3}{5} \cdot 45 = \dfrac{3}{\underset{1}{\cancel{5}}} \cdot \dfrac{\overset{9}{\cancel{45}}}{1} = \dfrac{27}{1} = 27$

24. $30 \cdot \dfrac{3}{10} = \dfrac{\overset{3}{\cancel{30}}}{1} \cdot \dfrac{3}{\underset{1}{\cancel{10}}} = \dfrac{9}{1} = 9$

26. $35 \cdot \dfrac{3}{5} \cdot \dfrac{1}{2} = \dfrac{\overset{7}{\cancel{35}}}{1} \cdot \dfrac{3}{\underset{1}{\cancel{5}}} \cdot \dfrac{1}{2} = \dfrac{21}{2} = 10\dfrac{1}{2}$

28. $200 \cdot \dfrac{7}{8} = \dfrac{\overset{25}{\cancel{200}}}{1} \cdot \dfrac{7}{\underset{1}{\cancel{8}}} = \dfrac{175}{1} = 175$

30. $\dfrac{3}{7} \cdot 490 = \dfrac{3}{\underset{1}{\cancel{7}}} \cdot \dfrac{\overset{70}{\cancel{490}}}{1} = \dfrac{210}{1} = 210$

32. $\dfrac{12}{25} \cdot 430 = \dfrac{12}{\underset{5}{\cancel{25}}} \cdot \dfrac{\overset{86}{\cancel{430}}}{1} = \dfrac{1032}{5} = 206\dfrac{2}{5}$

34. $\dfrac{21}{13} \cdot 520 \cdot \dfrac{7}{20} = \dfrac{21}{\underset{1}{\cancel{13}}} \cdot \dfrac{\overset{26}{\cancel{520}}}{1} \cdot \dfrac{7}{\underset{1}{\cancel{20}}}$

$\qquad = \dfrac{21 \cdot 2 \cdot 7}{1 \cdot 1 \cdot 1}$

$\qquad = \dfrac{294}{1} = 294$

36. $\dfrac{76}{43} \cdot 473 \cdot \dfrac{5}{19} = \dfrac{\overset{4}{\cancel{76}}}{\underset{1}{\cancel{43}}} \cdot \dfrac{\overset{11}{\cancel{473}}}{1} \cdot \dfrac{5}{\underset{1}{\cancel{19}}}$

$\qquad = \dfrac{4 \cdot 11 \cdot 5}{1 \cdot 1 \cdot 1}$

$\qquad = \dfrac{220}{1} = 220$

38. *area = length · width*

$\dfrac{7}{8} \cdot \dfrac{1}{4} = \dfrac{7 \cdot 1}{8 \cdot 1} = \dfrac{7}{32}$ ft^2

40. *area = length · width*

$$\frac{3}{8} \cdot 8 = \frac{3}{\overset{}{\underset{1}{8}}} \cdot \frac{\overset{1}{8}}{1} = 3 \text{ in.}^2$$

42. *area = length · width*

$$\frac{9}{16} \cdot \frac{14}{15} = \frac{\overset{3}{9}}{\underset{8}{16}} \cdot \frac{\overset{7}{14}}{\underset{5}{15}} = \frac{3 \cdot 7}{8 \cdot 5} = \frac{21}{40} \text{ yd}^2$$

44. You must divide a numerator and a denominator by the same number. If you do all possible cancellations, your answer will be in lowest terms. One example is

$$\frac{3}{4} \cdot \frac{2}{3} = \frac{\overset{1}{3} \cdot \overset{1}{2}}{\underset{2}{4} \cdot \underset{1}{3}} = \frac{1}{2}.$$

46. *area = length · width*

$$2 \cdot \frac{7}{8} = \frac{\overset{1}{2}}{1} \cdot \frac{7}{\underset{4}{8}} = \frac{7}{4} = 1\frac{3}{4} \text{ yd}^2$$

48. *area = length · width*

$$6 \cdot \frac{3}{4} = \frac{\overset{3}{6}}{1} \cdot \frac{3}{\underset{2}{4}}$$

$$= \frac{3 \cdot 3}{1 \cdot 2} = \frac{9}{2}$$

$$= 4\frac{1}{2} \text{ mi}^2$$

50. Find the area of Rocking Horse Ranch.

$$\frac{3}{4} \cdot \frac{1}{2} = \frac{3 \cdot 1}{4 \cdot 2} = \frac{3}{8} \text{ mi}^2$$

Find the area of Silver Spur Ranch.

$$\frac{5}{8} \cdot \frac{4}{5} = \frac{\overset{1}{5} \cdot \overset{1}{4}}{\underset{2}{8} \cdot \underset{1}{5}} = \frac{1}{2} \text{ mi}^2$$

Since $\frac{1}{2}$ is larger than $\frac{3}{8}$, Silver Spur Ranch has the larger area.

2.6 Applications of Multiplication

2. Multiply the length and the width.

$$\frac{7}{8} \cdot \frac{10}{9} = \frac{7}{\underset{4}{8}} \cdot \frac{\overset{5}{10}}{9} = \frac{7 \cdot 5}{4 \cdot 9} = \frac{35}{36}$$

The area is $\frac{35}{36}$ yd^2.

4. Multiply the length and the width.

$$\frac{4}{5} \cdot \frac{3}{8} = \frac{\overset{1}{4}}{5} \cdot \frac{3}{\underset{2}{8}} = \frac{1 \cdot 3}{5 \cdot 2} = \frac{3}{10}$$

The area is $\frac{3}{10}$ yd^2.

6. Multiply the items sold by the fraction which is junk food.

$$\frac{3}{25} \cdot 2500 = \frac{3}{\underset{1}{25}} \cdot \frac{\overset{100}{2500}}{1}$$

$$= \frac{3 \cdot 100}{1 \cdot 1}$$

$$= \frac{300}{1} = 300$$

There are 300 junk food items.

8. Multiply the fraction that is personal earnings by the employer's profits.

$$\frac{2}{5} \cdot 5680 = \frac{2}{\underset{1}{5}} \cdot \frac{\overset{1136}{5680}}{1}$$

$$= \frac{2 \cdot 1136}{1 \cdot 1}$$

$$= \frac{2272}{1} = 2272$$

Her earnings are $2272.

10. Find $\frac{3}{4}$ of $8400.

$$\frac{3}{4} \cdot 8400 = \frac{3 \cdot \overset{2100}{8400}}{\underset{1}{4} \cdot 1} = 6300$$

He must earn $6300.

12. Multiply the fraction of rooms for non-smokers by the number of rooms.

$$\frac{9}{17} \cdot 408 = \frac{9}{\overset{}{\underset{1}{17}}} \cdot \frac{\overset{24}{408}}{1} = \frac{9 \cdot 24}{1 \cdot 1} = \frac{216}{1} = 216$$

There are 216 rooms for non-smokers.

14. The largest sector of the circle graph is the age group 55 years and up. To find how many books this age group purchased, multiply $\frac{8}{25}$ by the total number of books, 1 billion.

$$\frac{8}{25} \cdot 1,000,000,000 = \frac{8}{25} \cdot \frac{1,000,000,000}{1}$$
$$= 320,000,000$$

They purchased 320 million or 320,000,000 books.

16. Multiply the fraction labeled in the 45–54 year age group, $\frac{6}{25}$, by the total number of books, 1 billion.

$$\frac{6}{25} \cdot 1,000,000,000 = \frac{6}{25} \cdot \frac{1,000,000,000}{1}$$
$$= 240,000,000$$

They purchased 240 million or 240,000,000 books.

18. Answers will vary.
Some possibilities are
1. You made an addition error.
2. The fractions on the pie graph are incorrect.
3. The fraction errors were caused by rounding.

20. Multiply the fraction $\left(\frac{1}{4}\right)$ by the total income ($38,000).

$$\frac{1}{4} \cdot 38,000 = \frac{1}{\overset{}{\underset{1}{4}}} \cdot \frac{\overset{9500}{38,000}}{1} = 9500$$

Their taxes were $9500.

22. Multiply the fraction $\left(\frac{5}{16}\right)$ by the total income.

$$\frac{5}{16} \cdot 38,000 = \frac{5}{\overset{}{\underset{1}{16}}} \cdot \frac{\overset{2375}{38,000}}{1} = 11,875$$

They spent $11,875 on food.

24. Multiply the fraction $\left(\frac{1}{8}\right)$ times the total income ($38,000).

$$\frac{1}{8} \cdot 38,000 = \frac{1}{\overset{}{\underset{1}{8}}} \cdot \frac{\overset{4750}{38,000}}{1} = 4750$$

They spent $4750 on clothing.

26. Yes, the statements are true. Since whole numbers are 1 or greater, when you multiply, the product will always be greater than either of the numbers multiplied. But, when you multiply two proper fractions, you are finding a fraction of a fraction, and the product will be smaller than either of the two proper fractions.

28. The number of miles Ruth jogged in 5 hours is $\frac{5}{8}$ of the number of miles she jogged in 8 hours. Multiply 40 times $\frac{5}{8}$.

$$40 \cdot \frac{5}{8} = \frac{\overset{5}{40}}{1} \cdot \frac{5}{\overset{}{\underset{1}{8}}} = 25$$

She jogged 25 miles in 5 hours.

30. Multiply the fraction $\left(\frac{9}{16}\right)$ by the cost ($32,000).

$$\frac{9}{16} \cdot 32,000 = \frac{9}{\overset{}{\underset{1}{16}}} \cdot \frac{\overset{2000}{32,000}}{1} = \$18,000$$

To find the amount that is to be paid by the owner subtract:

$32,000 - $18,000 = $14,000.

32. Subtract to find the amount remaining to be invested.

$$\frac{5}{5} - \frac{1}{5} = \frac{4}{5}$$

Then multiply $\frac{4}{5}$ and $\frac{1}{8}$.

$$\frac{4}{5} \cdot \frac{1}{8} = \frac{\overset{1}{4} \cdot 1}{5 \cdot \overset{}{\underset{2}{8}}} = \frac{1}{10}$$

The couple invested $\frac{1}{10}$ of their investment in bonds.

2.7 Dividing Fractions

2. The reciprocal of $\frac{3}{4}$ is $\frac{4}{3}$

because $\frac{3}{4} \cdot \frac{4}{3} = \frac{12}{12} = 1$.

4. The reciprocal of $\frac{12}{7}$ is $\frac{7}{12}$

because $\frac{7}{12} \cdot \frac{12}{7} = \frac{84}{84} = 1$.

6. The reciprocal of $\frac{13}{20}$ is $\frac{20}{13}$

because $\frac{13}{20} \cdot \frac{20}{13} = \frac{260}{260} = 1$.

8. The reciprocal of 10 is $\frac{1}{10}$

because $\frac{10}{1} \cdot \frac{1}{10} = \frac{10}{10} = 1$.

10. $\dfrac{3}{8} \div \dfrac{5}{8} = \dfrac{3}{\cancel{8}} \cdot \dfrac{\overset{1}{\cancel{8}}}{5} = \dfrac{3}{5}$

12. $\dfrac{7}{8} \div \dfrac{3}{4} = \dfrac{7}{\underset{2}{\cancel{8}}} \cdot \dfrac{\overset{1}{\cancel{4}}}{3} = \dfrac{7}{6} = 1\dfrac{1}{6}$

14. $\dfrac{4}{5} \div \dfrac{9}{4} = \dfrac{4}{5} \cdot \dfrac{4}{9} = \dfrac{16}{45}$

16. $\dfrac{5}{8} \div \dfrac{5}{16} = \dfrac{\overset{1}{\cancel{5}}}{\underset{1}{\cancel{8}}} \cdot \dfrac{\overset{2}{\cancel{16}}}{\underset{1}{\cancel{5}}} = \dfrac{2}{1} = 2$

18. $\dfrac{7}{12} \div \dfrac{14}{15} = \dfrac{\overset{1}{\cancel{7}}}{\underset{4}{\cancel{12}}} \cdot \dfrac{\overset{5}{\cancel{15}}}{\underset{2}{\cancel{14}}} = \dfrac{5}{8}$

20. $\dfrac{\frac{9}{10}}{\frac{3}{5}} = \dfrac{9}{10} \div \dfrac{3}{5} = \dfrac{\overset{3}{\cancel{9}}}{\underset{2}{\cancel{10}}} \cdot \dfrac{\overset{1}{\cancel{5}}}{\underset{1}{\cancel{3}}} = \dfrac{3}{2} = 1\dfrac{1}{2}$

22. $\dfrac{\frac{28}{15}}{\frac{21}{5}} = \dfrac{28}{15} \div \dfrac{21}{5} = \dfrac{\overset{4}{\cancel{28}}}{\underset{3}{\cancel{15}}} \cdot \dfrac{\overset{1}{\cancel{5}}}{\underset{3}{\cancel{21}}} = \dfrac{4}{9}$

24. $7 \div \dfrac{1}{4} = \dfrac{7}{1} \div \dfrac{1}{4} = \dfrac{7}{1} \cdot \dfrac{4}{1} = 28$

26. $\dfrac{9}{\frac{3}{4}} = 9 \div \dfrac{3}{4} = \dfrac{9}{1} \div \dfrac{3}{4} = \dfrac{\overset{3}{\cancel{9}}}{1} \cdot \dfrac{4}{\underset{1}{\cancel{3}}} = \dfrac{12}{1} = 12$

28. $\dfrac{\frac{7}{10}}{3} = \dfrac{7}{10} \div 3 = \dfrac{7}{10} \div \dfrac{3}{1} = \dfrac{7}{10} \cdot \dfrac{1}{3} = \dfrac{7}{30}$

30. Divide the fraction of revenue by the number of winners.

$\dfrac{7}{8} \div 14 = \dfrac{\overset{1}{\cancel{7}}}{8} \cdot \dfrac{1}{\underset{2}{\cancel{14}}} = \dfrac{1}{16}$

Each winner receives $\frac{1}{16}$ of the total revenue.

32. Divide the number of quarts of oil by the fraction of a quart each reservoir holds.

$10 \div \dfrac{1}{3} = \dfrac{10}{1} \cdot \dfrac{3}{1} = 30$

Robert can fill 30 reservoirs.

34. Divide the number of pounds of peanuts by the fraction of peanuts each person will get.

$10 \div \dfrac{5}{16} = \dfrac{\overset{2}{\cancel{10}}}{1} \cdot \dfrac{16}{\underset{1}{\cancel{5}}} = 32$

32 guests can be served with 10 pounds of peanuts.

36. Divide the 200-yard roll into $\frac{5}{8}$-yard pieces.

$200 \div \dfrac{5}{8} = \dfrac{\overset{40}{\cancel{200}}}{1} \cdot \dfrac{8}{\underset{1}{\cancel{8}}} = 320$

Manuel can cut 320 pieces from the roll.

38. Divide the total amount of brass tacks by amount needed for each stool.

$21 \div \dfrac{7}{8} = \dfrac{\overset{3}{\cancel{21}}}{1} \cdot \dfrac{8}{\underset{1}{\cancel{7}}} = 24$

She can upholster 24 bar stools.

40. Sometimes the answer is smaller and sometimes it is larger.

$\dfrac{1}{4} \div \dfrac{7}{8} = \dfrac{1}{\underset{1}{\cancel{4}}} \times \dfrac{\overset{2}{\cancel{8}}}{7} = \dfrac{2}{7}$ *smaller than $\frac{7}{8}$ but not smaller than $\frac{1}{4}$*

$\dfrac{1}{2} \div \dfrac{1}{4} = \dfrac{1}{\underset{1}{\cancel{2}}} \times \dfrac{\overset{2}{\cancel{4}}}{1} = \dfrac{2}{1} = 2$ *larger*

42. First, find the number of hours the whole job will take by dividing the number of hours worked by the fractional part that is finished.

$$63 \div \frac{7}{9} = \frac{63}{1} \div \frac{7}{9} = \frac{\overset{9}{\cancel{63}}}{1} \cdot \frac{9}{\underset{1}{\cancel{7}}} = 81 \text{ total hours}$$

$81 - 63 = 18$ more hours that she must work. She must work 18 more hours to complete the job.

44. First, divide the amount raised so far by the fractional part raised.

$$45{,}000 \div \frac{9}{16} = \frac{\overset{5000}{\cancel{45{,}000}}}{1} \cdot \frac{16}{\underset{1}{\cancel{9}}} = 80{,}000$$

They must raise an additional
$80{,}000 - $45{,}000 = $35{,}000.

2.8 Multiplying and Dividing Mixed Numbers

2. $3\frac{1}{2} \cdot 1\frac{1}{4}$

estimate $4 \cdot 1 = 4$

exact $3\frac{1}{2} \cdot 1\frac{1}{4} = \frac{7}{2} \cdot \frac{5}{4} = \frac{35}{8} = 4\frac{3}{8}$

4. $4\frac{1}{2} \cdot 2\frac{1}{4}$

estimate $5 \cdot 2 = 10$

exact $4\frac{1}{2} \cdot 2\frac{1}{4} = \frac{9}{2} \cdot \frac{9}{4} = \frac{81}{8} = 10\frac{1}{8}$

6. $6\frac{1}{4} \cdot 3\frac{1}{5}$

estimate $6 \cdot 3 = 18$

exact $6\frac{1}{4} \cdot 3\frac{1}{5} = \frac{\overset{5}{\cancel{25}}}{\underset{1}{\cancel{4}}} \cdot \frac{\overset{4}{\cancel{16}}}{\underset{1}{\cancel{5}}} = \frac{20}{1} = 20$

8. $6 \cdot 2\frac{1}{3}$

estimate $6 \cdot 2 = 12$

exact $6 \cdot 2\frac{1}{3} = \frac{\overset{2}{\cancel{6}}}{1} \cdot \frac{7}{\underset{1}{\cancel{3}}} = \frac{2 \cdot 7}{1 \cdot 1} = \frac{14}{1} = 14$

10. $5\frac{1}{2} \cdot 1\frac{1}{3} \cdot 2\frac{1}{4}$

estimate $6 \cdot 1 \cdot 2 = 12$

exact $5\frac{1}{2} \cdot 1\frac{1}{3} \cdot 2\frac{1}{4} = \frac{11}{2} \cdot \frac{\overset{1}{\cancel{4}}}{\underset{1}{\cancel{3}}} \cdot \frac{\overset{3}{\cancel{9}}}{\underset{1}{\cancel{4}}} = \frac{33}{2} = 16\frac{1}{2}$

12. $\frac{2}{3} \cdot 3\frac{2}{3} \cdot \frac{6}{11}$

estimate $1 \cdot 4 \cdot 1 = 4$

exact $\frac{2}{3} \cdot 3\frac{2}{3} \cdot \frac{6}{11} = \frac{2}{3} \cdot \frac{\overset{1}{\cancel{11}}}{\underset{1}{\cancel{3}}} \cdot \frac{\overset{2}{\cancel{6}}}{\underset{1}{\cancel{11}}}$

$= \frac{2 \cdot 1 \cdot 2}{3 \cdot 1 \cdot 1}$

$= \frac{4}{3} = 1\frac{1}{3}$

14. $1\frac{1}{8} \div 2\frac{1}{4}$

estimate $1 \div 2 = \frac{1}{2}$

exact $1\frac{1}{8} \div 2\frac{1}{4} = \frac{9}{8} \div \frac{9}{4} = \frac{\overset{1}{\cancel{9}}}{\underset{2}{\cancel{8}}} \cdot \frac{\overset{1}{\cancel{4}}}{\underset{1}{\cancel{9}}} = \frac{1 \cdot 1}{2 \cdot 1} = \frac{1}{2}$

16. $2\frac{3}{4} \div 2$

estimate $3 \div 2 = 1\frac{1}{2}$

exact $2\frac{3}{4} \div 2 = \frac{11}{4} \div \frac{2}{1} = \frac{11}{4} \cdot \frac{1}{2} = \frac{11}{8} = 1\frac{3}{8}$

18. $5 \div 1\frac{7}{8}$

estimate $5 \div 2 = 2\frac{1}{2}$

exact

$5 \div 1\frac{7}{8} = \frac{5}{1} \div \frac{15}{8} = \frac{\overset{1}{\cancel{5}}}{1} \cdot \frac{8}{\underset{3}{\cancel{15}}} = \frac{1 \cdot 8}{1 \cdot 3} = \frac{8}{3} = 2\frac{2}{3}$

20. $\frac{3}{4} \div 2\frac{1}{2}$

estimate $1 \div 3 = \frac{1}{3}$

exact $\frac{3}{4} \div 2\frac{1}{2} = \frac{3}{4} \div \frac{5}{2} = \frac{3}{\underset{2}{\cancel{4}}} \cdot \frac{\overset{1}{\cancel{2}}}{5} = \frac{3}{10}$

22. $8\frac{2}{5} \div 3\frac{1}{2}$

estimate $8 \div 4 = 2$

exact $8\frac{2}{5} \div 3\frac{1}{2} = \frac{42}{5} \div \frac{7}{2} = \frac{\overset{6}{\cancel{42}}}{5} \cdot \frac{2}{\underset{1}{\cancel{7}}} = \frac{12}{5} = 2\frac{2}{5}$

24. $5\frac{3}{4} \div 2$

estimate $6 \div 2 = 3$

exact $5\frac{3}{4} \div 2 = \frac{23}{4} \div \frac{2}{1} = \frac{23}{4} \cdot \frac{1}{2} = \frac{23}{8} = 2\frac{7}{8}$

26. To triple the recipe, multiply each amount by 3.

(a) *estimate* $2 \cdot 3 = 6$ cups

exact

$1\frac{3}{4} \cdot 3 = \frac{7}{4} \cdot \frac{3}{1} = \frac{21}{4} = 5\frac{1}{4}$ cups of flour

(b) *estimate* $3 \cdot 3 = 9$ cups

exact

$2\frac{1}{2} \cdot 3 = \frac{5}{2} \cdot \frac{3}{1} = \frac{15}{2} = 7\frac{1}{2}$ cups of Quaker Oats

(c) *estimate* $1 \cdot 3 = 3$ cups

exact

$\frac{1}{2} \cdot 3 = \frac{1}{2} \cdot \frac{3}{1} = \frac{3}{2} = 1\frac{1}{2}$ cups of granulated sugar

28. Divide each amount by 3.

(a) *estimate* $3 \div 3 = 1$ cup

exact

$2\frac{1}{2} \div 3 = \frac{5}{2} \div \frac{3}{1} = \frac{5}{2} \cdot \frac{1}{3} = \frac{5}{6}$ cup of Quaker Oats

(b) *estimate* $1 \div 3 = \frac{1}{3}$ teaspoon

exact

$\frac{1}{2} \div 3 = \frac{1}{2} \div \frac{3}{1} = \frac{1}{2} \cdot \frac{1}{3} = \frac{1}{6}$ teaspoon of salt

(c) *estimate* $1 \div 3 = \frac{1}{3}$ cup

exact

$1\frac{1}{4} \div 3 = \frac{5}{4} \div \frac{3}{1} = \frac{5}{4} \cdot \frac{1}{3} = \frac{5}{12}$ cup of brown sugar

30. Divide the number of total ounces by the size of each vial.

estimate $99 \div 1 = 99$ vials

exact $99 \div 1\frac{1}{8} = \frac{99}{1} \div \frac{9}{8} = \frac{\overset{11}{\cancel{99}}}{1} \cdot \frac{8}{\underset{1}{\cancel{9}}} = \frac{88}{1} = 88$

88 vials can be filled.

32. Multiply the number of homes by the amount of nails needed for each home.

estimate $38 \cdot 36 = 1368$ pounds

exact $37\frac{3}{4} \cdot 36 = \frac{151}{\underset{1}{\cancel{4}}} \cdot \frac{\overset{9}{\cancel{36}}}{1} = 1359$

1359 pounds are needed for 36 homes.

34. The additional step is to use the reciprocal of the second fraction (divisor).

36. Divide the number of square yards of carpet by the amount of carpet needed for each apartment unit.

estimate $6750 \div 63 \approx 107$ units

exact $6750 \div 62\frac{1}{2} = \frac{6750}{1} \div \frac{125}{2}$

$= \frac{\overset{54}{\cancel{6750}}}{1} \cdot \frac{2}{\underset{1}{\cancel{125}}}$

$= \frac{54 \cdot 2}{1 \cdot 1}$

$= 108$

108 units can be carpeted.

38. Divide the amount of sand (12 tons) by the amount his truck can carry each trip.

estimate $12 \div 1 = 12$ trips

exact $12 \div \frac{3}{4} = \frac{12}{1} \div \frac{3}{4} = \frac{\overset{4}{\cancel{12}}}{1} \cdot \frac{4}{\underset{1}{\cancel{3}}} = 16$

16 trips must be made.

40. *estimate*: $7 \cdot 36 =$ 252
$3 \cdot 22 = \underline{+\ 66}$
318 minutes

If it takes $6\frac{1}{2}$ minutes to complete 1 necklace, then it takes

$$6\frac{1}{2} \cdot 36 = \frac{13}{\overset{}{\underset{1}{\cancel{2}}}} \cdot \frac{\overset{18}{\cancel{36}}}{1} = 234 \text{ minutes}$$

to complete 36 necklaces.

For 22 bracelets it takes

$$3\frac{1}{8} \cdot 22 = \frac{25}{\underset{4}{\cancel{8}}} \cdot \frac{\overset{11}{\cancel{22}}}{1} = \frac{275}{4} = 68\frac{3}{4} \text{ minutes.}$$

The total time to complete the jewelry is:

234
$\underline{+\ 68\frac{3}{4}}$
$302\frac{3}{4}$ minutes.

Chapter 3

ADDING AND SUBTRACTING FRACTIONS

3.1 Adding and Subtracting Like Fractions

2. $\dfrac{5}{8} + \dfrac{2}{8} = \dfrac{5+2}{8} = \dfrac{7}{8}$

4. $\dfrac{9}{11} + \dfrac{1}{11} = \dfrac{9+1}{11} = \dfrac{10}{11}$

6. $\dfrac{1}{12} + \dfrac{1}{12} = \dfrac{1+1}{12} = \dfrac{2}{12} = \dfrac{2 \div 2}{12 \div 2} = \dfrac{1}{6}$

8. $\quad \dfrac{13}{12}$

$+ \quad \dfrac{5}{12}$

$\dfrac{13}{12} + \dfrac{5}{12} = \dfrac{13+5}{12} = \dfrac{18}{12} = \dfrac{18 \div 6}{12 \div 6} = \dfrac{3}{2} = 1\dfrac{1}{2}$

10. $\dfrac{3}{14} + \dfrac{5}{14} = \dfrac{3+5}{14} = \dfrac{8}{14} = \dfrac{8 \div 2}{14 \div 2} = \dfrac{4}{7}$

12. $\dfrac{1}{7} + \dfrac{2}{7} + \dfrac{3}{7} = \dfrac{1+2+3}{7} = \dfrac{6}{7}$

14. $\dfrac{5}{11} + \dfrac{1}{11} + \dfrac{4}{11} = \dfrac{5+1+4}{11} = \dfrac{10}{11}$

16. $\dfrac{4}{9} + \dfrac{1}{9} + \dfrac{7}{9} = \dfrac{4+1+7}{9} = \dfrac{12}{9} = 1\dfrac{3}{9} = 1\dfrac{1}{3}$

18. $\dfrac{7}{64} + \dfrac{15}{64} + \dfrac{20}{64} = \dfrac{7+15+20}{64} = \dfrac{42}{64} = \dfrac{42 \div 2}{64 \div 2} = \dfrac{21}{32}$

20. $\dfrac{2}{3} - \dfrac{1}{3} = \dfrac{2-1}{3} = \dfrac{1}{3}$

22. $\dfrac{4}{5} - \dfrac{3}{5} = \dfrac{4-3}{5} = \dfrac{1}{5}$

24. $\dfrac{7}{8} - \dfrac{3}{8} = \dfrac{7-3}{8} = \dfrac{4}{8} = \dfrac{4 \div 4}{8 \div 4} = \dfrac{1}{2}$

26. $\quad \dfrac{43}{24}$

$- \quad \dfrac{13}{24}$

$\dfrac{43}{24} - \dfrac{13}{24} = \dfrac{40-13}{24} = \dfrac{30}{24} = 1\dfrac{6}{24} = 1\dfrac{1}{4}$

28. $\quad \dfrac{38}{55}$

$- \quad \dfrac{16}{55}$

$\dfrac{38}{55} - \dfrac{16}{55} = \dfrac{38-16}{55} = \dfrac{22}{55} = \dfrac{22 \div 11}{55 \div 11} = \dfrac{2}{5}$

30. $\dfrac{76}{45} - \dfrac{21}{45} = \dfrac{76-21}{45} = \dfrac{55}{45} = \dfrac{55 \div 5}{45 \div 5} = \dfrac{11}{9} = 1\dfrac{2}{9}$

32. $\dfrac{181}{100} - \dfrac{31}{100} = \dfrac{181-31}{100} = \dfrac{150}{100} = \dfrac{150 \div 50}{100 \div 50} = \dfrac{3}{2} = 1\dfrac{1}{2}$

34. Like fractions have the same denominator. Unlike fractions have denominators that are different. Some examples are:

$$\text{like: } \dfrac{3}{8}, \dfrac{1}{8}, \dfrac{7}{8} \quad \text{unlike: } \dfrac{1}{2}, \dfrac{3}{4}, \dfrac{5}{8}.$$

36. Subtract two fractions.

$$\dfrac{17}{20} - \dfrac{3}{20} = \dfrac{17-3}{20} = \dfrac{14}{20} = \dfrac{14 \div 2}{20 \div 2} = \dfrac{7}{10}$$

The state owes the lotto winner $\dfrac{7}{10}$ of the winnings.

38. Add the distance down the ravine to the distance along the creek bed.

$$\dfrac{5}{12} + \dfrac{1}{12} = \dfrac{5+1}{12} = \dfrac{6}{12} = \dfrac{1}{2}$$

The search team traveled a total of $\dfrac{1}{2}$ mile.

40. Add the acres planted in the morning to the acres planted in the afternoon.

$$\frac{5}{12} + \frac{11}{12} = \frac{5+11}{12} = \frac{6}{12}$$

Then, subtract the acres destroyed by frost.

$$\frac{16}{12} - \frac{7}{12} = \frac{16-7}{12} = \frac{9}{12} = \frac{3}{4}$$

$\frac{3}{4}$ acre of seedlings remained.

3.2   Least Common Multiples

2. 6 and 12

Multiples of 12:

$$\underline{12}, 24, 36, 48, 60, \dots$$

12 is the first number divisible by 6.

$$(12 \div 6 = 2)$$

The least common multiple of 6 and 12 is 12.

4. 3 and 7

Multiples of 7:

$$7, 14, \underline{21}, 28, 35, 42, \dots$$

21 is the first number divisible by 3.

$$(21 \div 3 = 7)$$

The least common multiple of 3 and 7 is 21.

6. 4 and 10

Multiples of 10:

$$10, \underline{20}, 30, 40, \dots$$

20 is the first number divisible by 4.

$$(20 \div 4 = 5)$$

The least common multiple of 4 and 10 is 20.

8. 6 and 8

Multiples of 8:

$$8, 16, \underline{24}, 32, 40, 48, \dots$$

24 is the first number divisible by 6.

$$(24 \div 6 = 4)$$

The least common multiple of 6 and 8 is 24.

10. 12 and 16

Multiples of 16:

$$16, 32, \underline{48}, 64, \dots$$

48 is the first number divisible by 12.

$$(48 \div 12 = 4)$$

The least common multiple of 12 and 16 is 48.

12. 25 and 75

Multiples of 75:

$$\underline{75}, 150, 225, 300, 375, 450, \dots$$

75 is the first number divisible by 25.

$$(75 \div 25 = 3)$$

The least common multiple of 25 and 75 is 75.

14. 8, 10

2	8	10
2	4	$\cancel{8}$
2	2	$\cancel{8}$
5	$\cancel{1}$	5
	1	1

The least common multiple is

$$2 \cdot 2 \cdot 2 \cdot 5 = 40.$$

16. 9 and 15

3	9	15
3	3	$\cancel{9}$
5	$\cancel{1}$	5
	1	1

The least common multiple is

$$3 \cdot 3 \cdot 5 = 45.$$

18. 20, 24, 30

2	20	24	30
2	10	12	$\cancel{15}$
2	$\cancel{5}$	6	$\cancel{15}$
3	$\cancel{5}$	3	15
5	5	$\cancel{1}$	5
	1	1	1

The least common multiple is

$$2 \cdot 2 \cdot 2 \cdot 3 \cdot 5 = 120.$$

20. 8, 9, 12, 18

2	8	9̸	12	18
2	4	9̸	6	9̸
2	2̸	9̸	3	9̸
3	1̸	9	3	9
3	1̸	3	1̸	3
	1	1	1	1

The least common multiple is
$$2 \cdot 2 \cdot 2 \cdot 3 \cdot 3 = 72.$$

22. 6, 9, 27, 36
$$6 = 2 \cdot 3$$
$$9 = 3 \cdot 3$$
$$27 = 3 \cdot 3 \cdot 3$$
$$36 = 2 \cdot 2 \cdot 3 \cdot 3$$
$$\text{LCM} = 2 \cdot 2 \cdot 3 \cdot 3 \cdot 3 = 108$$
The least common multiple is 108.

24. 5, 6, 25, 30
$$5 = 5$$
$$6 = 2 \cdot 3$$
$$25 = 5 \cdot 5$$
$$30 = 2 \cdot 3 \cdot 5$$
$$\text{LCM} = 2 \cdot 3 \cdot 5 \cdot 5 = 150$$
The least common multiple is 150.

26. $\dfrac{3}{8} = \dfrac{}{24}$ $24 \div 8 = 3$

$$\frac{3}{8} = \frac{3 \cdot 3}{8 \cdot 3} = \frac{9}{24}$$

28. $\dfrac{5}{12} = \dfrac{}{24}$ $24 \div 12 = 2$

$$\frac{5}{12} = \frac{5 \cdot 2}{12 \cdot 2} = \frac{10}{24}$$

30. $\dfrac{7}{8} = \dfrac{}{24}$ $24 \div 8 = 3$

$$\frac{7}{8} = \frac{7 \cdot 3}{8 \cdot 3} = \frac{21}{24}$$

32. $\dfrac{2}{3} = \dfrac{}{12}$ $12 \div 3 = 4$

$$\frac{2}{3} = \frac{2 \cdot 4}{3 \cdot 4} = \frac{8}{12}$$

34. $\dfrac{7}{10} = \dfrac{}{30}$ $30 \div 10 = 3$

$$\frac{7}{10} = \frac{7 \cdot 3}{10 \cdot 3} = \frac{21}{30}$$

36. $\dfrac{5}{12} = \dfrac{}{48}$ $48 \div 12 = 4$

$$\frac{5}{12} = \frac{5 \cdot 4}{12 \cdot 4} = \frac{20}{48}$$

38. $\dfrac{7}{8} = \dfrac{}{96}$ $96 \div 8 = 12$

$$\frac{7}{8} = \frac{7 \cdot 12}{8 \cdot 12} = \frac{84}{96}$$

40. $\dfrac{7}{8} = \dfrac{}{40}$ $40 \div 8 = 5$

$$\frac{7}{8} = \frac{7 \cdot 5}{8 \cdot 5} = \frac{35}{40}$$

42. $\dfrac{3}{2} = \dfrac{}{64}$ $64 \div 2 = 32$

$$\frac{3}{2} = \frac{3 \cdot 32}{2 \cdot 32} = \frac{96}{64}$$

44. $\dfrac{7}{6} = \dfrac{}{120}$ $120 \div 6 = 20$

$$\frac{7}{6} = \frac{7 \cdot 20}{6 \cdot 20} = \frac{140}{120}$$

46. $\dfrac{4}{15} = \dfrac{}{165}$ $165 \div 15 = 11$

$$\frac{4}{15} = \frac{4 \cdot 11}{15 \cdot 11} = \frac{44}{165}$$

48. $\dfrac{7}{16} = \dfrac{}{112}$ $112 \div 16 = 7$

$$\frac{7}{16} = \frac{7 \cdot 7}{16 \cdot 7} = \frac{49}{112}$$

50. Divide the desired denominator by the given denominator. Next, multiply both the given numerator and denominator by this number.

Divide 12 by 4 to get 3. Then multiply:
$$\frac{3}{4} = \frac{3 \cdot 3}{4 \cdot 3} = \frac{9}{12}$$

52. $\dfrac{53}{288}, \dfrac{115}{1568}$

2	288	1568
2	144	784
2	72	392
2	36	196
2	18	98
3	9	4̶9̶
3	3	4̶9̶
7	1̶	49
7	1̶	7
	1	1

The least common multiple is
$$2 \cdot 2 \cdot 2 \cdot 2 \cdot 2 \cdot 3 \cdot 3 \cdot 7 \cdot 7 = 14{,}112.$$

54. $\dfrac{61}{810}, \dfrac{37}{1170}$

2	810	1170
3	405	585
3	135	195
3	45	65
3	15	6̶5̶
5	5	65
13	1̶	13
	1	1

The least common multiple is
$$2 \cdot 3 \cdot 3 \cdot 3 \cdot 3 \cdot 5 \cdot 13 = 10{,}530.$$

3.3 Adding and Subtracting Unlike Fractions

2. $\dfrac{1}{4} + \dfrac{1}{8} = \dfrac{2}{8} + \dfrac{1}{8}$ *LCD is* 8

$$= \dfrac{2+1}{8}$$

$$= \dfrac{3}{8}$$

4. $\dfrac{3}{7} + \dfrac{1}{14} = \dfrac{6}{14} + \dfrac{1}{14}$ *LCD is* 8

$$= \dfrac{6+1}{14}$$

$$= \dfrac{7}{14}$$

$$= \dfrac{1}{2}$$

6. $\dfrac{5}{8} + \dfrac{1}{4} = \dfrac{5}{8} + \dfrac{2}{8} = \dfrac{5+2}{8}$

$$= \dfrac{7}{8}$$ *LCD is* 8

8. $\dfrac{5}{7} + \dfrac{3}{14} = \dfrac{10}{14} + \dfrac{3}{14} = \dfrac{10+3}{14}$

$$= \dfrac{13}{14}$$ *LCD is* 14

10. $\dfrac{5}{8} + \dfrac{1}{12} = \dfrac{15}{24} + \dfrac{2}{24} = \dfrac{15+2}{24}$

$$= \dfrac{17}{24}$$ *LCD is* 24

12. $\dfrac{2}{5} + \dfrac{3}{7} = \dfrac{14}{35} + \dfrac{15}{35} = \dfrac{14+15}{35}$

$$= \dfrac{29}{35}$$ *LCD is* 35

14. $\dfrac{3}{7} + \dfrac{2}{5} + \dfrac{1}{10} = \dfrac{30}{70} + \dfrac{28}{70} + \dfrac{7}{70}$ *LCD is* 70

$$= \dfrac{30+28+7}{70} = \dfrac{65}{70} = \dfrac{13}{14}$$

16. $\dfrac{1}{3} + \dfrac{3}{8} + \dfrac{1}{4} = \dfrac{8}{24} + \dfrac{9}{24} + \dfrac{6}{24}$ *LCD is* 24

$$= \dfrac{8+9+6}{24} = \dfrac{23}{24}$$

18. $\dfrac{5}{12} + \dfrac{2}{9} + \dfrac{1}{6} = \dfrac{15}{36} + \dfrac{8}{36} + \dfrac{6}{36}$ *LCD is* 36

$$= \dfrac{15+8+6}{36} = \dfrac{29}{36}$$

20. $\dfrac{7}{12} = \dfrac{7 \cdot 2}{12 \cdot 2} = \dfrac{14}{24}$ *LCD is* 24

$+\dfrac{1}{8} = \dfrac{1 \cdot 3}{8 \cdot 3} = \dfrac{3}{24}$

$$\dfrac{17}{24}$$

22.
$$\frac{3}{7} = \frac{3\cdot 3}{7\cdot 3} = \frac{9}{21} \qquad LCD \text{ is } 21$$
$$+\frac{1}{3} = \frac{1\cdot 7}{3\cdot 7} = \frac{7}{21}$$
$$\frac{16}{21}$$

24. $\dfrac{7}{8} - \dfrac{1}{4} = \dfrac{7}{8} - \dfrac{2}{8} = \dfrac{7-2}{8} = \dfrac{5}{8} \qquad LCD \text{ is } 8$

26. $\dfrac{3}{4} - \dfrac{5}{8} = \dfrac{6}{8} - \dfrac{5}{8} \qquad LCD \text{ is } 8$
$$= \frac{6-5}{8}$$
$$= \frac{1}{8}$$

28. $\dfrac{5}{6} - \dfrac{7}{9} = \dfrac{30}{36} - \dfrac{28}{36} = \dfrac{30-28}{36} = \dfrac{2}{36} = \dfrac{1}{18}$
$LCD \text{ is } 36$

30. $\dfrac{5}{7} - \dfrac{1}{3} = \dfrac{15}{21} - \dfrac{7}{21} = \dfrac{15-7}{21} = \dfrac{8}{21} \qquad LCD \text{ is } 21$

32.
$$\frac{4}{5} = \frac{4\cdot 3}{5\cdot 3} = \frac{12}{15}$$
$$-\frac{1}{3} = \frac{1\cdot 5}{3\cdot 5} = \frac{5}{15}$$
$$\frac{7}{15}$$

34.
$$\frac{5}{8} = \frac{5\cdot 3}{8\cdot 3} = \frac{15}{24}$$
$$-\frac{1}{3} = \frac{1\cdot 8}{3\cdot 8} = \frac{8}{24}$$
$$\frac{7}{24}$$

36.
$$\frac{7}{12} = \frac{7}{12}$$
$$-\frac{1}{3} = \frac{4}{12}$$
$$\frac{3}{12} = \frac{1}{4}$$

38. To find the fraction spent, add the fractions.
$$\frac{1}{4} + \frac{1}{10} + \frac{1}{6} + \frac{1}{12} = \frac{15}{60} + \frac{6}{60} + \frac{10}{60} + \frac{5}{60}$$
$$= \frac{15+6+10+5}{60}$$
$$= \frac{36}{60} = \frac{3}{5}$$

Sergy spent $\frac{3}{5}$ of his savings.

40. Add the fractions of the amounts that she has saved.
$$\frac{2}{5} + \frac{1}{8} + \frac{1}{6} \qquad LCD \text{ is } 120$$
$$= \frac{48}{120} + \frac{15}{120} + \frac{20}{120}$$
$$= \frac{48+15+20}{120}$$
$$= \frac{83}{120}$$

$\frac{83}{120}$ of the start-up costs has been saved.

42. Add the fractions to find the total length of the bolt.
$$\frac{1}{5} + \frac{1}{3} + \frac{1}{4}$$
$$= \frac{12}{60} + \frac{20}{60} + \frac{15}{60}$$
$$= \frac{12+20+15}{60}$$
$$= \frac{47}{60}$$

The total length of the bolt is $\frac{47}{60}$ in.

44. First add to find the total amount delivered at each stop.
$$\frac{1}{4} + \frac{1}{3} = \frac{3}{12} + \frac{4}{12} = \frac{3+4}{12} = \frac{7}{12}$$

Then subtract the amount used from the amount in the tank to find the fraction of the capacity remaining.
$$\frac{7}{8} - \frac{7}{12} = \frac{21}{24} - \frac{14}{24} = \frac{7}{24}$$

$\frac{7}{24}$ of the tanker's capacity remains.

46. *Step 1* Rewrite the unlike fractions as like fractions.

Step 2 Add or subtract the like fractions.

Step 3 Simplify the answer.

48. Add the time spent in work and travel and other.

$$\frac{1}{3} + \frac{1}{8} = \frac{8}{24} + \frac{3}{24} = \frac{8+3}{24} = \frac{11}{24}$$

$\frac{11}{24}$ of the student's day was spent in work and travel and other.

50. One way to compare fractions accurately is to rewrite each fraction with a common denominator.

$$\frac{1}{3} = \frac{8}{24}, \frac{1}{6} = \frac{4}{24}, \frac{1}{8} = \frac{3}{24}, \frac{1}{12} = \frac{2}{24}, \frac{7}{24}$$

The fraction with the smallest numerator is the smallest fraction.

This is

$$\frac{2}{24} \text{ or } \frac{1}{12} \text{ which is study.}$$

To find the number of hours multiply.

$$\frac{1}{12} \cdot 24 = \frac{1}{12} \cdot \frac{24}{1} = \frac{1 \cdot 24}{12 \cdot 1} = \frac{24}{12} = 2$$

Study took 2 hours.

52. The diameter is the distance across the hole. Add the two measures not included in the diameter of the hole.

$$\frac{3}{16} + \frac{3}{16} = \frac{3+3}{16} = \frac{6}{16} = \frac{3}{8} \text{ in.}$$

Subtract this length from the length of the line segment.

$$\frac{7}{8} - \frac{3}{8} = \frac{7-3}{8} = \frac{4}{8} = \frac{1}{2}$$

The diameter of the hole in the pendant is $\frac{1}{2}$ in.

3.4 Adding and Subtracting Mixed Numbers

2. *estimate:* *exact:*

$$\begin{array}{r} 8 \\ + \ 2 \\ \hline 10 \end{array} \qquad \begin{array}{r} 8\frac{3}{10} = 8\frac{3}{10} \\ + \ 1\frac{3}{5} = 1\frac{6}{10} \\ \hline 9\frac{9}{10} \end{array}$$

4. *estimate:* *exact:*

$$\begin{array}{r} 10 \\ + \ 6 \\ \hline 16 \end{array} \qquad \begin{array}{r} 10\frac{1}{4} = 10\frac{2}{8} \\ + \ 5\frac{5}{8} = 5\frac{5}{8} \\ \hline 15\frac{7}{8} \end{array}$$

6. *estimate:* *exact:*

$$\begin{array}{r} 13 \\ + \ 1 \\ \hline 14 \end{array} \qquad \begin{array}{r} 12\frac{4}{5} = 12\frac{8}{10} \\ + \ \frac{7}{10} = \frac{7}{10} \\ \hline 12\frac{15}{10} \end{array}$$

$$12\frac{15}{10} = 12 + 1\frac{5}{10}$$
$$= 13\frac{5}{10} = 13\frac{1}{2}$$

8. *estimate:* *exact:*

$$\begin{array}{r} 15 \\ + \ 16 \\ \hline 31 \end{array} \qquad \begin{array}{r} 14\frac{6}{7} = 14\frac{12}{14} \\ + \ 15\frac{1}{2} = 15\frac{7}{14} \\ \hline 29\frac{19}{14} \end{array}$$

$$29\frac{19}{14} = 29 + 1\frac{5}{14}$$
$$= 30\frac{5}{14}$$

10. *estimate:* *exact:*

$$\begin{array}{r} 19 \\ + \ 7 \\ \hline 26 \end{array} \qquad \begin{array}{r} 18\frac{5}{8} = 18\frac{15}{24} \\ + \ 6\frac{2}{3} = 6\frac{16}{24} \\ \hline 22\frac{31}{24} \end{array}$$

$$22\frac{31}{24} = 22 + 1\frac{7}{24}$$
$$= 23\frac{7}{24}$$

12. *estimate:* *exact:*

$$\begin{array}{r} 7 \\ + \ 26 \\ \hline 33 \end{array} \qquad \begin{array}{r} 7\frac{1}{4} = 7\frac{2}{8} \\ + \ 25\frac{7}{8} = 25\frac{7}{8} \\ \hline 32\frac{9}{8} \end{array}$$

$$32\frac{9}{8} = 32 + 1\frac{1}{8}$$
$$= 33\frac{1}{8}$$

14. *estimate:*   *exact:*

$$
\begin{array}{r}
15 \\
8 \\
+\ 14 \\
\hline
37
\end{array}
$$

$$14\frac{9}{10} = 14\frac{18}{20}$$
$$8\frac{1}{4} = 8\frac{5}{20}$$
$$+\ 13\frac{3}{5} = 13\frac{12}{20}$$
$$\overline{\phantom{+\ 13\frac{3}{5} = }35\frac{35}{20}}$$

$$35\tfrac{35}{20} = 35 + 1\frac{15}{20}$$
$$= 36\frac{15}{20} = 36\frac{3}{4}$$

16. *estimate:*   *exact:*

$$
\begin{array}{r}
15 \\
-\ 11 \\
\hline
4
\end{array}
$$

$$14\frac{3}{4} = 14\frac{6}{8}$$
$$-\ 11\frac{3}{8} = 11\frac{3}{8}$$
$$\overline{\phantom{-\ 11\frac{3}{8} = }3\frac{3}{8}}$$

18. *estimate:*   *exact:*

$$
\begin{array}{r}
11 \\
-\ 5 \\
\hline
6
\end{array}
$$

$$11\frac{9}{20} = 11\frac{9}{20} = 10\frac{29}{20}$$
$$-\ 4\frac{3}{5} = 4\frac{12}{20} = 4\frac{12}{20}$$
$$\overline{\phantom{-\ 4\frac{3}{5} = 4\frac{12}{20} = }6\frac{17}{20}}$$

20. *estimate:*   *exact:*

$$
\begin{array}{r}
15 \\
-\ 6 \\
\hline
9
\end{array}
$$

$$15\frac{7}{20} = 15\frac{14}{40}$$
$$-\ 6\frac{1}{8} = 6\frac{5}{40}$$
$$\overline{\phantom{-\ 6\frac{1}{8} = }9\frac{9}{40}}$$

22. *estimate:*   *exact:*

$$
\begin{array}{r}
22 \\
-\ 5 \\
\hline
17
\end{array}
$$

$$
\begin{array}{r}
22 \\
-\ 4\frac{5}{8} \\
\hline
\end{array}
$$

Borrow:

$$22 = 21 + 1 = 21 + \frac{8}{8}$$
$$= 21\frac{8}{8}$$

$$
\begin{array}{r}
21\frac{8}{8} \\
-\ 4\frac{5}{8} \\
\hline
17\frac{3}{8}
\end{array}
$$

24. *estimate:*   *exact:*

$$
\begin{array}{r}
18 \\
-\ 6 \\
\hline
12
\end{array}
$$

$$17\frac{5}{8} = 17\frac{15}{24}$$
$$-\ 5\frac{2}{3} = 5\frac{16}{24}$$

Borrow:

$$17\tfrac{15}{24} = 16 + 1 + \frac{15}{24}$$
$$= 16 + \frac{24}{24} + \frac{15}{24}$$
$$= 16\frac{39}{24}$$

$$
\begin{array}{r}
16\frac{39}{24} \\
-\ 5\frac{16}{24} \\
\hline
11\frac{23}{24}
\end{array}
$$

26. *estimate:*   *exact:*

$$
\begin{array}{r}
21 \\
-\ 12 \\
\hline
9
\end{array}
$$

$$20\frac{3}{5} = 20\frac{9}{15}$$
$$-\ 12\frac{7}{15} = 12\frac{7}{15}$$
$$\overline{\phantom{-\ 12\frac{7}{15} = }8\frac{2}{15}}$$

28.

$$8\frac{3}{4} = \frac{35}{4} = \frac{70}{8}$$
$$+\ 1\frac{5}{8} = \frac{13}{8} = \frac{13}{8}$$
$$\overline{\phantom{+\ 1\frac{5}{8} = \frac{13}{8} = }\frac{83}{8} = 10\frac{3}{8}}$$

30.

$$7\frac{5}{12} = \frac{89}{12} = \frac{89}{12}$$
$$+\ 6\frac{2}{3} = \frac{20}{3} = \frac{80}{12}$$
$$\overline{\phantom{+\ 6\frac{2}{3} = \frac{20}{3} = }\frac{169}{12} = 14\frac{1}{12}}$$

32.

$$4\frac{1}{2} = \frac{9}{2} = \frac{18}{4}$$
$$+\ 2\frac{3}{4} = \frac{11}{4} = \frac{11}{4}$$
$$\overline{\phantom{+\ 2\frac{3}{4} = \frac{11}{4} = }\frac{29}{4} = 7\frac{1}{4}}$$

34.
$$2\frac{4}{5} = \frac{14}{5} = \frac{42}{15}$$
$$+ 5\frac{1}{3} = \frac{16}{3} = \frac{80}{15}$$
$$\frac{122}{15} = 8\frac{2}{15}$$

36.
$$1\frac{5}{12} = \frac{17}{12} = \frac{34}{24}$$
$$+ 1\frac{7}{8} = \frac{15}{8} = \frac{45}{24}$$
$$\frac{79}{24} = 3\frac{7}{24}$$

38.
$$4\frac{1}{4} = \frac{17}{4} = \frac{51}{12}$$
$$- 3\frac{7}{12} = \frac{43}{12} = \frac{43}{12}$$
$$\frac{8}{12} = \frac{2}{3}$$

40.
$$10\frac{1}{3} = \frac{31}{3} = \frac{62}{6}$$
$$- 6\frac{5}{6} = \frac{41}{6} = \frac{41}{6}$$
$$\frac{21}{6} = 3\frac{1}{2}$$

42.
$$4\frac{1}{10} = \frac{41}{10} = \frac{164}{40}$$
$$- 3\frac{7}{8} = \frac{31}{8} = \frac{155}{40}$$
$$\frac{9}{40}$$

44.
$$10\frac{2}{7} = \frac{72}{7} = \frac{144}{14}$$
$$- 5\frac{5}{14} = \frac{75}{14} = \frac{75}{14}$$
$$\frac{69}{14} = 4\frac{13}{14}$$

46.
$$8\frac{2}{15} = \frac{122}{15} = \frac{244}{30}$$
$$- 6\frac{1}{2} = \frac{13}{2} = \frac{195}{30}$$
$$\frac{49}{30} = 1\frac{19}{30}$$

48. You need to borrow when the fraction in the minuend (top number) is smaller than the fraction in the subtrahend (bottom number). One example is:

$$5\frac{1}{4} = 5\frac{1}{4} = 4\frac{5}{4}$$
$$- 3\frac{1}{2} = 3\frac{2}{4} = 3\frac{2}{4}$$
$$1\frac{3}{4}$$

50. Subtract to find the difference in the lengths.

estimate: $49 - 21 = 28$ ft

exact:
$$49\frac{1}{5} = 49\frac{2}{10} = 48\frac{12}{10}$$
$$- 21\frac{3}{10} = 21\frac{3}{10} = 21\frac{3}{10}$$
$$27\frac{9}{10}$$

The humpback whale is $27\frac{9}{10}$ ft longer than the southern elephant whale.

52. Subtract to find the difference in the rates.

estimate: $9 - 3 = 6$ deaths per 1000

exact:
$$8\frac{4}{5} = 8\frac{8}{10}$$
$$- 2\frac{7}{10} = 2\frac{7}{10}$$
$$6\frac{1}{10}$$

The difference in these death rates is $6\frac{1}{10}$ deaths per 1000.

54. Add the tons recycled on Monday to the tons recycled on Tuesday.

estimate: $6 + 10 = 16$ tons

exact:
$$5\frac{3}{4} = 5\frac{15}{20}$$
$$+ 9\frac{3}{5} = 9\frac{12}{20}$$
$$14\frac{27}{20} = 14 + 1\frac{7}{20}$$
$$= 15\frac{7}{20}$$

56. Add the hours driven each day.

estimate: $8 + 5 + 7 + 9 = 29$ hr

exact:

$$7\tfrac{3}{4} = \frac{31}{4} = \frac{31}{4}$$
$$5\tfrac{1}{4} = \frac{21}{4} = \frac{21}{4}$$
$$6\tfrac{1}{2} = \frac{13}{2} = \frac{26}{4}$$
$$+\ 9 = \frac{9}{1} = \frac{36}{4}$$
$$\frac{114}{4} = 28\tfrac{1}{2}$$

She drove $28\tfrac{1}{2}$ hr altogether.

58. Add the measurements of the four sides of the lamp base plate.

estimate: $10 + 5 + 10 + 5 = 30$ in.

exact: $9\tfrac{7}{8} + 5\tfrac{1}{8} + 9\tfrac{7}{8} + 5\tfrac{1}{8} = 28\tfrac{16}{8}$
$$= 30$$

The length of brass trim needed is 30 in.

60. First, add the yards of material used for each item of clothing. Then, subtract the yards of material used from the total yards of material bought.

estimate: $15 - 4 - 4 - 4 = 3$ yd

exact:
$$3\tfrac{3}{4} = 3\tfrac{6}{8}$$
$$4\tfrac{1}{8} = 4\tfrac{1}{8}$$
$$+\ 3\tfrac{7}{8} = 3\tfrac{7}{8}$$
$$10\tfrac{14}{8} = 11\tfrac{6}{8} = 11\tfrac{3}{4}$$

$$15 = 14\tfrac{4}{4}$$
$$-11\tfrac{3}{4} = 11\tfrac{3}{4}$$
$$3\tfrac{1}{4}$$

Marv has $3\tfrac{1}{4}$ yd of material left.

62. Find the total length of the 3 sides. Then, subtract this distance from the total distance around the lot to find the length of the fourth side.

estimate: $519 - 108 - 162 - 144 = 105$ ft

exact:
$$108\tfrac{1}{4} = 108\tfrac{2}{8}$$
$$162\tfrac{3}{8} = 162\tfrac{3}{8}$$
$$+\ 143\tfrac{1}{2} = 143\tfrac{4}{8}$$
$$413\tfrac{9}{8} = 413 + 1\tfrac{1}{8}$$
$$= 414\tfrac{1}{8}$$

$$518\tfrac{3}{4} = 518\tfrac{6}{8}$$
$$-414\tfrac{1}{8} = 414\tfrac{1}{8}$$
$$104\tfrac{5}{8}$$

The length of the fourth side is $104\tfrac{5}{8}$ ft.

64. Add the number of cases of each brand of oil sold.

estimate: $17 + 12 + 9 + 13 = 51$ cases

exact:
$$16\tfrac{1}{2} = 16\tfrac{4}{8}$$
$$12\tfrac{1}{8} = 12\tfrac{1}{8}$$
$$8\tfrac{3}{4} = 8\tfrac{6}{8}$$
$$+\ 12\tfrac{5}{8} = 12\tfrac{5}{8}$$
$$48\tfrac{16}{8} = 48 + 2 = 50$$

Comet Auto Supply sold 50 cases of oil during the week.

66. First, add the 2 known lengths.

$$6\tfrac{9}{10}$$
$$+\ 6\tfrac{9}{10}$$
$$12\tfrac{18}{10} = 13\tfrac{8}{10}$$

Then subtract $13\tfrac{8}{10}$ from the total length to find the unknown length.

$$28\tfrac{1}{4} = 28\tfrac{5}{20} = 27\tfrac{25}{20}$$
$$-13\tfrac{8}{10} = 13\tfrac{16}{20} = 13\tfrac{16}{20}$$
$$14\tfrac{9}{20}$$

The length of the section marked x is $14\tfrac{9}{20}$ in.

68. First, add the length of the sections at each end.

$$5\tfrac{3}{4} = 5\tfrac{6}{8}$$
$$+\ 1\tfrac{1}{8} = 1\tfrac{1}{8}$$
$$\overline{\hphantom{+\ 1\tfrac{1}{8} = }\,6\tfrac{7}{8}}$$

Next, subtract this total from the total length of the object.

$$8\tfrac{1}{3} = 8\tfrac{8}{24} = 7\tfrac{32}{24}$$
$$-6\tfrac{7}{8} = 6\tfrac{21}{24} = 6\tfrac{21}{24}$$
$$\overline{\hphantom{-6\tfrac{7}{8} = 6\tfrac{21}{24} = }\,1\tfrac{11}{24}}$$

The length of the unknown section is $1\tfrac{11}{24}$ ft.

3.5 Order Relations and the Order of Operations

2.– 12. See the following number line.

14. $\dfrac{5}{8} - \dfrac{3}{4}$

$$\dfrac{3}{4} = \dfrac{6}{8} \qquad LCD \text{ is } 8$$

$$\dfrac{5}{8} < \dfrac{6}{8}, \text{ so } \dfrac{5}{8} < \dfrac{3}{4}.$$

16. $\dfrac{13}{18} - \dfrac{5}{6}$

$$\dfrac{5}{6} = \dfrac{15}{18} \qquad LCD \text{ is } 18$$

$$\dfrac{13}{18} < \dfrac{15}{18}, \text{ so } \dfrac{13}{18} < \dfrac{5}{6}.$$

18. $\dfrac{7}{15} - \dfrac{9}{20}$

$$\dfrac{7}{15} = \dfrac{28}{60}, \dfrac{9}{20} = \dfrac{27}{60}$$

$$\dfrac{28}{60} > \dfrac{27}{60}, \text{ so } \dfrac{7}{15} > \dfrac{9}{20}.$$

20. $\dfrac{17}{24} - \dfrac{5}{6}$

$$\dfrac{5}{6} = \dfrac{20}{24} \qquad LCD \text{ is } 24$$

$$\dfrac{17}{24} < \dfrac{20}{24}, \text{ so } \dfrac{17}{24} < \dfrac{5}{6}.$$

22. $\dfrac{13}{15} - \dfrac{8}{9}$

$$\dfrac{13}{15} = \dfrac{39}{45}, \dfrac{8}{9} = \dfrac{40}{45} \qquad LCD \text{ is } 45$$

$$\dfrac{39}{45} < \dfrac{40}{45}, \text{ so } \dfrac{13}{15} < \dfrac{8}{9}.$$

24. $\dfrac{7}{12} - \dfrac{11}{20}$

$$\dfrac{7}{12} = \dfrac{35}{60}, \dfrac{11}{20} = \dfrac{33}{60} \qquad LCD \text{ is } 60$$

$$\dfrac{35}{60} > \dfrac{33}{60}, \text{ so } \dfrac{7}{12} > \dfrac{11}{20}.$$

26. $\left(\dfrac{2}{3}\right)^2 = \dfrac{2}{3} \cdot \dfrac{2}{3} = \dfrac{4}{9}$

28. $\left(\dfrac{7}{8}\right)^2 = \dfrac{7}{8} \cdot \dfrac{7}{8} = \dfrac{49}{64}$

30. $\left(\dfrac{3}{5}\right)^3 = \dfrac{3}{5} \cdot \dfrac{3}{5} \cdot \dfrac{3}{5} = \dfrac{27}{125}$

32. $\left(\dfrac{4}{7}\right)^3 = \dfrac{4}{7} \cdot \dfrac{4}{7} \cdot \dfrac{4}{7} = \dfrac{64}{343}$

34. $\left(\dfrac{4}{3}\right)^4 = \dfrac{4}{3} \cdot \dfrac{4}{3} \cdot \dfrac{4}{3} \cdot \dfrac{4}{3} = \dfrac{256}{81} = 3\tfrac{13}{81}$

36. $\left(\dfrac{2}{3}\right)^5 = \dfrac{2}{3} \cdot \dfrac{2}{3} \cdot \dfrac{2}{3} \cdot \dfrac{2}{3} \cdot \dfrac{2}{3} = \dfrac{32}{243}$

38. (1) Do all operations inside parentheses or other grouping symbols.

(2) Simplify any expressions with exponents or square roots.

(3) Multiply or divide from left to right.

(4) Add or subtract from left to right.

40. $2^2 + 5 \cdot 1 = 4 + 5 \cdot 1$
$$= 4 + 5$$
$$= 9$$

42. $5 \cdot 2^3 - \dfrac{6}{2} = 5 \cdot 8 - \dfrac{6}{2}$
$$= 40 - \dfrac{6}{2}$$
$$= 40 - 3$$
$$= 37$$

44. $\left(\dfrac{1}{4}\right)^2 \cdot 4 = \dfrac{1}{4} \cdot \dfrac{1}{4} \cdot 4$
$$= \dfrac{1}{16} \cdot 4$$
$$= \dfrac{1}{16} \cdot \dfrac{4}{1}$$
$$= \dfrac{1}{4}$$

46. $\left(\dfrac{2}{3}\right)^3 \cdot \left(\dfrac{1}{2}\right) = \dfrac{2}{3} \cdot \dfrac{2}{3} \cdot \dfrac{\overset{1}{\cancel{2}}}{3} \cdot \dfrac{1}{\underset{1}{\cancel{2}}} = \dfrac{4}{27}$

48. $\left(\dfrac{5}{8}\right)^2 \cdot \left(\dfrac{4}{25}\right)^2 = \dfrac{\overset{1}{\cancel{5}}}{\underset{2}{\cancel{8}}} \cdot \dfrac{\overset{1}{\cancel{5}}}{\underset{2}{\cancel{8}}} \cdot \dfrac{\overset{1}{\cancel{4}}}{\underset{5}{\cancel{25}}} \cdot \dfrac{\overset{1}{\cancel{4}}}{\underset{5}{\cancel{25}}}$
$$= \dfrac{1}{100}$$

50. $9 \cdot \left(\dfrac{1}{3}\right)^3 \cdot \left(\dfrac{4}{3}\right)^2 = \dfrac{\overset{\overset{1}{\cancel{3}}}{\cancel{9}}}{1} \cdot \dfrac{1}{\underset{1}{\cancel{3}}} \cdot \dfrac{1}{\underset{1}{\cancel{3}}} \cdot \dfrac{1}{3} \cdot \dfrac{4}{3} \cdot \dfrac{4}{3}$
$$= \dfrac{16}{27}$$

52. $\dfrac{1}{4} \cdot \dfrac{3}{4} + \dfrac{3}{8} \cdot \dfrac{4}{3} = \dfrac{1}{4} \cdot \dfrac{3}{4} + \dfrac{\overset{1}{\cancel{3}}}{\underset{2}{\cancel{8}}} \cdot \dfrac{\overset{1}{\cancel{4}}}{\underset{1}{\cancel{3}}}$
$$= \dfrac{3}{16} + \dfrac{1}{2}$$
$$= \dfrac{3}{16} + \dfrac{8}{16}$$
$$= \dfrac{11}{16}$$

54. $\dfrac{2}{3} + \left(\dfrac{1}{3}\right)^2 - \dfrac{5}{9} = \dfrac{2}{3} + \dfrac{1}{3} \cdot \dfrac{1}{3} - \dfrac{5}{9}$
$$= \dfrac{6}{9} + \dfrac{1}{9} - \dfrac{5}{9}$$
$$= \dfrac{7}{9} - \dfrac{5}{9} = \dfrac{2}{9}$$

56. $\left(\dfrac{3}{5} - \dfrac{3}{20}\right) \cdot \dfrac{4}{3} = \left(\dfrac{12}{20} - \dfrac{3}{20}\right) \cdot \dfrac{4}{3}$
$$= \dfrac{\overset{3}{\cancel{9}}}{\underset{5}{\cancel{20}}} \cdot \dfrac{\overset{1}{\cancel{4}}}{\underset{1}{\cancel{3}}}$$
$$= \dfrac{3}{5}$$

58. $\dfrac{6}{5} \div \left(\dfrac{3}{5} - \dfrac{3}{10}\right) = \dfrac{6}{5} \div \left(\dfrac{6}{10} - \dfrac{3}{10}\right)$
$$= \dfrac{6}{5} \div \dfrac{3}{10}$$
$$= \dfrac{\overset{2}{\cancel{6}}}{\underset{1}{\cancel{5}}} \cdot \dfrac{\overset{2}{\cancel{10}}}{\underset{1}{\cancel{3}}} = 4$$

60. $\left(\dfrac{4}{5} - \dfrac{3}{10}\right) \div \dfrac{4}{5} = \left(\dfrac{8}{10} - \dfrac{3}{10}\right) \div \dfrac{4}{5}$
$$= \dfrac{5}{10} \div \dfrac{4}{5}$$
$$= \dfrac{5}{\underset{2}{\cancel{10}}} \cdot \dfrac{\overset{1}{\cancel{5}}}{4}$$
$$= \dfrac{5}{8}$$

62. $\dfrac{1}{3} \cdot \left(\dfrac{4}{5} - \dfrac{3}{10}\right) \cdot \dfrac{4}{2} = \dfrac{1}{3} \cdot \left(\dfrac{8}{10} - \dfrac{3}{10}\right) \cdot \dfrac{4}{2}$
$$= \dfrac{1}{3} \cdot \dfrac{\overset{1}{\cancel{5}}}{\underset{\underset{1}{\cancel{2}}}{\cancel{10}}} \cdot \dfrac{\overset{\overset{1}{\cancel{2}}}{\cancel{4}}}{\underset{1}{\cancel{2}}} = \dfrac{1}{3}$$

64. $\left(\dfrac{2}{3}\right)^2 - \left(\dfrac{5}{8} - \dfrac{1}{2}\right) \div \dfrac{3}{2} = \left(\dfrac{2}{3}\right)^2 - \left(\dfrac{5}{8} - \dfrac{4}{8}\right) \div \dfrac{3}{2}$

$$= \dfrac{4}{9} - \dfrac{1}{8} \div \dfrac{3}{2}$$

$$= \dfrac{4}{9} - \dfrac{1}{\overset{}{\underset{4}{8}}} \cdot \dfrac{\overset{1}{2}}{3}$$

$$= \dfrac{4}{9} - \dfrac{1}{12}$$

$$= \dfrac{16}{36} - \dfrac{3}{36}$$

$$= \dfrac{13}{36}$$

66. $\left(\dfrac{5}{6} - \dfrac{7}{12}\right) - \left(\dfrac{1}{3}\right)^2 \cdot \dfrac{3}{4} = \left(\dfrac{10}{12} - \dfrac{7}{12}\right) - \left(\dfrac{1}{3}\right)^2 \cdot \dfrac{3}{4}$

$$= \dfrac{3}{12} - \dfrac{1}{3} \cdot \dfrac{1}{3} \cdot \dfrac{3}{4}$$

$$= \dfrac{3}{12} - \dfrac{1}{3} \cdot \dfrac{1}{\overset{}{\underset{1}{3}}} \cdot \dfrac{\overset{1}{3}}{4}$$

$$= \dfrac{3}{12} - \dfrac{1}{12} = \dfrac{2}{12} = \dfrac{1}{6}$$

68. $\left(\dfrac{2}{3}\right)^2 \cdot \left(\dfrac{1}{2} - \dfrac{1}{8}\right) - \dfrac{2}{3} \cdot \dfrac{1}{8} = \left(\dfrac{2}{3}\right)^2 \cdot \left(\dfrac{4}{8} - \dfrac{1}{8}\right) - \dfrac{2}{3} \cdot \dfrac{1}{8}$

$$= \left(\dfrac{2}{3}\right)^2 \cdot \dfrac{3}{8} - \dfrac{2}{3} \cdot \dfrac{1}{8}$$

$$= \dfrac{2}{3} \cdot \dfrac{\overset{1}{2}}{\overset{}{\underset{1}{3}}} \cdot \dfrac{\overset{1}{3}}{\overset{}{\underset{4}{8}}} - \dfrac{\overset{1}{2}}{3} \cdot \dfrac{1}{\overset{}{\underset{4}{8}}}$$

$$= \dfrac{2}{12} - \dfrac{1}{12} = \dfrac{1}{12}$$

70. $\dfrac{3}{4} \underline{} \dfrac{19}{25}$

$$\dfrac{3}{4} = \dfrac{75}{100}, \ \dfrac{19}{25} = \dfrac{76}{100}$$

$$\dfrac{75}{100} < \dfrac{76}{100}, \ \text{so} \ \dfrac{3}{4} < \dfrac{19}{25}.$$

$\dfrac{19}{25}$ is greater.

Summary Exercises on Fractions

2. $\dfrac{6}{5}$ is an improper fraction since the numerator is greater than the denominator.

4. $\dfrac{9}{10}$ is a proper fraction since the numerator is less than the denominator.

6. $\dfrac{175}{200} = \dfrac{175 \div 25}{200 \div 25} = \dfrac{7}{8}$

8. $\dfrac{115}{235} = \dfrac{115 \div 5}{235 \div 5} = \dfrac{23}{47}$

10. $\dfrac{7}{12} \cdot \dfrac{9}{14} = \dfrac{\overset{1}{7} \cdot \overset{3}{9}}{\underset{4}{12} \cdot \underset{2}{14}} = \dfrac{1 \cdot 3}{4 \cdot 2} = \dfrac{3}{8}$

12. $\dfrac{5}{8} \div \dfrac{3}{4} = \dfrac{5}{\overset{}{\underset{2}{8}}} \cdot \dfrac{\overset{1}{4}}{3}$

$$= \dfrac{5 \cdot 1}{2 \cdot 3}$$

$$= \dfrac{5}{6}$$

14. $21 \div \dfrac{3}{8} = \dfrac{21}{1} \div \dfrac{3}{8} = \dfrac{\overset{7}{21}}{1} \cdot \dfrac{8}{\overset{}{\underset{1}{3}}} = \dfrac{7 \cdot 8}{1 \cdot 1} = \dfrac{56}{1} = 56$

16. $\dfrac{5}{8} + \dfrac{3}{4} + \dfrac{7}{16} = \dfrac{10}{16} + \dfrac{12}{16} + \dfrac{7}{16}$

$$= \dfrac{10 + 12 + 7}{16}$$

$$= \dfrac{29}{16}$$

$$= 1\dfrac{13}{16}$$

18. $\dfrac{5}{6} - \dfrac{3}{4} = \dfrac{10}{12} - \dfrac{9}{12} = \dfrac{10 - 9}{12} = \dfrac{1}{12}$

20. $\dfrac{4}{5} - \dfrac{2}{3} = \dfrac{12}{15} - \dfrac{10}{15} = \dfrac{12 - 10}{15} = \dfrac{2}{15}$

22. *estimate:*
$$5 \cdot 3 = 15$$

exact:
$$5\frac{3}{8} \cdot 3\frac{1}{4} = \frac{43}{8} \cdot \frac{13}{4} = \frac{559}{32} = 17\frac{15}{32}$$

24. *estimate:*
$$4 \div 4 = 1$$

exact:
$$4\frac{3}{8} \div 3\frac{3}{4} = \frac{35}{8} \div \frac{15}{4} = \frac{\overset{7}{\cancel{35}}}{\underset{2}{\cancel{8}}} \cdot \frac{\overset{1}{\cancel{4}}}{\underset{3}{\cancel{15}}} = \frac{7}{6} = 1\frac{1}{6}$$

26. *estimate:*
$$5 \div 1 = 5$$

exact:
$$4\frac{5}{8} \div \frac{3}{4} = \frac{37}{8} \div \frac{3}{4} = \frac{37}{\underset{2}{\cancel{8}}} \cdot \frac{\overset{1}{\cancel{4}}}{3} = \frac{37}{6} = 6\frac{1}{6}$$

28. *estimate:*   *exact:*

$$\begin{array}{r} 22 \\ +\ \ 8 \\ \hline 30 \end{array}$$

$$\begin{array}{r} 21\frac{3}{4} = 21\frac{9}{12} \\ +\ \ 8\frac{5}{12} = \ \ 8\frac{5}{12} \\ \hline 29\frac{14}{12} = 29 + 1\frac{2}{12} \\ = 30\frac{2}{12} \\ = 30\frac{1}{6} \end{array}$$

30. *estimate:*   *exact:*

$$\begin{array}{r} 8 \\ -\ \ 3 \\ \hline 5 \end{array}$$

$$\begin{array}{r} 7\frac{1}{2} = 7\frac{5}{10} = 6\frac{15}{10} \\ -\ 2\frac{3}{5} = 2\frac{6}{10} = 2\frac{6}{10} \\ \hline 4\frac{9}{10} \end{array}$$

32. *estimate:*   *exact:*

$$\begin{array}{r} 32 \\ -\ 23 \\ \hline 9 \end{array}$$

$$\begin{array}{r} 31\frac{5}{6} = 31\frac{10}{12} \\ -\ 22\frac{7}{12} = 22\frac{7}{12} \\ \hline 9\frac{3}{12} = 9\frac{1}{4} \end{array}$$

34.
$$\frac{3}{4} \div \left(\frac{1}{2} + \frac{1}{3}\right) = \frac{3}{4} \div \left(\frac{3}{6} + \frac{2}{6}\right)$$
$$= \frac{3}{4} \div \frac{5}{6}$$
$$= \frac{3}{\underset{2}{\cancel{4}}} \cdot \frac{\overset{3}{\cancel{6}}}{5}$$
$$= \frac{9}{10}$$

36. 8, 10
$$8 = 2 \cdot 2 \cdot 2$$
$$10 = 2 \cdot 5$$
$$LCM = 2 \cdot 2 \cdot 2 \cdot 5 = 40$$
The least common multiple is 40.

38. 4, 12, 21
$$4 = 2 \cdot 2$$
$$12 = 2 \cdot 2 \cdot 3$$
$$21 = 3 \cdot 7$$
$$LCM = 2 \cdot 2 \cdot 3 \cdot 7 = 84$$
The least common multiple is 84

40. $28 \div 7 = 4$
$$\frac{3}{7} = \frac{3 \cdot 4}{7 \cdot 4} = \frac{12}{28}$$

42. $\dfrac{7}{8} \underline{\quad\quad} \dfrac{15}{16}$
$$\frac{7}{8} = \frac{14}{16} \quad \textit{LCD is } 16$$
$$\frac{14}{16} < \frac{15}{16}, \text{ so } \frac{7}{8} < \frac{15}{16}.$$

44. $\dfrac{11}{15} \underline{\quad\quad} \dfrac{7}{10}$
$$\frac{11}{15} = \frac{22}{30}, \frac{7}{10} = \frac{21}{30} \quad \textit{LCD is } 30$$
$$\frac{22}{30} > \frac{21}{30}, \text{ so } \frac{11}{15} > \frac{7}{10}.$$

Chapter 4

DECIMALS

4.1 Reading and Writing Decimals

2. 135.296

   ones: 5
   tenths: 2
   tens: 3

4. 0.9347

   hundredths: 3
   thousandths: 4
   ten-thousandths: 7

6. 0.51968

   tenths: 5
   ten-thousandths: 6
   hundredths: 1

8. 51.325

   tens: 5
   tenths: 3
   hundredths: 2

10. 3458.712

    hundreds: 4
    hundredths: 1
    tenths: 7

12. 5417.6832

    thousands: 5
    thousandths: 3
    ones: 7

14. 7 tens, 9 tenths, 3 ones, 6 hundredths, 8 hundreds

    873.96

16. 8 ten-thousandths, 4 hundredths, 0 ones, 2 tenths, 6 thousandths

    0.2468

18. 7 tens, 7 tenths, 6 thousands, 6 thousandths, 3 hundreds, 3 hundredths, 2 ones

    6372.736

20. $0.1 = \dfrac{1}{10}$

22. $9.8 = 9\dfrac{8}{10} = 9\dfrac{8 \div 2}{10 \div 2} = 9\dfrac{4}{5}$

24. $0.55 = \dfrac{55}{100} = \dfrac{55 \div 5}{100 \div 5} = \dfrac{11}{20}$

26. $0.33 = \dfrac{33}{100}$

28. $31.99 = 31\dfrac{99}{100}$

30. $0.08 = \dfrac{8}{100} = \dfrac{8 \div 4}{100 \div 4} = \dfrac{2}{25}$

32. $0.805 = \dfrac{805}{1000} = \dfrac{805 \div 5}{1000 \div 5} = \dfrac{161}{200}$

34. $4.008 = 4\dfrac{8}{1000} = 4\dfrac{8 \div 8}{1000 \div 8} = 4\dfrac{1}{125}$

36. $0.492 = \dfrac{492}{1000} = \dfrac{492 \div 4}{1000 \div 4} = \dfrac{123}{250}$

38. 0.2 is two tenths.

40. 0.55 is fifty-five hundredths.

42. 0.609 is six hundred nine thousandths.

44. 86.09 is eighty-six and nine hundredths.

46. 4.025 is four and twenty-five thousandths.

48. eight and twelve hundredths

    $8\dfrac{12}{100} = 8.12$

50. one hundred eleven thousandths

    $\dfrac{111}{1000} = 0.111$

52. two hundred and twenty-four thousandths

    $200\dfrac{24}{1000} = 200.024$

54. eight hundred and six hundredths

    $800\dfrac{6}{100} = 800.06$

56. sixty and fifty hundredths

    $60\dfrac{50}{100} = 60.50$

58. Jerry used "and" twice; only the first "and" is correct.

60. 17-pound test line has a diameter of 0.015 in. 0.015 in. is read fifteen thousandths of an inch.

$$0.015 = \frac{15}{1000} = \frac{15 \div 5}{1000 \div 5} = \frac{3}{200}$$

62. sixteen thousandths in. $= \dfrac{16}{1000} = 0.016$ in.

A diameter of 0.016 in. corresponds to a test strength of 20 pounds.

64. One and six hundredths is 1.06, so the correct part number is 4-C.

66. Twenty-six hundredths is 0.26, so the correct part number is 3-B.

68. The size of part number 4-B is 1.026 centimeters, which in words is one and twenty-six thousandths centimeters.

4.2 Rounding Decimals

2. 193.845 to the nearest hundredth

Draw cut-off line after hundredths place.
193.84|5

First digit cut is 5 or more, so round up the hundredths place.

$$\begin{array}{r} 193.84 \\ +\ 0.01 \\ \hline 193.85 \end{array}$$

Answer: ≈ 193.85

4. 96.81584 to the nearest ten-thousandth

Draw cut-off line after ten-thousandths place.
96.8158|4

First digit cut is less than 5, so the part you keep stays the same.

Answer: ≈ 96.8158

6. 0.952 to the nearest tenth

Draw cut-off line after tenths place.
0.9|52

First digit cut is 5 or more, so round up the tenths place.

$$\begin{array}{r} 0.9 \\ +\ 0.1 \\ \hline 1.0 \end{array}$$

Answer: ≈ 1.0

8. 1.5074 to the nearest hundredth

Draw cut-off line after hundredths place.
1.50|74

First digit cut is 5 or more, so round up the hundredths place.

$$\begin{array}{r} 1.50 \\ +\ 0.01 \\ \hline 1.51 \end{array}$$

Answer: ≈ 1.51

10. 476.1196 to the nearest thousandth

Draw cut-off line after thousandths place.
476.119|6

First digit cut is 5 or more, so round up the thousandths place.

$$\begin{array}{r} 476.119 \\ +\ 0.001 \\ \hline 476.120 \end{array}$$

Answer: ≈ 476.120

12. 176.004 to the nearest tenth

Draw cut-off line after the tenths place.
176.0|04

First digit cut is less than 5, so the part you keep stays the same.

Answer: ≈ 176.0

14. 3.385 to the nearest one

Draw cut-off line after the ones place.
3.|385

First digit cut is less than 5, so the part you keep stays the same.

Answer: ≈ 3

16. 30.1290 to the nearest thousandth

Draw cut-off line after the thousandths place.
30.129|0

First digit cut is less than 5, so the part you keep stays the same.

Answer: ≈ 30.129

18. 0.400594 to the nearest ten-thousandth

Draw cut-off line after the ten-thousandth place.
0.4005|94

First digit cut is 5 or more, so round up the ten-thousandths place.

$$\begin{array}{r} 0.4005 \\ +\ 0.0001 \\ \hline 0.4006 \end{array}$$

Answer: ≈ 0.4006

20. Round $1.345 to the nearest cent.

Draw cut-off line.
1.34|5

First digit cut is 5 or more, so round up.

$1.34
+ 0.01
$1.35

Nardos pays $1.35.

22. Round $0.58333 to the nearest cent.

Draw cut-off line.
0.58|333

First digit cut is less than 5, so the part you keep stays the same.

Nardos pays $0.58.

24. Round $0.8975 to the nearest cent.

Draw cut-off line.
0.89|95

First digit cut is 5 or more, so round up.

$0.89
+ 0.01
$0.90

Nardos pays $0.90.

26. Round $69.58 to the nearest dollar.

Draw cut-off line.
69.|58

First digit cut is 5 or more, so round up.

$69
+ 1
$70

Income from interest on bank account: ≈ $70

28. Round $6064.49 to the nearest dollar.

Draw cut-off line.
6064.|49

First digit cut is less than 5, so the part you keep stays the same.

Federal withholding: ≈ $6064

30. Round $609.38 to the nearest dollar.

Draw cut-off line.
609.|38

First digit cut is less than 5, so the part you keep stays the same.

Medical expenses: ≈ $609

32. $9899.59 to the nearest dollar

Draw cut-off line.
9899.|59

First digit cut is 5 or more, so round up.

$9899
+ 1
$9900

Answer: ≈ $9900

34. $0.09929 to the nearest cent

Draw cut-off line.
0.09|929

First digit cut is 5 or more, so round up.

$0.09
+ 0.01
$0.10

Answer: ≈ $0.10

36. $9999.80 to the nearest dollar

Draw cut-off line.
9999.|80

First digit cut is 5 or more, so round up.

$9999
+ 1
$10,000

Answer: ≈ $10,000

38. (a) Round 177.602 to the nearest hundredth.

Draw cut-off line.
177.60|2

First digit cut is less than 5, so the part you keep stays the same.

The Daytona 500 average winning speed is 177.60 miles per hour.

(b) Round 185.984 to the nearest hundredth.

Draw cut-off line.
185.98|4

First digit cut is less than 5 so the part you keep stays the same.

The Indianapolis 500 average winning speed is 185.98 miles per hour.

40. (a) Round 4520 to the nearest hundred.

Draw cut-off line.
45|20

First digit cut is less than 5, so the part you keep stays the same.

The record speed for a X-15 military jet is 4500 miles per hour.

(b) Round 495 to the nearest hundred.

Draw cut-off line.

4|95

First digit cut is 5 or more, so round up

$$\begin{array}{r} 400 \\ +\ 100 \\ \hline 500 \end{array}$$

The record speed for a Boeing 737-300 airplane is 500 miles per hour.

4.3 Adding and Subtracting Decimals

2. $372.1 - 33.7$

Line up decimal points.

$$\begin{array}{r} 372.1 \\ -\ 33.7 \\ \hline 338.4 \end{array}$$

4. $0.7759 + 9.8883$

Line up decimal points.

$$\begin{array}{r} 0.7759 \\ +\ 9.8883 \\ \hline 10.6642 \end{array}$$

6. $47.658 - 20.9$

Line up decimal points.
Write in 0's.

$$\begin{array}{r} 47.658 \\ -\ 20.900 \\ \hline 26.758 \end{array}$$

8. $1.87 + 9.749$

Line up decimal points.
Write in 0's.

$$\begin{array}{r} 1.870 \\ +\ 9.749 \\ \hline 11.619 \end{array}$$

10. $9 - 1.183$

Line up decimal points.
Write in 0's.

$$\begin{array}{r} 9.000 \\ -\ 1.183 \\ \hline 7.817 \end{array}$$

12. $0.35 - 0.088$

Line up decimal points.
Write in 0's.

$$\begin{array}{r} 0.350 \\ -\ 0.088 \\ \hline 0.262 \end{array}$$

14. $489.76 + 0.9993 + 38 + 8.55087 + 80.697$

Line up decimal points.
Write in 0's.

$$\begin{array}{r} 489.76000 \\ 0.99930 \\ 38.00000 \\ 8.55087 \\ +\ 80.69700 \\ \hline 618.00717 \end{array}$$

16. (a) Femur 19.88 in., tibia 16.94 in.

$$\begin{array}{r} 19.88 \\ +\ 16.94 \\ \hline 36.82 \end{array}$$

The total length is 36.82 in.

(b)

$$\begin{array}{r} 19.88 \\ -\ 16.94 \\ \hline 2.94 \end{array}$$

The difference is 2.94 in.

18. (a) Ulna 11.1 in., radius 10.4 in.

$$\begin{array}{r} 11.1 \\ -\ 10.4 \\ \hline 0.7 \end{array}$$

The difference is 0.7 in.

(b) Tibia 16.94 in., fibula 15.94 in.

$$\begin{array}{r} 16.94 \\ -\ 15.94 \\ \hline 1.00 \end{array}$$

The difference is 1.00 or 1 in.

20. The two problems are done in a different order: $8 - 2.9$ is not the same as $2.9 - 8$ because subtraction is not commutative.

22.

estimate	exact
$30	$27.96
− 8	− 8.39
$22	$19.57

24.

estimate	exact
40	38.550
8	7.716
+ 1	+ 0.600
49	46.866

26.

estimate	exact
30	31.700
− 4	− 4.271
26	27.429

28.

estimate	exact
300	332.6070
10	12.5000
+ 800	+ 823.3949
1110	1168.5019

30. Estimate is $20 - 1 = 19$, so 18.63 is most reasonable answer.

32. Estimate is $10 + 0 = 10$, so 9.76 is most reasonable answer.

34. Estimate is $803 - 1 = 802$, so 802.65 is most reasonable answer.

36. Estimate is $130 + 100 = 230$, so 225.3593 is most reasonable answer.

38. Add the 3 heights.

estimate	exact
2	1.98
2	2.06
+ 2	+ 2.16
6 meters	6.20 meters

The NBA stars' combined height is less than the rhino's.

40.

estimate	exact
30	28.000
− 10	− 13.582
20	14.418 meters

42. Add the cost of the muffins, croissants, and cookie.

estimate	exact
$7	$7.42
10	10.09
+ 1	+ 0.69
$18	$18.20

Altogether, she spent $18.20.

44. Subtract the two weights.

estimate	exact
4	4.05
− 4	− 3.90
0 ounce	0.15 ounce

The difference was 0.15 ounce.

46. To find the perimeter, add the lengths of all the sides.

estimate
$2 + 1 + 2 + 1 + 2 + 1 + 1 = 10$ meters
exact

```
  2.000
  1.000
  1.700
  0.860
  2.095
  1.180
+ 0.900
  9.735
```

The perimeter is 9.735 meters.

48. 330 yd of line, $5.32
3 bobbers, $0.87
estimate $5 − $1 = $4
exact

```
   5.32
 − 0.87
   4.45
```

The difference in cost is $4.45.

50. Add the costs.
estimate $8 + $7 + $20 = $35
exact

```
    8.49
    6.97
 + 19.99
   35.45
```

He spent $35.45 on these items.

52. Add the costs.

```
   57.32
   39.95
 + 19.95
  117.22
```

Olivia paid $117.22 for telephone, cable TV, and Internet access.

54. Subtract to find the difference.

```
  205.00
 − 97.75
  107.25
```

She paid $107.25 more on car repairs and gas than she did on entertainment.

56. Add the costs for car expenses. Then subtract that amount from the cost for clothing and laundry.

190.78	395.78
+ 205.00	− 107.00
395.78	288.78

She spent $288.78 less less on clothing and laundry than she did on all her car expenses.

58. Add the given lengths and subtract the sum from the total length.

$$
\begin{array}{r}
1.002 \\
+\ 1.002 \\
\hline
2.004 \text{ meters}
\end{array}
\qquad
\begin{array}{r}
5.000 \\
-\ 2.004 \\
\hline
2.996 \text{ meters}
\end{array}
$$

$z = 2.996$ meters

4.4 Multiplying Decimals

2.
$$
\begin{array}{r}
0.571 \leftarrow 3\ \textit{decimal places} \\
\times\ 2.9 \leftarrow 1\ \textit{decimal place} \\
\hline
5139 \\
1\,142 \\
\hline
1.6559 \leftarrow \overline{4\ \textit{decimal places}}
\end{array}
$$

4.
$$
\begin{array}{r}
85.4 \leftarrow 1\ \textit{decimal place} \\
\times\ 3.5 \leftarrow 1\ \textit{decimal place} \\
\hline
42\,70 \\
256\,2 \\
\hline
298.90 \leftarrow \overline{2\ \textit{decimal places}}
\end{array}
$$

6.
$$
\begin{array}{r}
0.896 \leftarrow 3\ \textit{decimal places} \\
\times\ 0.799 \leftarrow 3\ \textit{decimal places} \\
\hline
8064 \\
8064 \\
6272 \\
\hline
0.715904 \leftarrow \overline{3\ \textit{decimal places}}
\end{array}
$$

8.
$$
\begin{array}{r}
\$736.75 \leftarrow 2\ \textit{decimal places} \\
\times\ 118 \\
\hline
5\,894\,00 \\
7\,367\,5 \\
73\,675 \\
\hline
\$86,936.50 \leftarrow \overline{2\ \textit{decimal places}}
\end{array}
$$

10. 7.2×6
$$
\begin{array}{rr}
72 & 7.2 \leftarrow 1\ \textit{decimal place} \\
\times\ 6 & \times\ 6 \\
\hline
432 & 43.2 \leftarrow \overline{1\ \textit{decimal place}}
\end{array}
$$

12. $(0.72)(0.6)$
$$
\begin{array}{rr}
72 & 0.72 \leftarrow 2\ \textit{decimal places} \\
\times\ 6 & \times\ 0.6 \leftarrow 1\ \textit{decimal place} \\
\hline
432 & 0.432 \leftarrow \overline{3\ \textit{decimal places}}
\end{array}
$$

14. 72×0.0006
$$
\begin{array}{rr}
72 & 72 \\
\times\ 6 & \times\ 0.0006 \leftarrow 4\ \textit{decimal places} \\
\hline
432 & 0.0432 \leftarrow \overline{4\ \textit{decimal places}}
\end{array}
$$

16. 0.072×0.006
$$
\begin{array}{rr}
72 & 0.072 \leftarrow 3\ \textit{decimal places} \\
\times\ 6 & \times\ 0.006 \leftarrow 3\ \textit{decimal places} \\
\hline
432 & 0.000432 \leftarrow \overline{6\ \textit{decimal places}}
\end{array}
$$

18. $(0.0052)(0.009)$
$$
\begin{array}{r}
0.0052 \leftarrow 4\ \textit{decimal places} \\
\times\ 0.009 \leftarrow 3\ \textit{decimal places} \\
\hline
0.0000468 \leftarrow \overline{7\ \textit{decimal places}}
\end{array}
$$

20. $0.0079 \cdot 0.006$
$$
\begin{array}{r}
0.0079 \leftarrow 4\ \textit{decimal places} \\
\times\ 0.006 \leftarrow 3\ \textit{decimal places} \\
\hline
0.0000474 \leftarrow \overline{7\ \textit{decimal places}}
\end{array}
$$

24.
$$
\begin{array}{ll}
\textit{estimate} & \textit{exact} \\
20 & 18.7 \leftarrow 1\ \textit{decimal place} \\
\times\ 2 & \times\ 2.3 \leftarrow 1\ \textit{decimal place} \\
\hline
40 & 5\,61 \\
& 37\,4 \\
\hline
& 43.01 \leftarrow \overline{2\ \textit{decimal places}}
\end{array}
$$

26.
$$
\begin{array}{ll}
\textit{estimate} & \textit{exact} \\
5 & 5.08 \leftarrow 2\ \textit{decimal places} \\
\times\ 70 & \times\ 71 \\
\hline
350 & 5\,08 \\
& 355\,6 \\
\hline
& 360.68 \leftarrow \overline{2\ \textit{decimal places}}
\end{array}
$$

28.
$$
\begin{array}{ll}
\textit{estimate} & \textit{exact} \\
8 & 7.51 \leftarrow 2\ \textit{decimal places} \\
\times\ 8 & \times\ 8.2 \leftarrow 1\ \textit{decimal place} \\
\hline
64 & 1\,502 \\
& 60\,08 \\
\hline
& 61.582 \leftarrow \overline{3\ \textit{decimal places}}
\end{array}
$$

30.
$$
\begin{array}{ll}
\textit{estimate} & \textit{exact} \\
70 & 73.52 \leftarrow 2\ \textit{decimal places} \\
\times\ 20 & \times\ 22.34 \leftarrow 2\ \textit{decimal places} \\
\hline
1400 & 2\,9408 \\
& 22\,056 \\
& 147\,04 \\
& 1470\,4 \\
\hline
& 1642.4368 \leftarrow \overline{4\ \textit{decimal places}}
\end{array}
$$

32. A 25 hour work day is *unreasonable*. A reasonable answer would be 2.5 hours.

34. Rent for $6.92 is *unreasonable*. A reasonable answer would be $692.

36. A living room 16.8 feet in length is *reasonable*.

38. A sale price of $1.49 for a jacket is *unreasonable*. A reasonable answer would be $14.90 or $149.

40. Multiply the hours worked by the hourly rate.

$$\begin{array}{r} \$10.03 \\ \times\ \ 42.2 \\ \hline 2\ 006 \\ 20\ 06 \\ 401\ 2\ \ \\ \hline \$423.266 \end{array}$$

Round $423.266 to the nearest cent. His gross earnings are $423.27.

42. Multiply the amount of lace trim purchased by the cost per yard.

$$\begin{array}{r} \$0.87 \\ \times\ \ 3.5 \\ \hline 435 \\ 2\ 61\ \ \\ \hline \$3.045 \end{array}$$

Round $3.045 to the nearest cent. She will pay $3.05.

44. Multiply the number of pounds purchased by the cost per pound.

$$\begin{array}{r} \$0.98 \\ \times\ \ 1.7 \\ \hline 686 \\ 98\ \ \\ \hline \$1.666 \end{array}$$

Round $1.666 to the nearest cent. The chicken wings cost $1.67.

46. Multiply the shortstop's batting average by the number of times at bat.

$$\begin{array}{r} 554 \\ \times\ 0.316 \\ \hline 3\ 324 \\ 5\ 54 \\ 166\ 2\ \ \\ \hline 175.064 \end{array}$$

Round 175.064 to the nearest whole number. Alex Rodriguez had 175 hits.

48. To find the total payment for three years, multiply the monthly payment by 36.

$$\begin{array}{r} \$220.27 \\ \times\ \ \ \ 36 \\ \hline 1321\ 62 \\ 6608\ 1\ \ \\ \hline \$7929.72 \end{array}$$

Chuck will pay $7929.72.

50. Multiply the pounds of plastic collected by the rate paid per pound.

$$\begin{array}{r} \$0.142 \\ \times\ \ 2200 \\ \hline 28\ 400 \\ 284\ \ \ \ \ \\ \hline \$312.400 \end{array}$$

The recycling center will pay $312.40.

52. One adult: $8

4 children: $4.50
$$\begin{array}{r} \times\ \ \ \ 4 \\ \hline \$18.00 \end{array}$$

3 seniors: $5.75
$$\begin{array}{r} \times\ \ \ \ 3 \\ \hline \$17.25 \end{array}$$

Total: 8.00
$$\begin{array}{r} 18.00 \\ +\ 17.25 \\ \hline 43.25 \end{array}$$

Difference: 73.45
$$\begin{array}{r} -\ 43.25 \\ \hline \$30.20 \end{array}$$

The family would spend $30.20 less.

54. Find the rental cost for 3 weeks.

$$\begin{array}{r} \$375 \\ \times\ \ 3 \\ \hline \$1125 \end{array}$$

Find the mileage fee.

$$\begin{array}{r} \$0.35 \\ \times\ 2650 \\ \hline \$927.50 \end{array}$$

Add the two amounts.

$$\begin{array}{r} \$1125.00 \\ +\ 927.50 \\ \hline \$2052.50 \end{array}$$

The rental cost was $2052.50.

56. Find the total payments.

$37.98
× 6
$227.88

Add the down payment.

$227.88
+ 45.00
$272.88

Subtract the cost of the VCR from this amount.

$272.88
− 229.88
$43.00

Susan could have saved $43.

58. Find the cost of five long-sleeve, solid color shirts.

$18.95
× 5
$94.75

Find the cost of three long-sleeve striped shirts.

$21.95
× 3
$65.85

Add the two amounts.

$94.75
+ 65.85
$160.60

The subtotal cost is $160.60.
Shipping is $9.95 based on this subtotal.
Also, add $4.25 to ship to an additional address.

$160.60
9.95
+ 4.25
$174.80

The total cost is $174.80.

60. (a) Find the cost of 3 long-sleeved striped shirts.

$21.95
× 3
65.85

Now add the cost for extra-large size.

$2 $65.85
× 3   + 6.00
$6 $71.85

Now find the cost of the shirts for yourself.

$14.75
16.75
18.95
+ 21.95
$72.40

The subtotal is: $71.85
+ 72.40
$144.25

The shipping, based on this subtotal, is $9.95. Add the two amounts plus $5 for a gift box, and $4.25 for shipping to an additional address, and $4.95 for each of the 2 monograms ($9.90).

$144.25
9.95
5.00
4.25
+ 9.90
$173.35

The total cost is $173.35.

(b) Subtract to find difference.

Yourself   Dad
$72.40 $71.85
+ 9.90   + 5.00
$82.30 $76.85

$82.30
− 76.85
$5.45

The difference is $5.45.

4.5 Dividing Decimals

2.
$$
\begin{array}{r}
6.3 \\
8\overline{)50.4} \\
\underline{48} \\
2\ 4 \\
\underline{2\ 4} \\
0
\end{array}
$$
6.3 *Line up decimal points.*

4. $\dfrac{1.62}{6}$

$$
\begin{array}{r}
0.27 \\
6\overline{)1.62} \\
\underline{1\ 2} \\
42 \\
\underline{42} \\
0
\end{array}
$$
0.27 *Line up decimal points.*

6.

$$\begin{array}{r} 200.5 \\ 0.08_\wedge \overline{)16.04_\wedge 0} \end{array}$$

Line up decimal points.
Move decimal point 2
places in dividend
and divisor.

$$\begin{array}{r} \underline{16} \\ 00 \\ \underline{00} \\ 4 \\ \underline{0} \\ 4\,0 \\ \underline{4\,0} \\ 0 \end{array}$$

Write 0 in dividend.

8.

$$\begin{array}{r} 5\,5. \\ 2.4_\wedge \overline{)132.0_\wedge} \end{array}$$

Move decimal point
1 place in dividend
and divisor; write 0.

$$\begin{array}{r} \underline{120} \\ 12\,0 \\ \underline{12\,0} \\ 0 \end{array}$$

10. $10.8 \div 18$

$108 \div 18 = 6$ *Move decimal point left one*
$10.8 \div 18 = 0.6$ *place for divisor.*

12. $0.18\overline{)1.08}$

Move decimal point
left two places for
divisor.

$108 \div 18 = 6$
$1.08 \div 0.18 = 108 \div 18 = 6$

14.

$$\begin{array}{r} 1.92 \\ 2.6_\wedge \overline{)4.9_\wedge 92} \end{array}$$

Line up decimal points.
Move decimal point
left two places for
divisor.

$$\begin{array}{r} \underline{2\,6} \\ 2\,3\,9 \\ \underline{2\,3\,4} \\ 52 \\ \underline{52} \\ 0 \end{array}$$

16. $\dfrac{1.7}{0.09}$

$$\begin{array}{r} 18.888 \\ 0.09_\wedge \overline{)1.70_\wedge 000} \end{array}$$

Move decimal point 2
places in dividend and
divisor; write one 0.

$$\begin{array}{r} \underline{9} \\ 80 \\ \underline{72} \\ 8\,0 \\ \underline{7\,2} \\ 80 \\ \underline{72} \\ 80 \\ \underline{72} \\ 8 \end{array}$$

Write 0 in dividend.
Write 0 in dividend.
Write 0 in dividend.
Stop and round answer
to the nearest hundredth.

18.888 rounds to 18.89.

18. $7643 \div 5.36 = 1425.9328$

Round to the nearest thousandth.
1425.932|8
1425.9328 rounds to 1425.933.

20. $0.043\overline{)1748.4} = 40,660.4651$

If you are using an 8-digit calculator, your
answer will appear already rounded as
40,660.465.

24. $345.6 \div 3 = 11.52$

estimate   ↑   *not reasonable*

$$\begin{array}{r} 100 \\ 3\overline{)300} \end{array} \qquad \begin{array}{r} 115.2 \\ 3\overline{)345.6} \\ \underline{3} \\ 04 \\ \underline{3} \\ 15 \\ \underline{15} \\ 6 \\ \underline{6} \\ 0 \end{array}$$

The answer is 115.2.

26. $2428.8 \div 4.8 = 50.6$

estimate   ↑   *not reasonable*

$$\begin{array}{r} 400 \\ 5\overline{)2000} \end{array} \qquad \begin{array}{r} 50\,6. \\ 4.8_\wedge \overline{)2428.8_\wedge} \\ \underline{240} \\ 28 \\ \underline{0} \\ 28\,8 \\ \underline{28\,8} \\ 0 \end{array}$$

The answer is 506.

28. $395.415 \div 5.05 = 78.3$

↑
estimate   *reasonable*

$$\begin{array}{r} 80 \\ 5\overline{)400} \end{array}$$

30. $78 \div 14.2 = 0.182$
                    ↑
estimate   *not reasonable*

$$\begin{array}{r} 8 \\ 10\overline{)80} \end{array}$$

$$\begin{array}{r} 5.4929 \\ 14.2_\wedge\overline{)78.0_\wedge 0000} \\ \underline{71\ 0} \\ 7\ 0\ 0 \\ \underline{5\ 6\ 8} \\ 1\ 3\ 20 \\ \underline{1\ 2\ 78} \\ 420 \\ \underline{284} \\ 1360 \\ \underline{1278} \\ 82 \end{array}$$

Write 0 in dividend.

Write 0 in dividend.

Write 0 in dividend.

Write 0 in dividend.

Stop and round answer.

5.4929 rounds to 5.493, which is a reasonable answer.

32. Divide the cost of four notepads by the number of notepads purchased.

$$\begin{array}{r} 0.422 \\ 4\overline{)1.690} \\ \underline{1\ 6} \\ 9 \\ \underline{8} \\ 10 \\ \underline{8} \\ 2 \end{array}$$

0.422 rounds to 0.42.

One notepad costs $0.42.

34. Divide the cost of the fabric by the number of meters of fabric purchased.

$$\begin{array}{r} 6.996 \\ 2.6_\wedge\overline{)18.1_\wedge 900} \\ \underline{15\ 6} \\ 2\ 5\ 9 \\ \underline{2\ 3\ 4} \\ 2\ 50 \\ \underline{2\ 34} \\ 160 \\ \underline{156} \\ 4 \end{array}$$

6.996 rounds to 7.00.

Marcella paid ≈ $7.00 per meter.

36. Divide the amount she paid by the number of copies of the newspaper.

$$\begin{array}{r} 0.155 \\ 842\overline{)130.510} \\ \underline{84\ 2} \\ 46\ 31 \\ \underline{42\ 10} \\ 4\ 210 \\ \underline{4\ 210} \\ 0 \end{array}$$

$0.155 rounds to $0.16.

The cost per copy is ≈ $0.16.

38. Divide the cost of the records by the number of records.

$$\begin{array}{r} 0.722 \\ 400\overline{)289.000} \\ \underline{280\ 0} \\ 9\ 00 \\ \underline{8\ 00} \\ 1\ 000 \\ \underline{800} \\ 200 \end{array}$$

0.722 rounds to 0.72.

The cost per record is ≈ $0.72.

40. Mr. Rodriguez pays $53.19 in one month.
$1436.13 ÷ $53.19 = the number of monthly payments.
$1436.13 \div 53.19 = 27$
It will take 27 months.

42. Add all the lengths, then divide by the total number.

$$
\begin{array}{r}
8.95 \\
8.90 \\
8.87 \\
8.86 \\
8.74 \\
8.74 \\
8.71 \\
8.63 \\
+\ 8.62 \\
\hline
79.02
\end{array}
$$

$$
\begin{array}{r}
8.78 \\
9\overline{)79.02} \\
\underline{72} \\
7\,0 \\
\underline{6\,3} \\
72 \\
\underline{72} \\
0
\end{array}
$$

The average lengths of all the long jumps is 8.78 meters.

44. Multiply 6 and the length of the jump

$$
\begin{array}{r}
8.95 \\
\times\ 6 \\
\hline
53.70
\end{array}
$$

The total distance jumped was 53.70 meters.

46. Subtract to find difference.

$$
\begin{array}{r}
8.63 \\
-\ 8.62 \\
\hline
0.01
\end{array}
$$

The last place jump was 0.01 meter less than the next-to-last-place jump.

48. $6.2 + 4.3^2 - 9.72 = 6.2 + 18.49 - 9.72$
$$= 24.69 - 9.72 = 14.97$$

50. $2.25 - 1.06 \cdot (4.85 - 3.95) = 2.25 - 1.06 \cdot 0.9$
$$= 2.25 - 0.954 = 1.296$$

52. $25.1 + 11.4 \div 7.5 \cdot 3.75 = 25.1 + 1.52 \cdot 3.75$
$$= 25.1 + 5.7 = 30.8$$

54. $0.6 + (1.89 + 0.11) \div 0.004 \cdot 0.5$
$$= 0.6 + 2 \div 0.004 \cdot 0.5$$
$$= 0.6 + 500 \cdot 0.5$$
$$= 0.6 + 250 = 250.6$$

56. Find the weight of 1 nugget by dividing the package weight by the number of nuggests.

$$
\begin{array}{r}
0.7 \\
15\overline{)10.5} \\
\underline{10\,5} \\
0
\end{array}
$$

Then divide the number of ounces Nadia can eat by the weight of each nugget.

$$
\begin{array}{r}
5 \\
0.7_\wedge\overline{)3.5_\wedge}
\end{array}
$$

Nadia can eat 5 nuggets.

58. Divide the vehicle's speed by the speed of sound.

$$
\begin{array}{r}
1.019 \\
748.11_\wedge\overline{)763.03_\wedge500} \\
\underline{748\,11} \\
14\,92\,50 \\
\underline{7\,48\,11} \\
7\,44\,390 \\
\underline{6\,73\,299} \\
71\,091
\end{array}
$$

1.019 rounds to 1.02.

The car's Mach speed is 1.02.

60. Divide 100,000 by 550.

$$
\begin{array}{r}
181.8 \\
550\overline{)100,000.0} \\
\underline{55\,0} \\
45\,00 \\
\underline{44\,00} \\
1\,000 \\
\underline{550} \\
450\,0 \\
\underline{440\,0} \\
10\,0
\end{array}
$$

181.8 rounds to 182.

Each child needs to collect 182 box tops.

62. Divide 182 by 38.

$$
\begin{array}{r}
4.7 \\
38\overline{)182.0} \\
\underline{152} \\
30\,0 \\
\underline{26\,6} \\
3\,4
\end{array}
$$

4.7 rounds to 5.

Each child needs to collect 5 box tops per week.

4.6   Writing Fractions as Decimals

2. $\dfrac{1}{4} = 0.25$

$$
\begin{array}{r}
0.25 \\
4\overline{)1.00} \\
\underline{8} \\
20 \\
\underline{20} \\
0
\end{array}
$$

4. $\dfrac{1}{10} = 0.1$

$$
\begin{array}{r}
0.1 \\
10\overline{)1.0} \\
\underline{1\,0} \\
0
\end{array}
$$

6. $\dfrac{7}{10} = 0.7$

$$
\begin{array}{r}
0.7 \\
10\overline{)7.0} \\
\underline{7\,0} \\
0
\end{array}
$$

8. $\dfrac{4}{5} = 0.8$

$$
\begin{array}{r}
0.8 \\
5\overline{)4.0} \\
\underline{4\,0} \\
0
\end{array}
$$

10. $\dfrac{2}{5} = 0.4$

$$
\begin{array}{r}
0.4 \\
5\overline{)2.0} \\
\underline{2\,0} \\
0
\end{array}
$$

12. $\dfrac{3}{8} = 0.375$

$$
\begin{array}{r}
0.375 \\
8\overline{)3.000} \\
\underline{2\,4} \\
60 \\
\underline{56} \\
40 \\
\underline{40} \\
0
\end{array}
$$

14. $1\dfrac{1}{2} = \dfrac{3}{2} = 1.5$

$$
\begin{array}{r}
1.5 \\
2\overline{)3.0} \\
\underline{2} \\
1\,0 \\
\underline{1\,0} \\
0
\end{array}
$$

16. $23\dfrac{3}{5}$

$$
\begin{array}{r}
0.6 \\
5\overline{)3.0} \\
\underline{3\,0} \\
0
\end{array}
$$

$$23\dfrac{3}{5} = 23 + \dfrac{3}{5} = 23 + 0.6 = 23.6$$

18. $2\dfrac{7}{8} = \dfrac{23}{8} = 2.875$

$$
\begin{array}{r}
2.875 \\
8\overline{)23.000} \\
\underline{16} \\
7\,0 \\
\underline{6\,4} \\
60 \\
\underline{56} \\
40 \\
\underline{40} \\
0
\end{array}
$$

20. $\dfrac{2}{3}$ $2 \div 3 = 0.6666667 \approx 0.667$

22. $\dfrac{1}{6}$ $1 \div 6 = 0.1666667 \approx 0.167$

24. $5\dfrac{4}{7} = \dfrac{39}{7}$

$$39 \div 7 \approx 5.5714286$$
$$\approx 5.571$$

30. $0.75 = \dfrac{75}{100} = \dfrac{75 \div 25}{100 \div 25} = \dfrac{3}{4}$

32. $0.111 = \dfrac{111}{1000}$

34. $0.9 = \dfrac{9}{10}$

36. $\dfrac{1}{40} = 0.025$

$$
\begin{array}{r}
0.025 \\
40\overline{)1.000} \\
\underline{80} \\
200 \\
\underline{200} \\
0
\end{array}
$$

38. $0.52 = \dfrac{52}{100} = \dfrac{52 \div 4}{100 \div 4} = \dfrac{13}{25}$

40. $0.85 = \dfrac{85}{100} = \dfrac{85 \div 5}{100 \div 5} = \dfrac{17}{20}$

42. $\dfrac{1}{8} = 0.125$

$$
\begin{array}{r}
0.125 \\
8\overline{)1.000} \\
\underline{8} \\
20 \\
\underline{16} \\
40 \\
\underline{40} \\
0
\end{array}
$$

44. $0.02 = \dfrac{2}{100} = \dfrac{2 \div 2}{100 \div 2} = \dfrac{1}{50}$

46. Compare the two amounts.

$$8.3 \rightarrow 8.30 \textit{ more} \qquad 8.30$$
$$8.03 \rightarrow 8.03 \textit{ less} \quad \underline{- \ 8.03}$$
$$0.27$$

She got too little medicine.

The difference was 0.27 milligrams.

48. Compare the two thicknesses.

$$0.625 \rightarrow 0.6250 \textit{ thicker} \qquad 0.6250$$
$$0.6248 \rightarrow 0.6248 \textit{ thinner} \quad \underline{- \ 0.6248}$$
$$0.0002$$

The edge was too thin by 0.0002 cm.

50. Compare the weights.

Between 2.950 ounces and 3.050 ounces

$$3.000 \rightarrow \textit{Yes}$$
$$2.995 \rightarrow \textit{Yes}$$
$$3.055 \rightarrow \textit{No}$$
$$3.005 \rightarrow \textit{Yes}$$

52. Compare the two amounts.

$$\frac{3}{8} = 0.375 \textit{ more} \qquad 0.375$$
$$0.3 = 0.300 \textit{ less} \quad \underline{- \ 0.300}$$
$$0.075$$

Their actual gain of 0.075 ounce was more.

54. 0.76, 0.7, 0.7006

$$0.76 = 0.7600$$
$$0.7 = 0.7000$$
$$0.7006 = 0.7006$$

From smallest to largest:
0.7, 0.7006, 0.76

56. 12.99, 12.5, 13.0001, 12.77

$$12.99 = 12.9900$$
$$12.5 = 12.5000$$
$$13.0001 = 13.0001$$
$$12.77 = 12.7700$$

From smallest to largest:
12.5, 12.77, 12.99, 13.0001

58. 0.27, 0.281, 0.296, 0.3

$$0.27 = 0.270$$
$$0.281 = 0.281$$
$$0.296 = 0.296$$
$$0.3 = 0.300$$

From smallest to largest:
0.27, 0.281, 0.296, 0.3

60. 0.98, 0.89, 0.904, 0.9

$$0.98 = 0.980$$
$$0.89 = 0.890$$
$$0.904 = 0.904$$
$$0.9 = 0.900$$

From smallest to largest:
0.89, 0.9, 0.904, 0.98

62. 0.629, $\frac{5}{8}$, 0.65, $\frac{7}{10}$

$$0.629 = 0.629$$
$$\frac{5}{8} = 0.625$$
$$0.65 = 0.650$$
$$\frac{7}{10} = 0.700$$

From smallest to largest:

$$\frac{5}{8}, \ 0.629, \ 0.65, \ \frac{7}{10}$$

64. 0.1501, 0.25, $\frac{1}{10}$, $\frac{1}{5}$

$$0.1501 = 0.1501$$
$$0.25 = 0.2500$$
$$\frac{1}{10} = 0.1000$$
$$\frac{1}{5} = 0.2000$$

From smallest to largest:

$$\frac{1}{10}, \ 0.1501, \ \frac{1}{5}, \ 0.25$$

66. Find the smallest of:
0.018, 0.01, 0.008, 0.010

$$0.018 = 0.018$$
$$0.01 = 0.010$$
$$0.008 = 0.008$$
$$0.010 = 0.010$$

List from smallest to largest:
0.008, 0.01 = 0.010, 0.018

The green box, labeled 0.008 in. diameter, has the line with the least strength.

68. Find the difference between 0.01 and 0.010.

$$0.010$$
$$\underline{- \ 0.01}$$
$$0.000$$

There is no difference; they are equal.

70. $1\frac{1}{8} = \frac{9}{8}$

$$
\begin{array}{r}
1.12 \\
8\overline{)9.00} \\
\underline{8} \\
1\,0 \\
\underline{8} \\
20 \\
\underline{16} \\
4
\end{array}
$$

1.12 rounded to the nearest tenth is 1.1.
Length (b) is ≈ 1.1.

72. $\frac{1}{2} = \frac{5}{10} = 0.5$

Length (d) is 0.5 inch.

74. $\frac{11}{16}$

$$
\begin{array}{r}
0.68 \\
16\overline{)11.00} \\
\underline{9\,6} \\
1\,40 \\
\underline{1\,28} \\
12
\end{array}
$$

0.6 rounded to the nearest tenth is 0.7.
Length (f) is ≈ 0.7 inch.

Chapter 5

RATIO AND PROPORTION

5.1 Ratios

2. 11 to $15 = \dfrac{11}{15}$

4. 35¢ to 7¢

$$\dfrac{35¢}{7¢} = \dfrac{35}{7} = \dfrac{35 \div 7}{7 \div 7} = \dfrac{5}{1}$$

6. 9 pounds to 36 pounds

$$\dfrac{9 \text{ pounds}}{36 \text{ pounds}} = \dfrac{9}{36} = \dfrac{9 \div 9}{36 \div 9} = \dfrac{1}{4}$$

8. 300 people to 450 people

$$\dfrac{300 \text{ people}}{450 \text{ people}} = \dfrac{300}{450} = \dfrac{300 \div 150}{450 \div 150} = \dfrac{2}{3}$$

10. 45 books to 35 books

$$\dfrac{45 \text{ books}}{35 \text{ books}} = \dfrac{45}{35} = \dfrac{45 \div 5}{35 \div 5} = \dfrac{9}{7}$$

12. $0.08 to $0.06

$$\dfrac{\$0.08}{\$0.06} = \dfrac{0.08}{0.06} = \dfrac{0.08 \cdot 100}{0.06 \cdot 100} = \dfrac{8}{6}$$

$$\dfrac{8 \div 2}{6 \div 2} = \dfrac{4}{3}$$

14. 5 to $1\dfrac{1}{4}$

$$\dfrac{5}{1\frac{1}{4}} = \dfrac{\frac{5}{1}}{\frac{5}{4}} = \dfrac{5}{1} \div \dfrac{5}{4} = \dfrac{\overset{1}{\cancel{5}}}{1} \cdot \dfrac{4}{\cancel{5}_{1}} = \dfrac{4}{1}$$

16. $2\dfrac{1}{3}$ to $2\dfrac{2}{3}$

$$\dfrac{2\frac{1}{3}}{2\frac{2}{3}} = \dfrac{\frac{7}{3}}{\frac{8}{3}} = \dfrac{7}{3} \div \dfrac{8}{3} = \dfrac{7}{\cancel{3}} \cdot \dfrac{\overset{1}{\cancel{3}}}{8} = \dfrac{7}{8}$$

18. 8 feet to 4 yards

4 yards = 4 · 3 = 12 feet

$$\dfrac{8 \text{ feet}}{4 \text{ yards}} = \dfrac{8 \text{ feet}}{12 \text{ feet}} = \dfrac{8}{12} = \dfrac{8 \div 4}{12 \div 4} = \dfrac{2}{3}$$

20. 8 quarts to 5 pints

8 quarts = 8 · 2 pints = 16 pints

$$\dfrac{8 \text{ quarts}}{5 \text{ pints}} = \dfrac{16 \text{ pints}}{5 \text{ pints}} = \dfrac{16}{5}$$

22. 3 pounds to 6 ounces

3 pounds = 3 · 16 = 48 ounces

$$\dfrac{3 \text{ pounds}}{6 \text{ ounces}} = \dfrac{48 \text{ ounces}}{6 \text{ ounces}} = \dfrac{48}{6} = \dfrac{48 \div 6}{6 \div 6} = \dfrac{8}{1}$$

24. 3 cups to 3 pints

3 pints = 3 · 2 cups = 6 cups

$$\dfrac{3 \text{ cups}}{3 \text{ pints}} = \dfrac{3 \text{ cups}}{6 \text{ cups}} = \dfrac{3}{6} = \dfrac{3 \div 3}{6 \div 3} = \dfrac{1}{2}$$

26. Halloween cards to Mother's Day cards

$$\dfrac{25 \text{ million}}{150 \text{ million}} = \dfrac{25}{150} = \dfrac{25 \div 25}{150 \div 25} = \dfrac{1}{6}$$

28. Mother's Day cards to Father's Day cards

$$\dfrac{150 \text{ million}}{95 \text{ million}} = \dfrac{150}{95} = \dfrac{150 \div 5}{95 \div 5} = \dfrac{30}{19}$$

30. Answers will vary. Possibilities include: a person may send Valentine's Day cards every year but graduation cards only once every few years; Valentine's Day may have more advertising than graduations.

32. (a) guitar to clarinet:

$$\dfrac{20 \text{ million}}{4 \text{ million}} = \dfrac{20}{4} = \dfrac{20 \div 4}{4 \div 4} = \dfrac{5}{1}$$

(b) organ to drums:

$$\dfrac{6 \text{ million}}{3 \text{ million}} = \dfrac{6}{3} = \dfrac{6 \div 3}{3 \div 3} = \dfrac{2}{1}$$

clarinet to violin:

$$\dfrac{4 \text{ million}}{2 \text{ million}} = \dfrac{4}{2} = \dfrac{4 \div 2}{2 \div 2} = \dfrac{2}{1}$$

34. Answers will vary. One possibility is hiring teachers in the same ratios as the instruments, for example, five guitar teachers for every clarinet teacher.

36. (a) taxes to rent

$$\dfrac{\$400}{\$750} = \dfrac{400}{750} = \dfrac{400 \div 50}{750 \div 50} = \dfrac{8}{15}$$

(b) food to transportation:

$$\frac{\$300}{\$200} = \frac{300}{200} = \frac{300 \div 100}{200 \div 100} = \frac{3}{2}$$

(c) taxes and food to rent and utilities:

taxes and food: $400 + \$300 = \$700$

rent and utilities: $750 + \$125 = \$875$

$$\frac{\$700}{\$875} = \frac{700}{875} = \frac{700 \div 175}{875 \div 175} = \frac{4}{5}$$

38. $\dfrac{\text{longest side}}{\text{shortest side}} = \dfrac{25 \text{ kilometers}}{5 \text{ kilometers}} = \dfrac{25}{5} = \dfrac{5}{1}$

The ratio of the lengths of the longest side to the shortest side is $\frac{5}{1}$.

40. $\dfrac{\text{longest side}}{\text{shortest side}} = \dfrac{0.12 \text{ inch}}{0.09 \text{ inch}} = \dfrac{0.12}{0.09}$

$$= \frac{0.12 \cdot 100}{0.09 \cdot 100} = \frac{12}{9}$$

$$= \frac{4}{3}$$

The ratio of the lengths of the longest side to the shortest side is $\frac{4}{3}$.

42. $\dfrac{\text{longest side}}{\text{shortest side}} = \dfrac{6\frac{3}{4} \text{ feet}}{1\frac{1}{2} \text{ feet}}$

$$= \frac{6\frac{3}{4}}{1\frac{1}{2}} = \frac{\frac{27}{4}}{\frac{3}{2}}$$

$$= \frac{27}{4} \div \frac{3}{2}$$

$$= \frac{\overset{9}{\cancel{27}}}{\underset{2}{\cancel{4}}} \cdot \frac{\overset{1}{\cancel{2}}}{\underset{1}{\cancel{3}}} = \frac{9}{2}$$

The ratio of the of the longest side to the shortest side is $\frac{9}{2}$.

44. The decrease in price is
$8.80 - \$5.60 = \$3.20$.

$$\frac{\$3.20}{\$8.80} = \frac{3.20}{8.80} = \frac{3.20 \cdot 10}{8.80 \cdot 10} = \frac{32}{88}$$

$$= \frac{32 \div 8}{88 \div 8} = \frac{4}{11}$$

The ratio of the decrease in price to the original price is $\frac{4}{11}$.

46. $5\frac{3}{4}$ feet to $15\frac{3}{4}$ inches

$$5\frac{3}{4} \text{ feet} = 5\frac{3}{4} \cdot 12 \text{ inches} = 69 \text{ inches}$$

$$\frac{69 \text{ inches}}{15\frac{3}{4} \text{ inches}} = \frac{\frac{69}{1}}{\frac{63}{4}} = \frac{69}{1} \div \frac{63}{4}$$

$$= \frac{\overset{23}{\cancel{69}}}{1} \cdot \frac{4}{\underset{21}{\cancel{63}}} = \frac{92}{21}$$

The ratio of the percheron's height to its prehistoric ancestor's height is $\frac{92}{21}$.

5.2   Rates

2. $12 for 30 pens

$$\frac{\$12 \div 6}{30 \text{ pens} \div 6} = \frac{\$2}{5 \text{ pens}}$$

4. 100 miles in 30 hours

$$\frac{100 \text{ miles} \div 10}{30 \text{ hours} \div 10} = \frac{10 \text{ miles}}{3 \text{ hours}}$$

6. 12 wagons for 48 horses

$$\frac{12 \text{ wagons} \div 12}{48 \text{ horses} \div 12} = \frac{1 \text{ wagon}}{4 \text{ horses}}$$

8. 68 pills for 17 people

$$\frac{68 \text{ pills} \div 17}{17 \text{ people} \div 17} = \frac{4 \text{ pills}}{1 \text{ person}}$$

10. 25 doctors for 310 patients

$$\frac{25 \text{ doctors} \div 5}{310 \text{ patients} \div 5} = \frac{5 \text{ doctors}}{62 \text{ patients}}$$

12. 132 miles on 8 gallons

$$\frac{132 \text{ miles} \div 4}{8 \text{ gallons} \div 4} = \frac{33 \text{ miles}}{2 \text{ gallons}}$$

14. $2500 in 20 days

$$\begin{array}{r} 125 \\ 20\overline{)2500} \\ \underline{20} \\ 50 \\ \underline{40} \\ 100 \\ \underline{100} \\ 0 \end{array}$$

The unit rate is $125 per day or $125/day.

16. 36 children from 12 families

$$12\overline{)36} \;\; 3$$

The unit rate is 3 children per family or 3 children/family.

18. 44 bushels from 8 trees

$$\begin{array}{r} 5.5 \\ 8\overline{)44.0} \\ \underline{40} \\ 40 \\ \underline{40} \\ 0 \end{array}$$

The unit rate is 5.5 bushels/tree.

20. $74.25 for 9 hours

$$\begin{array}{r} 8.25 \\ 9\overline{)74.25} \\ \underline{72} \\ 2\,2 \\ \underline{18} \\ 45 \\ \underline{45} \\ 0 \end{array}$$

The unit rate is $8.25/hour.

22. Miles traveled:

28,058.1 − 27.758.2 = 299.9

Miles per gallon:

$$\frac{299.9 \text{ miles}}{13.4 \text{ gallons}} = 299.9 \div 13.4$$
$$\approx 22.380597$$
$$\approx 22.4$$

24. Miles traveled:

28,704.5 − 28,396.7 = 307.8

Miles per gallon:

$$\frac{307.8 \text{ gallons}}{13.3 \text{ gallons}} = 307.8 \div 13.3$$
$$\approx 23.142857$$
$$\approx 23.1$$

26.

size	cost per unit
8 ounces	$\dfrac{\$0.99}{8 \text{ ounces}} \approx \$0.124$
12 ounces	$\dfrac{\$1.47}{12 \text{ ounces}} \approx \$0.123$

The best buy is 12 ounces for $1.47.

28.

size	cost per unit
2 cans	$\dfrac{\$0.95}{2 \text{ cans}} = \$0.475$
3 cans	$\dfrac{\$1.45}{3 \text{ cans}} \approx \$0.483$
5 cans	$\dfrac{\$2.29}{5 \text{ cans}} = \$0.458$

The best buy is 5 cans for $2.29.

30.

size	cost per unit
8 ounces	$\dfrac{\$0.37}{8 \text{ ounces}} \approx \$0.0463$
16 ounces	$\dfrac{\$0.77}{16 \text{ ounces}} \approx \$0.0481$
21 ounces	$\dfrac{\$0.99}{21 \text{ ounces}} \approx \$0.0471$
31 ounces	$\dfrac{\$1.50}{31 \text{ ounces}} \approx \$0.0484$

The best buy is 8 ounces for $0.37.

32. If you use only half of the larger bag, you really pay $0.30 per pound, so the smaller bag is the better buy.

34. 4 pounds for 10 people

$$\begin{array}{r} 0.4 \\ 10\overline{)4.0} \\ \underline{40} \\ 0 \end{array}$$

The rate is 0.4 pound/person.

36. 18 gallons cost $26.28

$$\begin{array}{r} 1.46 \\ 18\overline{)26.28} \\ \underline{18} \\ 82 \\ \underline{72} \\ 108 \\ \underline{108} \\ 0 \end{array}$$

The cost is $1.46/gallon.

38. $6450 for 2500 shares

$$
\begin{array}{r}
2.58 \\
2500\overline{)6450.00} \\
\underline{5000} \\
14500 \\
\underline{12500} \\
200\,00 \\
\underline{200\,00} \\
0
\end{array}
$$

The dividend is $2.58/share.

40. five hearing aids in four hours

$$
\begin{array}{r}
1 \\
4\overline{)5} = 1\frac{1}{4} \\
\underline{4} \\
1
\end{array}
$$

Sofia can clean and adjust 1.25 hearing aids per hour or $1\frac{1}{4}$ hearing aids per hour.

4 hours for 5 hearing aids

$$
\begin{array}{r}
0.8 \\
5\overline{)4.0} \qquad 0.8 = \frac{8}{10} = \frac{4}{5} \\
\underline{4\,0} \\
0
\end{array}
$$

In 0.8 or $\frac{4}{5}$ hour, Sofia can clean and adjust one hearing aid.

42. **(a)** $10 \times 7¢ = 70¢$

$0.70 + $5.95 = 6.65

$$\frac{\$6.65}{10 \text{ minutes}} \approx \$0.67 \text{ / minute}$$

The cost per minute is $\approx \$0.67$.

(b) $30 \times 7¢ = \$2.10$

$2.10 + $5.95 = 8.05

$$\frac{\$8.05}{30 \text{ minutes}} \approx \$0.27 \text{ / minute}$$

The cost per minute is $\approx \$0.27$.

(c) $60 \times 7¢ = \$4.20$

$4.20 + $5.95 = 10.15

$$\frac{\$10.15}{60 \text{ minutes}} \approx \$0.17 \text{ / minute}$$

The cost per minute is $\approx \$0.17$.

44. 64 fluid ounces

$2 \cdot 64 = 128$ ounces

$$\frac{\$5.99}{128 \text{ ounces}} \approx \frac{\$0.047}{\text{ounce}}$$

150 fluid ounces

$$\frac{\$7.29}{150 \text{ ounces}} \approx \frac{\$0.049}{\text{ounce}}$$

The better buy is the 64 ounce size.

46. Brand K: $\$5 \div 3 \approx \dfrac{\$1.67}{\text{box}}$

$1.67 - $0.45 = 1.22

$$\frac{\$1.22}{175 \text{ tissues}} \approx \$0.007 \text{ per tissue}$$

Brand S: $\$1.29 - \$0.20 = \$1.09$

$$\frac{\$1.09}{125 \text{ tissues}} \approx \$0.009 \text{ per tissue}$$

The best buy is Brand K with a 45¢ coupon.

5.3 Proportions

2. 28 people is to 7 cars as 16 people is to 4 cars.

$$\frac{28 \text{ people}}{7 \text{ cars}} = \frac{16 \text{ people}}{4 \text{ cars}}$$

4. 150 trees is to 1 acre as 1500 trees is to 10 acres.

$$\frac{150 \text{ trees}}{1 \text{ acre}} = \frac{1500 \text{ trees}}{10 \text{ acres}}$$

6. $6 is $9 as $10 is to $15.

$$\frac{6}{9} = \frac{10}{15} \qquad Common\ units\ cancel$$

8. $\dfrac{1}{4} = \dfrac{9}{36}$

$$\frac{1}{4} \text{ and } \frac{9 \div 9}{36 \div 9} = \frac{1}{4}$$

Both ratios are equivalent to $\frac{1}{4}$, so the proportion is true.

10. $\dfrac{2}{3} = \dfrac{20}{27}$

$$\frac{2}{3} \text{ and } \frac{20}{27}$$

Because $\frac{2}{3}$ is not equivalent to $\frac{20}{27}$, the proportion is false.

12. $\dfrac{100}{120} = \dfrac{75}{100}$

$\dfrac{100 \div 20}{120 \div 20} = \dfrac{5}{6}$ and $\dfrac{75 \div 25}{100 \div 25} = \dfrac{3}{4}$

Because $\frac{5}{6}$ is not equivalent to $\frac{3}{4}$, the proportion is false.

14. $\dfrac{18}{16} = \dfrac{36}{32}$

$\dfrac{18 \div 2}{16 \div 2} = \dfrac{9}{8}$ and $\dfrac{36 \div 4}{32 \div 4} = \dfrac{9}{8}$

Both ratios are equivalent to $\frac{9}{8}$, so the proportion is true.

16. $\dfrac{15}{48} = \dfrac{10}{24}$

$\dfrac{15 \div 3}{48 \div 3} = \dfrac{5}{16}$ and $\dfrac{10 \div 2}{24 \div 2} = \dfrac{5}{12}$

Because $\frac{5}{16}$ is not equivalent to $\frac{5}{12}$, the proportion is false.

18. $\dfrac{28}{21} = \dfrac{44}{33}$

$\dfrac{28 \div 7}{21 \div 7} = \dfrac{4}{3}$ and $\dfrac{44 \div 11}{33 \div 11} = \dfrac{4}{3}$

Both ratios are equivalent to $\frac{4}{3}$, so the proportion is true.

20. $\dfrac{20}{25} = \dfrac{4}{5}$

$20 \cdot 5 = 100 \leftarrow$ *Cross products*
$4 \cdot 25 = 100 \leftarrow$ *are equal*

True

22. $\dfrac{16}{40} = \dfrac{22}{55}$

$16 \cdot 55 = 880 \leftarrow$ *Cross products*
$40 \cdot 22 = 880 \leftarrow$ *are equal*

True

24. $\dfrac{600}{420} = \dfrac{20}{14}$

$600 \cdot 14 = 8400 \leftarrow$ *Cross products*
$420 \cdot 20 = 8400 \leftarrow$ *are equal*

True

26. $\dfrac{36}{23} = \dfrac{9}{5.75}$

$36 \cdot 5.75 = 207 \leftarrow$ *Cross products*
$23 \cdot 9 = 207 \leftarrow$ *are equal*

True

28. $\dfrac{0.26}{0.39} = \dfrac{1.3}{1.9}$

$0.26 \cdot 1.9 = 0.494 \leftarrow$ *Cross products*
$0.39 \cdot 1.3 = 0.507 \leftarrow$ *are not equal*

False

30. $\dfrac{16}{13} = \dfrac{2}{1\frac{5}{8}}$

$16 \cdot 1\dfrac{5}{8} = \dfrac{\overset{2}{\cancel{16}}}{1} \cdot \dfrac{13}{\underset{1}{\cancel{8}}} = 26$

$13 \cdot 2 = 26$

Cross products are equal.
True

32. $\dfrac{28}{17} = \dfrac{9\frac{1}{3}}{5\frac{2}{3}}$

$28 \cdot 5\dfrac{2}{3} = \dfrac{28}{1} \cdot \dfrac{17}{3} = \dfrac{476}{3}$

$17 \cdot 9\dfrac{1}{3} = \dfrac{17}{1} \cdot \dfrac{28}{3} = \dfrac{476}{3}$

Cross products are equal.
True

34. $\dfrac{3.75}{1\frac{1}{4}} = \dfrac{7.5}{2\frac{1}{2}}$

$3.75 \cdot 2\dfrac{1}{2} = \dfrac{3.75}{1} \cdot \dfrac{5}{2}$

$\qquad = \dfrac{18.75}{2} = 9.375$

$1\dfrac{1}{4} \cdot 7.5 = \dfrac{5}{4} \cdot \dfrac{7.5}{1}$

$\qquad = \dfrac{37.5}{4} = 9.375$

Cross products are equal.
True

36. $\dfrac{3}{\frac{5}{6}} = \dfrac{1.5}{\frac{7}{12}}$

$$3 \cdot \dfrac{7}{12} = \dfrac{\cancel{3}^{1}}{1} \cdot \dfrac{7}{\cancel{12}_{4}} = \dfrac{7}{4}$$

$$\dfrac{5}{6} \cdot 1.5 = \dfrac{5}{6} \cdot 1\dfrac{1}{2} = \dfrac{5}{\cancel{6}} \cdot \dfrac{\cancel{3}^{1}}{2} = \dfrac{5}{4}$$

The cross products are unequal.
False

38. The left-hand ratio compares hours to cartons, but the right-hand ratio compares cartons to hours. Correct proportion is:

$$\dfrac{3.5 \text{ hours}}{91 \text{ cartons}} = \dfrac{5.25 \text{ hours}}{126 \text{ cartons}}$$

Cross products are not equal so the proportion is false.

5.4   Solving Proportions

2. $\dfrac{x}{6} = \dfrac{15}{18}$

$$18 \cdot x = 6 \cdot 15$$

$$\dfrac{\cancel{18}^{1} \cdot x}{\cancel{18}_{1}} = \dfrac{\cancel{90}^{5}}{\cancel{18}_{1}}$$

$$x = 5$$

Check: $\dfrac{5}{6} = \dfrac{15}{18}$

$18 \cdot 5 = 90$
$15 \cdot 6 = 90$

The cross products are equal, so 5 is the correct solution.

4. $\dfrac{5}{x} = \dfrac{20}{8}$

$$\dfrac{5}{x} = \dfrac{5}{2}$$

$$\dfrac{\cancel{5}^{1} \cdot x}{\cancel{5}_{1}} = \dfrac{\cancel{5}^{1} \cdot 2}{\cancel{5}_{1}}$$

$$x = 2$$

Check: $\dfrac{5}{2} = \dfrac{20}{8}$

$5 \cdot 8 = 40$
$2 \cdot 20 = 40$

The cross products are equal, so 2 is the correct solution.

6. $\dfrac{12}{9} = \dfrac{8}{x}$

$$12 \cdot x = 9 \cdot 8$$

$$\dfrac{\cancel{12}^{1} \cdot x}{\cancel{12}_{1}} = \dfrac{\cancel{72}^{6}}{\cancel{12}_{1}}$$

$$x = 6$$

Check: $\dfrac{12}{9} = \dfrac{8}{6}$

$12 \cdot 6 = 72$
$8 \cdot 9 = 72$

The cross products are equal, so 6 is the correct solution.

8. $\dfrac{49}{x} = \dfrac{14}{18}$

$$14 \cdot x = 49 \cdot 18$$

$$\dfrac{\cancel{14}^{1} \cdot x}{\cancel{14}_{1}} = \dfrac{882}{14}$$

$$x = 63$$

Check: $\dfrac{49}{63} = \dfrac{14}{18}$

$49 \cdot 18 = 882$
$14 \cdot 63 = 882$

The cross products are equal, so 63 is the correct solution.

10. $\dfrac{6}{x} = \dfrac{4}{8}$

$$4 \cdot x = 6 \cdot 8$$

$$\dfrac{\cancel{4}^{1} \cdot x}{\cancel{4}_{1}} = \dfrac{48}{4}$$

$$x = 12$$

Check: $\dfrac{6}{12} = \dfrac{4}{8}$

$6 \cdot 8 = 48$
$4 \cdot 12 = 48$

The cross products are equal, so 12 is the correct solution.

12. $\dfrac{32}{5} = \dfrac{x}{10}$

$5 \cdot x = 32 \cdot 10$

$\dfrac{\cancel{5}^1 \cdot x}{\cancel{5}_1} = \dfrac{320}{5}$

$x = 64$

Check: $\dfrac{32}{5} = \dfrac{64}{10}$

$32 \cdot 10 = 320$

$5 \cdot 64 = 320$

The cross products are equal, so 64 is the correct solution.

14. $\dfrac{x}{12} = \dfrac{101}{147}$

$147 \cdot x = 101 \cdot 12$

$x = 1212 \div 147$

≈ 8.24

Check: Use the exact number $\dfrac{1212}{147}$ for x.

$\dfrac{\frac{1212}{147}}{12} = \dfrac{101}{147}$

$147 \cdot \dfrac{1212}{147} = 1212$

$12 \cdot 101 = 1212$

Cross products are equal, so $\dfrac{1212}{147} \approx 8.24$ is the correct solution.

16. $\dfrac{x}{3.6} = \dfrac{4.5}{6}$

$6 \cdot x = 3.6 \cdot 4.5$

$\dfrac{\cancel{6}^1 \cdot x}{\cancel{6}_1} = \dfrac{16.2}{6}$

$x = 2.7$

Check: $\dfrac{2.7}{3.6} = \dfrac{4.5}{6}$

$3.6 \cdot 4.5 = 16.2$

$6 \cdot 2.7 = 16.2$

The cross products are equal, so 2.7 is the correct solution.

18. $\dfrac{4.75}{17} = \dfrac{43}{x}$

$4.75 \cdot x = 43 \cdot 17$

$x = 731 \div 4.75$

≈ 153.89474

≈ 153.89

Check: Use the exact number $\dfrac{731}{4.75}$ for x.

$\dfrac{4.75}{17} = \dfrac{43}{\frac{731}{4.75}}$

$4.75 \cdot \dfrac{731}{4.75} = 731$

$17 \cdot 43 = 731$

Cross products are equal, so $\dfrac{731}{4.75} \approx 153.89$ is the correct solution.

20. $\dfrac{x}{\frac{3}{10}} = \dfrac{2\frac{2}{9}}{1}$

$1 \cdot x = \dfrac{3}{10} \cdot 2\dfrac{2}{9}$

$1 \cdot x = \dfrac{\cancel{3}^1}{\cancel{10}_1} \cdot \dfrac{\cancel{20}^2}{\cancel{9}_3}$

$x = \dfrac{2}{3}$

22. $\dfrac{1\frac{5}{6}}{x} = \dfrac{\frac{3}{14}}{\frac{6}{7}}$

$\dfrac{3}{14} \cdot x = 1\dfrac{5}{6} \cdot \dfrac{6}{7}$

$\dfrac{3}{14} \cdot x = \dfrac{11}{\cancel{6}} \cdot \dfrac{\cancel{6}^1}{7}$

$\dfrac{\frac{3}{14} \cdot x}{\frac{3}{14}} = \dfrac{\frac{11}{7}}{\frac{3}{14}}$

$x = \dfrac{11}{7} \div \dfrac{3}{14} = \dfrac{11}{7} \cdot \dfrac{\cancel{14}^2}{3}$

$= \dfrac{22}{3} = 7\dfrac{1}{3}$

24. Decimals:

$$\frac{\frac{3}{20}}{0.1} = \frac{0.03}{x}$$

$$\frac{0.15}{0.1} = \frac{0.03}{x}$$

$$0.15 \cdot x = 0.1 \cdot 0.03$$

$$\frac{0 \cdot 15 \cdot x}{0.15} = \frac{0.003}{0.15}$$

$$x = 0.02$$

Fractions:

$$\frac{\frac{3}{20}}{\frac{1}{10}} = \frac{\frac{3}{100}}{x}$$

$$\frac{3}{20} \cdot x = \frac{3}{100} \cdot \frac{1}{10}$$

$$\frac{\frac{3}{20} \cdot x}{\frac{3}{20}} = \frac{\frac{3}{1000}}{\frac{3}{20}}$$

$$x = \frac{3}{1000} \div \frac{3}{20}$$

$$= \frac{\cancel{3}}{\underset{50}{\cancel{1000}}} \cdot \frac{\overset{1}{\cancel{20}}}{\cancel{3}}$$

$$= \frac{1}{50}$$

26. Decimals:

$$\frac{8\frac{4}{5}}{1\frac{1}{10}} = \frac{x}{0.4}$$

$$\frac{8.8}{1.1} = \frac{x}{0.4}$$

$$1.1 \cdot x = 8.8 \cdot 0.4$$

$$\frac{1.1 \cdot x}{1.1} = \frac{3.52}{1.1}$$

$$x = 3.2$$

Fractions:

$$\frac{8\frac{4}{5}}{1\frac{1}{10}} = \frac{x}{0.4}$$

$$\frac{8\frac{4}{5}}{1\frac{1}{10}} = \frac{x}{\frac{4}{10}}$$

$$1\frac{1}{10} \cdot x = 8\frac{4}{5} \cdot \frac{4}{10}$$

$$1\frac{1}{10} \cdot x = \frac{\overset{22}{\cancel{44}}}{5} \cdot \frac{4}{\underset{5}{\cancel{10}}}$$

$$\frac{1\frac{1}{10} \cdot x}{1\frac{1}{10}} = \frac{\frac{88}{25}}{1\frac{1}{10}}$$

$$x = \frac{88}{25} \div 1\frac{1}{10}$$

$$= \frac{\overset{8}{\cancel{88}}}{\underset{5}{\cancel{25}}} \cdot \frac{\overset{2}{\cancel{10}}}{\underset{1}{\cancel{11}}} = \frac{16}{5} = 3\frac{1}{5}$$

5.5 Solving Application Problems with Proportions

2. $$\frac{8 \text{ songs}}{26 \text{ hours}} = \frac{14 \text{ songs}}{x}$$

$$8 \cdot x = 14 \cdot 26$$

$$\frac{8 \cdot x}{8} = \frac{364}{8}$$

$$x = 45.5$$

It will take The Cosmic Toads 45.5 hours to record 14 songs.

4. $$\frac{22 \text{ guitar lessons}}{\$396} = \frac{12 \text{ guitar lessons}}{x}$$

$$22 \cdot x = 396 \cdot 12$$

$$\frac{22 \cdot x}{22} = \frac{4752}{22}$$

$$x = 216$$

It will cost $216 for 12 guitar lessons.

6. $\dfrac{\$1242.08}{14 \text{ days}} = \dfrac{x}{260 \text{ days}}$

$14 \cdot x = 1242.08 \cdot 260$

$\dfrac{14 \cdot x}{14} = \dfrac{322{,}940.8}{14}$

$x = 23{,}067.2$

In 260 days, Anna earns $23,067.20.

8. $\dfrac{5 \text{ ounces medicine}}{8 \text{ ounces water}} = \dfrac{x}{20 \text{ ounces water}}$

$8 \cdot x = 5 \cdot 20$

$\dfrac{8 \cdot x}{8} = \dfrac{100}{8}$

$x = 12.5$

You would mix 12.5 ounces of medicine with 20 ounces of water.

10. $\dfrac{23 \text{ ounces}}{4 \text{ servings}} = \dfrac{x}{9 \text{ servings}}$

$4 \cdot x = 23 \cdot 9$

$\dfrac{4 \cdot x}{4} = \dfrac{207}{4}$

$x \approx 52$

About 52 ounces are needed for 9 servings.

12. $\dfrac{1 \text{ gallon}}{550 \text{ square feet}} = \dfrac{x}{(3 \cdot 400) \text{ square feet}}$

$\dfrac{1}{550} = \dfrac{x}{1200}$

$550 \cdot x = 1 \cdot 1200$

$\dfrac{550x}{550} = \dfrac{1200}{550}$

$x \approx 2.2$

You need ≈ 2.2 gallons to apply three coats of finish to 400 square feet.

14. First find the length of the family room.

$\dfrac{4.5 \text{ inches}}{x} = \dfrac{1 \text{ inch}}{4 \text{ feet}}$

$1 \cdot x = 4 \cdot 4.5$

$x = 18$

Then find the width.

$\dfrac{3 \text{ inches}}{x} = \dfrac{1 \text{ inch}}{4 \text{ feet}}$

$1 \cdot x = 3 \cdot 4$

$x = 12$

The family room has a length of 18 feet and a width of 12 feet.

16. Find the length of the floor plan.

$\dfrac{6.5 \text{ inches}}{x} = \dfrac{1 \text{ inch}}{4 \text{ feet}}$

$x \cdot 1 = 6.5 \cdot 4$

$x = 26$

Now find the width.

$\dfrac{4.5 \text{ inches}}{x} = \dfrac{1 \text{ inch}}{4 \text{ feet}}$

$1 \cdot x = 4.5 \cdot 4$

$x = 18$

The length is 26 feet and the width is 18 feet.

18. $\dfrac{7 \text{ rebounds}}{26 \text{ minutes}} = \dfrac{x}{40 \text{ minutes}}$

$26 \cdot x = 7 \cdot 40$

$\dfrac{26 \cdot x}{26} = \dfrac{280}{26}$

$x \approx 11$

He is expected to make ≈ 11 rebounds in 40 minutes.

20. 3 people liked

$\dfrac{\text{poached eggs}}{100 \text{ people}} = \dfrac{x}{60 \text{ customers}}$

$100 \cdot x = 3 \cdot 60$

$\dfrac{100 \cdot x}{100} = \dfrac{180}{100}$

$x = 1.8 \approx 2$

≈ 2 customers at Soon-Won's ordered poached eggs. This is a reasonable answer.

Incorrect setup

$\dfrac{3}{100} = \dfrac{60}{x}$

$3 \cdot x = 60 \cdot 100$

$\dfrac{3 \cdot x}{3} = \dfrac{6000}{3}$

$x = 2000$

The incorrect setup gives 2000 people and there were only 60 people in the restaurant.

22. $\dfrac{200}{1} = \dfrac{5600}{x}$

$200 \cdot x = 5600 \cdot 1$

$\dfrac{200 \cdot x}{200} = \dfrac{5600}{200}$

$x = 28$

28 sewing machines have defects. This is a reasonable answer.

Incorrect setup

$\dfrac{200}{1} = \dfrac{x}{5600}$

$1 \cdot x = 200 \cdot 5600$

$x = 1,120,000$

The incorrect setup gives 1,120,000 sewing machines have defects and only 5600 were shipped.

24. $\dfrac{3}{100} = \dfrac{x}{31,200,000}$

$100 \cdot x = 3 \cdot 31,200,00$

$\dfrac{100 \cdot x}{100} = \dfrac{93,600,000}{100}$

$x = 936,000$

936,000 dog owners washed their pets by having the dogs go into the shower with them. This is a reasonable answer.

Incorrect setup

$\dfrac{3}{100} = \dfrac{31,200,000}{x}$

$3 \cdot x = 100 \cdot 31,200,00$

$\dfrac{3 \cdot x}{3} = \dfrac{3,120,000,000}{3}$

$x = 1,040,000,000$

The incorrect setup gives 1,040,000,000 dog owners washing their pets with them in the shower and there are only 31,200,000 U.S. dog owners.

26. $\dfrac{90 \text{ pounds of water}}{100 \text{ pounds of body weight}}$

$= \dfrac{x \text{ pounds of water}}{80 \text{ pounds of body weight}}$

$100 \cdot x = 90 \cdot 80$

$\dfrac{100 \cdot x}{100} = \dfrac{7200}{100}$

$x = 72$

There are 72 pounds of water in a child who weighs 80 pounds.

28. $\dfrac{19 \text{ students}}{1 \text{ teacher}} = \dfrac{1850 \text{ students}}{x}$

$19 \cdot x = 1850 \cdot 1$

$\dfrac{19 \cdot x}{19} = \dfrac{1850}{19}$

$x \approx 97$

They need ≈ 97 teachers.

30. $\dfrac{150 \text{ pounds}}{189 \text{ calories}} = \dfrac{115 \text{ pounds}}{x}$

$150 \cdot x = 189 \cdot 115$

$\dfrac{150 \cdot x}{150} = \dfrac{21,735}{150}$

$x \approx 145$

A 115-pound person would burn ≈ 145 calories.

32. $\begin{array}{ccc} \text{Corretta's} & & \text{tree's} \\ \text{shadow} & = & \text{shadow} \\ \downarrow & & \downarrow \\ \dfrac{2.95 \text{ meters}}{1.68 \text{ meters}} & = & \dfrac{x}{10.53 \text{ meters}} \\ \uparrow & & \uparrow \\ \text{Coretta's} & & \text{tree's} \\ \text{height} & & \text{height} \end{array}$

$1.68 \cdot x = 2.95 \cdot 10.53$

$\dfrac{1.68 \cdot x}{1.68} = \dfrac{31.0635}{1.68}$

$x \approx 18.49$

Later in the day the tree's shadow was ≈ 18.49 meters.

34. Answers will vary. Exercises 1-32 are all examples of application problems.

36. First find how many employees think exercise is a good idea.

$$\frac{9}{10} = \frac{x}{300}$$

$$10 \cdot x = 9 \cdot 300$$

$$\frac{10 \cdot x}{10} = \frac{2700}{10}$$

$$x = 270$$

Then find how many of these employees actually exercise.

$$\frac{1}{6} = \frac{x}{270}$$

$$6 \cdot x = 270 \cdot 1$$

$$\frac{6 \cdot x}{6} = \frac{270}{6}$$

$$x = 45$$

In this company, 45 employees exercise regularly.

38.

$$\frac{\frac{2}{3} \text{ cup}}{210 \text{ calories}} = \frac{1 \text{ cup}}{x}$$

$$\frac{2}{3} \cdot x = 210 \cdot 1$$

$$\frac{3}{2} \cdot \frac{2}{3} x = 210 \cdot \frac{3}{2}$$

$$x = 315$$

$$\frac{\frac{2}{3} \text{ cup}}{2 \text{ grams of fiber}} = \frac{1 \text{ cup}}{x}$$

$$\frac{2}{3} \cdot x = 2 \cdot 1$$

$$\frac{3}{2} \cdot \frac{2}{3} \cdot x = 2 \cdot \frac{3}{2}$$

$$x = 3$$

A 1-cup serving provides 315 calories and 3 grams of fiber.

Chapter 6

PERCENT

6.1 Basics of Percent

2. 41% = 0.41
   Drop the percent sign and move the decimal point two places to the left.

4. 40% = 0.40 or 0.4
   Drop the percent sign and move the decimal point two places to the left.

6. 35% = 0.35
   Drop the percent sign and move the decimal point two places to the left.

8. 250% = 2.50 or 2.5
   Drop the percent sign and move the decimal point two places to the left.

10. 6.7% = 0.067
    Drop the percent sign and attach 0 so the decimal point can be moved two places to the left.

12. 600% = 6.00 or 6
    The percent sign is dropped. Move the decimal point two places to the left.

14. 0.25% = 0.0025
    The percent sign is dropped, 0's are attached so the decimal point can be moved two places to the left.

16. 0.75% = 0.0075
    The percent is dropped. 0's are attached so the decimal point can be moved two places to the left.

18. 0.4 = 40%
    Attach 0 so the decimal point can be moved two places to the right. Attach percent sign.

20. 0.25 = 25%
    Move the decimal point two places to the right and attach a percent sign.

22. 0.07 = 7%
    Move the decimal point two places to the right and attach percent sign.

24. 0.875 = 87.5%
    Move the decimal point two places to the right and attach percent sign.

26. 0.625 = 62.5%
    Move the decimal point two places to the right and attach percent sign.

28. 5 = 500%
    Attach 0's so the decimal point can be moved two places to the right. Attach percent sign.

30. 2.2 = 220%
    Attach 0 so the decimal point can be moved two places to the right. Attach percent sign.

32. 0.0625 = 6.25%
    Move the decimal point two places to the right and attach percent sign.

34. 8.715 = 871.5%
    Move the decimal point two places to the right and attach percent sign.

36. 0.0064 = 0.64%
    Move the decimal point two places to the right. Drop 0's and attach percent sign.

38. Some answers might be:
    When using discounts on purchases, calculating sales tax, figuring interest on loans, examining investments, finding tips in restaurants, calculating interest on savings, and doing math problems in this book.

40. Drop the percent sign and move the decimal point two places to the left.
    82% of the students = 0.82

42. Drop the percent sign and move the decimal point two places to the left.
    43.2% voter turnout = 0.432

44. Move the decimal point two places to the right and attach percent sign.
    0.49 of the money = 49%

46. Attach two 0's so that the decimal point can be moved two places to the right.
    Attach percent sign.
    4 times as great as last quarter = 400%

48. Move the decimal point two places to the right.
    Drop two 0's and attach percent sign.
    0.0075 of total output = 0.75%

50. Drop the percent sign and move the decimal point two places to the left.
    248.7% greater than anticipated = 2.487.

52. 100% is all of the vans.
    So, 100% of 345 vans is 345 vans.
    345 vans are painted white with blue lettering.

54. 200% is twice as much money.
So, 200% of $380 is $760.
This week's expenses are $760.

56. 300% is three times the miles per gallon.
So, 300% of 12 miles per gallon is 36 miles per gallon.
His new car gets 36 miles per gallon.

58. 50% is half of the animals.
So, 50% of 20,000 animals is 10,000 animals.
The number of dogs taken was 10,000.

60. 10% is found by moving the decimal point one place to the left.
So, 10% of 240 dozen plants is 24 dozen plants.
The number of unsold plants will be 24 dozen.

62. 1% is found by moving the decimal point two places to the left.
So, 1% of 4800 accidents is 48 accidents.
48 accidents were caused by mechanical failure.

64. (a) 50% means 50 parts out of 100 parts. That's half of the number. A shortcut for finding 50% of a number is to divide the number by 2.

(b) Answers will vary.

66. (a) Since 300% is three times a number, find 300% of the number by multiplying the number by 3 (triple it).

(b) Answers will vary.

68. (a) Since 1% means 1 part out of 100 parts or $\frac{1}{100}$, the shortcut for finding 1% of a number is to move the decimal point in the number two places to the left.

(b) Answers will vary.

70. 49% or 0.49 of the students ranked environmental issues as a top issue.

72. (a) The third most important issue the students chose was gun control.

(b) 51% or 0.51 of the students chose gun control.

74. 17.2% or 0.172 of the population of Greece is 65 or older.

76. (a) The country with the highest portion is Italy.

(b) 18.2% = 0.182

78. Twenty parts of the one hundred parts are shaded.
$$\frac{20}{100} = 0.20 = 20\%$$
Eighty parts of the one hundred parts are unshaded.
$$\frac{80}{100} = 0.80 = 80\%$$

80. Eighty parts of the one hundred parts are shaded.
$$\frac{80}{100} = 0.80 = 80\%$$
Twenty parts of the one hundred parts are unshaded.
$$\frac{20}{100} = 0.20 = 20\%$$

82. Thirty-seven parts of the one hundred parts are shaded.
$$\frac{37}{100} = 0.37 = 37\%$$
Sixty-three parts of the one hundred parts are unshaded.
$$\frac{63}{100} = 0.63 = 63\%$$

6.2 Percents and Fractions

2. $60\% = \frac{60 \div 20}{100 \div 20} = \frac{3}{5}$

4. $80\% = \frac{80 \div 20}{100 \div 20} = \frac{4}{5}$

6. $45\% = \frac{45 \div 5}{100 \div 5} = \frac{9}{20}$

8. $87.5\% = \frac{87.5}{100} = \frac{87.5 \cdot 10}{100 \cdot 10} = \frac{875 \div 125}{1000 \div 125} = \frac{7}{8}$

10. $43.75\% = \frac{43.75}{100} = \frac{43.75 \cdot 100}{100 \cdot 100}$
$$= \frac{4375 \div 625}{10,000 \div 625} = \frac{7}{16}$$

12. $83\frac{1}{3}\% = \frac{83\frac{1}{3}}{100} = 83\frac{1}{3} \div \frac{100}{1}$
$$= \frac{\overset{5}{\cancel{250}}}{3} \cdot \frac{1}{\underset{2}{\cancel{100}}} = \frac{5}{6}$$

14. $46\frac{2}{3}\% = \dfrac{46\frac{2}{3}}{100} = \dfrac{\frac{140}{3}}{100} = \dfrac{140}{3} \div \dfrac{100}{1}$

$= \dfrac{\overset{7}{\cancel{140}}}{3} \cdot \dfrac{1}{\underset{5}{\cancel{100}}} = \dfrac{7}{15}$

16. $0.8\% = \dfrac{0.8 \cdot 10}{100 \cdot 10} = \dfrac{8}{1000} = \dfrac{1}{125}$

18. $140\% = \dfrac{140 \div 20}{100 \div 20} = \dfrac{7}{5} = 1\frac{2}{5}$

20. $225\% = \dfrac{225 \div 25}{100 \div 25} = \dfrac{9}{4} = 2\frac{1}{4}$

22. $\dfrac{4}{10} = \dfrac{p}{100}$

$10 \cdot p = 4 \cdot 100$

$\dfrac{10 \cdot p}{10} = \dfrac{400}{10}$

$p = 40$

$\dfrac{4}{10} = 40\%$

24. $\dfrac{3}{10} = \dfrac{p}{100}$

$10 \cdot p = 3 \cdot 100$

$\dfrac{10 \cdot p}{10} = \dfrac{300}{10}$

$p = 30$

$\dfrac{3}{10} = 30\%$

26. $\dfrac{3}{4} = \dfrac{p}{100}$

$4 \cdot p = 3 \cdot 100$

$\dfrac{4 \cdot p}{4} = \dfrac{300}{4}$

$p = 75$

$\dfrac{3}{4} = 75\%$

28. $\dfrac{63}{100} = 0.63 = 63\%$

30. $\dfrac{1}{8} = \dfrac{p}{100}$

$8 \cdot p = 1 \cdot 100$

$\dfrac{8 \cdot p}{8} = \dfrac{100}{8}$

$p = 12.5$

$\dfrac{1}{8} = 12.5\%$

32. $\dfrac{3}{8} = \dfrac{p}{100}$

$8 \cdot p = 3 \cdot 100$

$\dfrac{8 \cdot p}{8} = \dfrac{300}{8}$

$p = 37.5$

$\dfrac{3}{8} = 37.5\%$

34. $\dfrac{15}{25} = \dfrac{p}{100}$

$25 \cdot p = 15 \cdot 100$

$\dfrac{25 \cdot p}{25} = \dfrac{1500}{25}$

$p = 60$

$\dfrac{15}{25} = 60\%$

36. $\dfrac{18}{50} = \dfrac{18 \cdot 2}{50 \cdot 2} = \dfrac{36}{100} = 0.36 = 36\%$

38. $\dfrac{9}{20} = \dfrac{p}{100}$

$20 \cdot p = 9 \cdot 100$

$\dfrac{20 \cdot p}{20} = \dfrac{900}{20}$

$p = 45$

$\dfrac{9}{20} = 45\%$

40. $\dfrac{1}{6} = \dfrac{p}{100}$

$6 \cdot p = 1 \cdot 100$

$\dfrac{6 \cdot p}{6} = \dfrac{100}{6}$

$p \approx 16.7$

$\dfrac{1}{6} \approx 16.7\%$

42. $\dfrac{7}{9} = \dfrac{p}{100}$

$9 \cdot p = 7 \cdot 100$

$\dfrac{9 \cdot p}{9} = \dfrac{700}{9}$

$p \approx 77.8$

$\dfrac{7}{9} \approx 77.8\%$

44. $\dfrac{5}{7} = \dfrac{p}{100}$

$7 \cdot p = 5 \cdot 100$

$\dfrac{7 \cdot p}{7} = \dfrac{500}{7}$

$p \approx 71.4$

$\dfrac{5}{7} \approx 71.4\%$

46. $\dfrac{3}{50} = \dfrac{3 \cdot 2}{50 \cdot 2} = \dfrac{6}{100} = 0.06$ *decimal*

$\qquad\qquad\qquad\quad = 6\%$ *percent*

48. $\dfrac{3}{4} = \dfrac{3 \cdot 25}{4 \cdot 25} = \dfrac{75}{100} = 0.75$ *decimal*

$\qquad\qquad\qquad\quad = 75\%$ *percent*

50. $60\% = 0.6$ *decimal*

$\qquad = \dfrac{6}{10} = \dfrac{3}{5}$ *fraction*

52. $\dfrac{1}{3} \approx 0.333$ *decimal*

$\qquad \approx 33.3\%$ *percent*

54. $37.5\% = \dfrac{37.5}{100}$

$\qquad = \dfrac{37.5 \cdot 10}{100 \cdot 10}$

$\qquad = \dfrac{375 \div 125}{1000 \div 125}$

$\qquad = \dfrac{3}{8}$ *fraction*

$37.5\% = 0.375$ *decimal*

56. $\dfrac{5}{8} = \dfrac{p}{100}$

$8 \cdot p = 5 \cdot 100$

$\dfrac{8 \cdot p}{8} = \dfrac{500}{8}$

$p = 62.5$

$\dfrac{5}{8} = 62.5\%$ *percent*

$\qquad = 0.625$ *decimal*

58. $\approx 0.833 = \dfrac{83\frac{1}{3}}{100} = \dfrac{\frac{250}{3}}{100}$

$\qquad = \dfrac{250}{3} \div \dfrac{100}{1}$

$\qquad = \dfrac{\overset{5}{\cancel{250}}}{3} \cdot \dfrac{1}{\underset{2}{\cancel{100}}}$

$\qquad = \dfrac{5}{6}$ *fraction*

$\approx 83.3\%$ *percent*

60. $\dfrac{3}{10} = \dfrac{3 \cdot 10}{10 \cdot 10} = \dfrac{30}{100} = 30\%$ *percent*

$\qquad\qquad\qquad\quad = 0.30 = 0.3$ *decimal*

62. $100\% = \dfrac{100}{100} = 1$ *fraction*

$100\% = 1.00 = 1$ *decimal*

64. $\dfrac{1}{400} = \dfrac{p}{100}$

$400 \cdot p = 1 \cdot 100$

$\dfrac{400 \cdot p}{400} = \dfrac{100}{400}$

$p = \dfrac{1}{4}$

$p = 0.25$

$\dfrac{1}{400} = 0.25\%$ *percent*

$\qquad = 0.0025$ *decimal*

66. $1.7 = 1\dfrac{7}{10}$ *fraction*

$\qquad = \dfrac{170}{100} = 170\%$ *decimal*

68. $2\dfrac{4}{5} = 2\dfrac{8}{10} = 2.8$ *decimal*

$\qquad = 280\%$ *percent*

70. There are many correct answers. The table of percent equivalents shows some of the possibilities.

72. 27 of every 100 purchased included a coloring activity.

$$\frac{27}{100} \qquad \textit{fraction}$$

$$\frac{27}{100} = 0.27 \quad \textit{decimal}$$

$$\frac{27}{100} = 27\% \quad \textit{percent}$$

74. 360 parents out of 800 parents said they were most influenced by relatives, friends, and spouses.

$$\frac{360}{800} = \frac{360 \div 40}{800 \div 40} = \frac{9}{20} \qquad \textit{fraction}$$

$$\frac{9}{20} = \frac{9 \cdot 5}{20 \cdot 5} = \frac{45}{100} = 0.45 \quad \textit{decimal}$$

$$0.45 = 45\% \qquad \textit{percent}$$

76. 14 employees of 25 employees are students.

$$\frac{14}{25} \qquad \textit{fraction}$$

$$\frac{14}{25} = \frac{56}{100} = 0.56 \quad \textit{decimal}$$

$$0.56 = 56\% \qquad \textit{percent}$$

78. $125 - 25 = 100$ animals out of 125 animals are not endangered.

$$\frac{100}{125} = \frac{100 \div 25}{125 \div 25} = \frac{4}{5} \quad \textit{fraction}$$

$$\frac{4}{5} = \frac{8}{10} = 0.8 \qquad \textit{decimal}$$

$$0.8 = 80\% \qquad \textit{percent}$$

80. $250 - 100 = 150$ members out of 250 members do not use their insecticide.

$$\frac{150}{250} = \frac{150 \div 50}{250 \div 50} = \frac{3}{5} \quad \textit{fraction}$$

$$\frac{3}{5} = \frac{6}{10} = 0.6 \qquad \textit{decimal}$$

$$0.6 = 60\% \qquad \textit{percent}$$

82. 336 students out of 4200 students use a bicycle.

$$\frac{336}{4200} = \frac{336 \div 168}{4200 \div 168} = \frac{2}{25} \quad \textit{fraction}$$

$$\frac{2}{25} = \frac{8}{100} = 0.08 \qquad \textit{decimal}$$

$$0.08 = 8\% \qquad \textit{percent}$$

84. 840 students out of 4200 students carpool.

$$\frac{840}{4200} = \frac{840 \div 840}{4200 \div 840} = \frac{1}{5} \quad \textit{fraction}$$

$$\frac{1}{5} = \frac{20}{100} = 0.2 \qquad \textit{decimal}$$

$$0.2 = 20\% \qquad \textit{percent}$$

6.3 Using the Percent Proportion and Identifying the Components in a Percent Problem

2. part = 20, percent = 25

$$\frac{20}{x} = \frac{25}{100}$$

$$x \cdot 25 = 20 \cdot 100$$

$$\frac{x \cdot 25}{25} = \frac{2000}{25}$$

$$x = 80$$

The whole is 80.

4. part = 25, percent = 25

$$\frac{25}{x} = \frac{25}{100}$$

$$x \cdot 25 = 25 \cdot 100$$

$$\frac{x \cdot 25}{25} = \frac{2500}{25}$$

$$x = 100$$

The whole is 100.

6. part = 11, percent = 5

$$\frac{11}{x} = \frac{5}{100}$$

$$x \cdot 5 = 11 \cdot 100$$

$$\frac{x \cdot 5}{5} = \frac{1100}{5}$$

$$x = 220$$

The whole is 220.

8. part = 105, whole = 35

$$\frac{105}{35} = \frac{x}{100}$$

$$35 \cdot x = 105 \cdot 100$$

$$\frac{35 \cdot x}{35} = \frac{10,500}{35}$$

$$x = 300$$

The percent is 300 or 300%.

10. part = 1.5, whole = 4.5

$$\frac{1.5}{4.5} = \frac{x}{100}$$

$$4.5 \cdot x = 1.5 \cdot 100$$

$$\frac{4.5 \cdot x}{4.5} = \frac{150}{4.5}$$

$$x = 33.3 \text{ (rounded)}$$

The percent is ≈ 33.3, or ≈ 33.3%.

12. part = 12.8, whole = 9.6

$$\frac{12.8}{9.6} = \frac{x}{100}$$

$$9.6 \cdot x = 12.8 \cdot 100$$

$$\frac{9.6 \cdot x}{9.6} = \frac{1280}{9.6}$$

$$x = 133.3 \text{ (rounded)}$$

The percent is ≈ 133.3, or ≈ 133.3%

14. whole = 160, percent = 35

$$\frac{x}{160} = \frac{35}{100}$$

$$x \cdot 100 = 160 \cdot 35$$

$$\frac{x \cdot 100}{100} = \frac{5600}{100}$$

$$x = 56$$

The part is 56.

16. whole = 115, percent = 38

$$\frac{x}{115} = \frac{38}{100}$$

$$x \cdot 100 = 115 \cdot 38$$

$$\frac{x \cdot 100}{100} = \frac{4370}{100}$$

$$x = 43.7$$

The part is 43.7.

18. whole = 89.6, part = 50

$$\frac{50}{89.6} = \frac{x}{100}$$

$$89.6 \cdot x = 50 \cdot 100$$

$$\frac{89.6 \cdot x}{89.6} = \frac{5000}{89.6}$$

$$x = 55.8 \text{ (rounded)}$$

The percent is ≈ 55.8, or ≈ 55.8%.

20. percent = 45, whole = 160

$$\frac{x}{160} = \frac{45}{100}$$

$$\frac{x}{160} = \frac{9}{20}$$

$$20 \cdot x = 9 \cdot 160$$

$$\frac{20 \cdot x}{20} = \frac{1440}{20}$$

$$x = 72$$

The part is 72.

22. part = 15, whole = 2500

$$\frac{15}{2500} = \frac{x}{100}$$

$$\frac{3}{500} = \frac{x}{100}$$

$$\frac{500 \cdot x}{500} = \frac{300}{500}$$

$$x = 0.6$$

The percent is 0.6%.

24. percent = $12\frac{3}{4}$, whole = 5600

$$\frac{x}{5600} = \frac{12\frac{3}{4}}{100}$$

$$x \cdot 100 = 5600 \cdot 12\frac{3}{4}$$

$$\frac{x \cdot 100}{100} = \frac{71,400}{100}$$

$$x = 714$$

The part is 714.

26. part = 281.25, percent = $1\frac{1}{4}$

$$\frac{281.25}{x} = \frac{1\frac{1}{4}}{100}$$

$$x \cdot 1\frac{1}{4} = 100 \cdot 281.25$$

$$\frac{x \cdot 1\frac{1}{4}}{1\frac{1}{4}} = \frac{28,125}{1\frac{1}{4}}$$

$$x = 22,500$$

The whole is 22,500.

28.

58%	of how many preschoolers	is 203 preschoolers?
↑	↑	↑
percent	whole	part
58	unknown	203

30. 93%   of   is
         $1500 $1395.
         ↑   ↑   ↑
      percent   whole   part
         93   1500   1395

32. What   is   61%   of   830   homes?
          ↑   ↑   ↑
        part   percent   whole
      unknown   61   830

34. 92   is   26%   of   what number
                               of servings?
          ↑   ↑   ↑
        part   percent   whole
         92   26   unknown

36. 410   is 33⅓%   1230
       pallets percent of pallets
          ↑   ↑   ↑
        part   percent   whole
         410   33⅓   1230

38. What percent of $120.80 is $30.20
              ↑   ↑   ↑
           percent   whole   part
          unknown   120.8   30.2

40. 16.74   is   11.9%   of   what number
          ↑   ↑   ↑
        part   percent   whole
        16.74   11.9   unknown

42. What number   is   6.21   of   704.35
              ↑   ↑   ↑
            part   percent   whole
          unknown   6.21   704.35

44. A possible sentence is: Of the 580 cars
         entering the parking lot, 464 cars, or 80%, had
         parking stickers on their windshield.
         percent = 80; whole = 580; part = 464

46. 99 44/100 %   of   9 ounces   is   what number?
              ↑   ↑   ↑
           percent   whole   part
          99 44/100   9   unknown

48. How much   is   15%   of $225?
            ↑   ↑   ↑
           part   percent   whole
         unknown   15   225

50. 680 computer   is   what   of   2000
            chips   percent   computer
                                            chips
              ↑   ↑   ↑
            part   percent   whole
            680   unknown   2000

52. 36   is   30%   of   what
        cups   capacity?
          ↑   ↑   ↑
        part   percent   whole
         36   30   unknown

54. 48   is   what   of   64
       credits   percent   credits?
          ↑   ↑   ↑
        part   percent   whole
         48   unknown   64

56. $820   is   5%   of   what number?
          ↑   ↑   ↑
        part   percent   whole
         820   5   unknown

58. 231   is   what   of   924 cars?
        cars   percent
          ↑   ↑   ↑
        part   percent   whole
         231   unknown   924

6.4 Using Proportions to Solve Percent Problems

2. 25% of 3500 salespeople
        0.25 · 3500 = 875
            part = 875 salespeople

4. 12% of 3650 Web sites
        0.12 · 3650 = 438
            part = 438 Web sites

6. 9% of $150
        0.09 · 150 = 13.5
            part = $13.50

8. 130% of 60 trees

$1.30 \cdot 60 = 78$

part = 78 trees

10. 38.2% of 4250 loads

$0.382 \cdot 4250 = 1623.5$

part = 1623.5 loads

12. 6% of $434

$0.06 \cdot 434 = 26.04$

part = $26.04

14. 135% of 800 commuters

$1.35 \cdot 800 = 1080$

part = 1080 commuters

16. 46.1% of 843 kilograms

$0.461 \cdot 843 = 388.623$

part = 388.623 kilograms

18. 0.3% of $1400

$0.003 \cdot 1400 = 4.2$

part = $4.20

20. part is 32; percent is 5

$$\frac{32}{x} = \frac{5}{100}$$

$$\frac{32}{x} = \frac{1}{20}$$

$$x \cdot 1 = 32 \cdot 20$$

$$x = 640$$

32 medical exams is 5% of 640 medical exams.

22. part is 209; percent is 55

$$\frac{209}{x} = \frac{55}{100}$$

$$\frac{209}{x} = \frac{11}{20}$$

$$x \cdot 11 = 209 \cdot 20$$

$$\frac{x \cdot 11}{11} = \frac{4180}{11}$$

$$x = 380$$

55% of 380 experiments is 209 experiments.

24. part is 84; percent is 28

$$\frac{84}{b} = \frac{28}{100}$$

$$\frac{84}{b} = \frac{7}{25}$$

$$7 \cdot b = 84 \cdot 25$$

$$\frac{7 \cdot b}{7} = \frac{2100}{7}$$

$$b = 300$$

84 letters is 28% of 300 letters.

26. part is 154; percent is 140

$$\frac{154}{x} = \frac{140}{100}$$

$$\frac{154}{x} = \frac{7}{5}$$

$$\frac{7 \cdot x}{7} = \frac{770}{7}$$

$$x = 110$$

154 bicycles is 140% of 110 bicycles.

28. part is 176; percent is $5\frac{1}{2}$

$$\frac{176}{x} = \frac{5\frac{1}{2}}{100}$$

$$\frac{5\frac{1}{2} \cdot x}{5\frac{1}{2}} = \frac{17,600}{5\frac{1}{2}}$$

$$x = 17,600 \div 5\frac{1}{2}$$

$$= \frac{17,600}{1} \cdot \frac{2}{11}$$

$$= 3200$$

$5\frac{1}{2}$% of 3200 is 176.

30. part is 62; whole is 248

$$\frac{62}{248} = \frac{x}{100}$$

$$\frac{1}{4} = \frac{x}{100}$$

$$4 \cdot x = 1 \cdot 100$$

$$\frac{4 \cdot x}{4} = \frac{100}{4}$$

$$x = 25$$

62 rooms is 25% of 248 rooms.

32. part is 650; whole is 1000

$$\frac{650}{1000} = \frac{x}{100}$$

$$\frac{13}{20} = \frac{x}{100}$$

$$20 \cdot x = 13 \cdot 100$$

$$\frac{20 \cdot x}{20} = \frac{1300}{20}$$

$$x = 65$$

650 liters is 65% of 1000 liters.

34. part is 7; whole is 350

$$\frac{7}{350} = \frac{x}{100}$$

$$\frac{1}{50} = \frac{x}{100}$$

$$50 \cdot x = 1 \cdot 100$$

$$\frac{50 \cdot x}{50} = \frac{100}{50}$$

$$x = 2$$

7 bridges is 2% of 350 bridges.

36. part is 60; whole is 2400

$$\frac{60}{2400} = \frac{x}{100}$$

$$\frac{1}{40} = \frac{x}{100}$$

$$\frac{40 \cdot x}{40} = \frac{100}{40}$$

$$x = 2.5$$

60 cartons is 2.5% of 2400 cartons.

38. part is 14; whole is 398

$$\frac{14}{398} = \frac{x}{100}$$

$$398 \cdot x = 14 \cdot 100$$

$$\frac{398 \cdot x}{398} = \frac{1400}{398}$$

$$x \approx 3.5$$

$14 is ≈ 3.5% of $398.

40. part is 54; whole is 105

$$\frac{54}{105} = \frac{x}{100}$$

$$105 \cdot x = 54 \cdot 100$$

$$\frac{105 \cdot x}{105} = \frac{5400}{105}$$

$$x \approx 51.4$$

54 employees is ≈ 51.4% of 105 employees.

42. One answer is:

There are 600 vehicles in the parking lot and 45 of them are pickup trucks. What percent are pickup trucks?

Total vehicles, 600, is the whole, and the number of pickup trucks, 45, is the part

$$\frac{45}{600} = \frac{x}{100}$$

$$600 \cdot x = 4500$$

$$\frac{600 \cdot x}{600} = \frac{4500}{600}$$

$$x = 7.5 \text{ or } 7.5\%$$

44. whole is 124; percent is 75; part is unknown

$$\frac{x}{124} = \frac{75}{100}$$

$$\frac{x}{124} = \frac{3}{4}$$

$$x \cdot 4 = 124 \cdot 3$$

$$\frac{x \cdot 4}{4} = \frac{372}{4}$$

$$x = 93$$

She has completed 93 credits.

$$\frac{x}{377} = \frac{62}{100}$$

$$x \cdot 100 = 377 \cdot 62$$

$$\frac{x \cdot 100}{100} = \frac{23,374}{100}$$

$$x = 233.74$$

There are 234 executives that were upbeat about global growth.

46. whole is 377; percent is 62; part is unknown

$$\frac{x}{377} = \frac{62}{100}$$

$$x \cdot 100 = 377 \cdot 62$$

$$\frac{x \cdot 100}{100} = \frac{23,374}{100}$$

$$x = 233.74$$

There are 234 executives that were upbeat about global growth.

48. percent is 5; whole is 1600; part is unknown

$$\frac{x}{1600} = \frac{5}{100}$$

$$\frac{x}{1600} = \frac{1}{20}$$

$$20 \cdot x = 1600 \cdot 1$$

$$\frac{20 \cdot x}{20} = \frac{1600}{20}$$

$$x = 80$$

80 cans of tuna contained the extraneous matter.

50. whole is 100; percent is 35; part is unknown

$$\frac{x}{100} = \frac{35}{100}$$

$$x \cdot 100 = 100 \cdot 35$$

$$\frac{x \cdot 100}{100} = \frac{3500}{100}$$

$$x = 35$$

$100 million + $35 million = $135 million.
The estimated amount of orange juice sales for next year is $135 million.

52. part is 20,000; whole is 55,000; percent is unknown

$$\frac{20,000}{55,000} = \frac{x}{100}$$

$$\frac{4}{11} = \frac{x}{100}$$

$$11 \cdot x = 4 \cdot 100$$

$$\frac{11 \cdot x}{11} = \frac{400}{11}$$

$$x = 36.363636$$

$$x \approx 36.4$$

They can identify $\approx 36.4\%$ of the words.

54. (a) If 54% of the labor force is male, then 100% − 54% = 46% is female.

(b) whole is 132; percent is 54; part is unknown

$$\frac{x}{132} = \frac{54}{100}$$

$$100 \cdot x = 54 \cdot 132$$

$$\frac{100 \cdot x}{100} = \frac{7128}{100}$$

$$x = 71.28$$

$$x \approx 71.3$$

In the labor force, there are ≈ 71.3 million male workers.

56. part is 2640; whole is 2112; percent is unknown

$$\frac{2640}{2112} = \frac{x}{100}$$

$$\frac{165}{132} = \frac{x}{100}$$

$$132 \cdot x = 165 \cdot 100$$

$$\frac{132 \cdot x}{132} = \frac{16,500}{132}$$

$$x = 125$$

2640 vacancies is 125% of 2112 vacancies.

58. whole is 43,000,000; percent is 61; part is unknown

$$\frac{x}{43,000,000} = \frac{61}{100}$$

$$100 \cdot x = 61 \cdot 43,000,000$$

$$\frac{100 \cdot x}{100} = \frac{2,623,000,000}{100}$$

$$x = 26,230,000$$

26,230,000 people are paid with a direct deposit.

60. If 60% of the sales take place in the flu season, then

$$100\% - 60\% = 40\%$$

of the sales take place in the *non-flu* season.

62. 10% were sold in October.
9% were sold in November.
10% − 9% = 1%

$$\text{answer} = 1\% \text{ of } 350 \text{ million}$$

$$= 0.01 \cdot 350 \text{ million}$$

$$= 3.5 \text{ million}$$

3.5 million more cans were sold in October than November.

64. The sectors with the lowest sales are Hardee's with 6% and Wendy's with 12%.
The percent is 6% + 12% = 18%.

66. whole is 42; percent is 20; part is unknown

$$\frac{x}{42} = \frac{20}{100}$$

$$\frac{x}{42} = \frac{1}{5}$$

$$x \cdot 5 = 42 \cdot 1$$

$$\frac{x \cdot 5}{5} = \frac{42}{5}$$

$$x = 8.4$$

The total annual sales for Burger King is $8.4 billion.

68. part is 50,475; percent is 2.5; whole is unknown

$$\frac{50,475}{x} = \frac{2.5}{100}$$

$$2.5 \cdot x = 50,475 \cdot 100$$

$$\frac{2.5 \cdot x}{2.5} = \frac{5,047,500}{2.5}$$

$$x = 2,019,000$$

Steel production last week was 2,019,000 tons.

70. (a) If a family spends 90% of its earnings, then it saves 100% − 90% = 10%.
part is unknown; whole is 2900; percent is 10.

$$\frac{x}{2900} = \frac{10}{100}$$

$$\frac{x}{2900} = \frac{1}{10} \quad Lowest\ terms$$

$$\frac{10 \cdot x}{10} = \frac{2900}{10}$$

$$x = 290$$

The monthly savings is $290.

(b) The annual savings is 12 · $290 $3480.

6.5 Using the Percent Equation

2. part = percent · whole
$x = 0.19 \cdot 700$ 19% = 0.19
$x = 133$

19% of 700 pages is 133 pages.

4. part = percent · whole
$x = 0.75 \cdot 360$ 75% = 0.75
$x = 270$

75% of 360 dosages is 270 dosages.

6. part = percent · whole
$x = 0.44 \cdot 430$ 44% = 0.44
$x = 189.2$

44% of 430 liters is 189.2 liters.

8. part = percent · whole
$x = 1.45 \cdot 580$ 145% = 1.45
$x = 841$

145% of 580 donors is 841 donors.

10. part = percent · whole
$x = 0.264 \cdot 4700$ 26.4% = 0.264
$x = 1240.8$

26.4% of 4700 miles is 1240.8 miles.

12. part = percent · whole
$x = 0.003 \cdot 480$ 0.3% = 0.003
$x = 1.44$

0.3% of $480 is $1.44.

14. part = percent · whole
$32 = 0.2 \cdot x$ 20% = 0.2
$$\frac{32}{0.2} = \frac{0.2 \cdot x}{0.2}$$
$160 = x$

32 classrooms is 20% of 160 classrooms.

16. part = percent · whole
$675 = 0.75 \cdot x$ 75% = 0.75
$$\frac{675}{0.75} = \frac{0.75 \cdot x}{0.75}$$
$900 = x$

75% of 900 wrenches is 675 wrenches.

18. part = percent · whole
$270 = 0.45 \cdot x$
$$\frac{270}{0.45} = \frac{0.45 \cdot x}{0.45}$$
$600 = x$ 45% = 0.45

270 lab tests is 45% of 600.

20. part = percent · whole
$370 = 0.185 \cdot x$ $18\frac{1}{2}\% = 18.5\% = 0.185$
$$\frac{370}{0.185} = \frac{0.185 \cdot x}{0.185}$$
$2000 = x$

$18\frac{1}{2}\%$ of 2000 circuit breakers is 370 circuit breakers.

22. part = percent · whole
$9 = 0.0225 \cdot x$ $2\frac{1}{4}\% = 0.0225$
$$\frac{9}{0.0225} = \frac{0.0225 \cdot x}{0.0225}$$
$400 = x$

$2\frac{1}{4}\%$ of 400 files is 9 files.

24. part = percent · whole
$90 = x \cdot 225$
$$\frac{90}{225} = \frac{x \cdot 225}{225}$$
$0.4 = x$
$0.4 = 40\%$

90 mail carriers is 40% of 225 mail carriers.

26. part = percent · whole
$75 = x \cdot 125$
$$\frac{75}{125} = \frac{x \cdot 125}{125}$$
$0.6 = x$
$0.6 = 60\%$

75 offices is 60% of 125 offices.

28. part = percent · whole

$696 = x \cdot 480$

$\dfrac{696}{480} = \dfrac{x \cdot 480}{480}$

$1.45 = x$

$1.45 = 145\%$

145% of \$480 is \$696.

30. part = percent · whole

$7.5 = x \cdot 600$

$\dfrac{7.5}{600} = \dfrac{x \cdot 600}{600}$

$0.0125 = x$

$0.0125 = 1.25\%$

1.25% of 600 is 7.5.

32. part = percent · whole

$612 = x \cdot 425$

$\dfrac{612}{425} = \dfrac{x \cdot 425}{425}$

$1.44 = x$

$1.44 = 144\%$

612 orders is 144% of 425 orders.

34. The correct answer is \$6.50. The error is in changing $\frac{1}{2}\%$ to a decimal.

$$\frac{1}{2}\% = 0.5\% = 0.005;$$

$$0.005 \cdot \$1300 = \$6.50 \quad correct$$

The incorrect answers and how your classmates got them are these.

$\frac{1}{2}\% = 0.0005;$ $0.0005 \cdot \$1300 = \$0.65$

$\frac{1}{2}\% = 0.05;$ $0.05 \cdot \$1300 = \$65$

$\frac{1}{2}\% = 0.5;$ $0.5 \cdot \$1300 = \$650$

36. 78% of 16 ounces of shampoo

part = percent · whole

$x = 0.78 \cdot 16$

$x \approx 12.5$

$\approx$ 12.5 ounces in the 16-ounce bottle are water.

38. 62.2% of \$148 million

part = percent · whole

$x = 0.622 \cdot 148$

$x \approx 92.06$

\$92.06 million or \$92,060,000 (rounded) is the total annual sales of these products.

40. 35% of 3300 miles

$x = 0.35 \cdot 3300$

$x = 1155$

1155 miles would be traveled by air

42. (a)   18 of 50

part = percent · whole

$18 = x \cdot 50$

$\dfrac{18}{50} = \dfrac{x \cdot 50}{50}$

$0.36 = x$

$0.36 = 36\%$

36% of the companies were Japanese companies.

(b) $100\% - 36\% = 64\%$

64% of the companies were not Japanese.

44. part = percent · whole

$450 = x \cdot 3200$

$\dfrac{450}{3200} = \dfrac{x \cdot 3200}{3200}$

$0.141 \approx x$

$0.141 = 14.1\%$

They have planned $\approx$ 14.1% additional stores.

46. $0.5\% + 0.5\% = 1\%$

1% of 5400

part = percent · whole

$x = 0.01 \cdot 5400$

$x = 54$

54 people answered "No response" and "Other".

48. 15 minutes + 16 – 30 minutes = 6% + 39%

   = 45%

45% of 5400

part = percent · whole

$x = 0.45 \cdot 5400$

$x = 2430$

2430 people said they spend 30 minutes or less preparing weekday dinners.

50. First find the monthly earnings.

\$131.75 is 8.5% of what number?

part = percent · whole

$131.75 = 0.085 \cdot x$

$\dfrac{131.75}{0.085} = \dfrac{0.85 \cdot x}{0.085}$

$1550 = x$

$12 \cdot \$1550 = \$18,600$

Her annual earnings are \$18,600.

52. 8.9 million workers is 7.1% of what number of workers?

$$8.9 = 0.071 \cdot x$$

$$\frac{8.9}{0.071} = \frac{0.071 \cdot x}{0.071}$$

$$125.4 \approx x$$

The total workforce is ≈ 125.4 million workers.

54. Find the increase in the mileage, then add it to the old mileage.

$$\text{part} = \text{percent} \cdot \text{whole}$$
$$x = 0.15 \cdot 25.6$$
$$x \approx 3.8$$

Mileage of ≈ 3.8 + 25.6 ≈ 29.4 miles per gallon can be expected.

56. Find the markdown.
25% of $332 is what number?

$$\text{part} = \text{percent} \cdot \text{whole}$$
$$x = 0.25 \cdot 332$$
$$x = 83$$

Subtract the markdown from the selling price.

$$\$332 - \$83 = \$249$$

The price of the organizer after the markdown is $249.

6.6 Solving Application Problems with Percent

2. *sales tax = rate of tax · cost of item*
$$= 4\% \cdot \$15$$
$$= 0.04 \cdot \$15$$
$$= \$0.60$$
The amount of sales tax is $0.60 and the total cost is $15.60 ($15 + $0.60)

4. *sales tax = rate of tax · cost of item*
$$\$19.32 = r \cdot \$322$$
$$\frac{19.32}{322} = \frac{r \cdot 322}{322}$$
$$0.06 = r$$
$$0.06 = 6\%$$
The tax rate is 6% and the total cost is $341.32 ($322 + $19.32).

6. *sales tax = rate of tax · cost of item*
$$\$5.88 = r \cdot \$84$$
$$\frac{5.88}{84} = \frac{r \cdot 84}{84}$$
$$0.07 = r$$
$$0.07 = 7\%$$
The tax rate is 7% and the total cost is $89.88 ($84 + $5.88)

8. *sales tax = rate of tax · cost of item*
$$= 7\tfrac{1}{2}\% \cdot \$11,789$$
$$= 0.075 \cdot \$11,789$$
$$\approx \$884.18$$
The amount of sales tax is $884.18 and the total cost is $12,673.18 ($11,789 + $884.18).

10. *commission = rate of commission · sales*
$$= 4\% \cdot \$325$$
$$= 0.04 \cdot \$325$$
$$= \$13$$
The amount of commission is $13.

12.
$$\frac{\text{part}}{\text{whole}} = \frac{x}{100}$$
$$\frac{1170}{7800} = \frac{x}{100}$$
$$7800 \cdot x = 1170 \cdot 100$$
$$\frac{7800 \cdot x}{7800} = \frac{117,000}{7800}$$
$$x = 15$$
The rate of commission is 15%.

14. *commission = rate of commission · sales*
$$= 7\% \cdot \$4416.70$$
$$= 0.07 \cdot \$4416.70$$
$$\approx \$309.17$$
The amount of commission is $309.17.

16. *commission = rate of commission · sales*
$$= 6\% \cdot \$55,800$$
$$= 0.06 \cdot \$55,800$$
$$= \$3348$$
The amount of commission is $3348.

18. *discount = rate of discount · original price*
$$= 15\% \cdot \$29.95$$
$$= 0.15 \cdot \$29.95$$
$$\approx \$4.49$$
The amount of discount is $4.49 and the sale price is $25.46 ($29.95 − $4.49).

20. *discount = rate of discount · original price*

$$\$9.50 = r \cdot \$38$$

$$\frac{9.50}{38} = \frac{r \cdot 38}{38}$$

$$0.25 = r$$

$$0.25 = 25\%$$

The rate of discount is 25% and the sale price is $28.50 ($38 − $9.50).

22. *discount = rate of discount · original price*

$$= 60\% \cdot \$76$$

$$= 0.6 \cdot \$76$$

$$= \$45.60$$

The amount of the discount is $45.60 and the sale price is $30.40 ($76 − $45.60).

24. *discount = rate of discount · original price*

$$= 30\% \cdot \$99.80$$

$$= 0.3 \cdot \$99.80$$

$$= \$29.94$$

The amount of discount is $29.94 and the sale price is $69.86 ($99.80 − $29.94).

26. Some answers might be:
Calculating percent pay increases or decreases; changes in the cost of utilities, groceries, gasoline, insurance; changes in the value of investments; the economy (inflation or deflation); to name a few.

The price of a loaf of bread increased from $1.50 to $1.65. Find the percent of increase.

$$\$1.65 - \$1.50 = \$0.15 \ increase$$

$$\frac{0.15}{1.5} = \frac{x}{100}$$

$$10 = x$$

The percent of increase is 10%.

28. *sales tax = rate of tax · cost of item*

$$= 7\% \cdot \$590$$

$$= 0.07 \cdot \$590$$

$$= \$41.30$$

The sales tax is $41.30.

30. *discount = rate of discount · original price*

$$= 12\% \cdot \$18,350$$

$$= 0.12 \cdot \$18,350$$

$$= \$2202$$

The cost of the car is $16,148 ($18,350 − $2202).

32. *sales tax = tax rate · cost of item*

$$\$11.55 = r \cdot \$165$$

$$\frac{11.55}{165} = \frac{r \cdot 165}{165}$$

$$0.07 = r$$

$$0.07 = 7\%$$

The sales tax rate is 7%.

34. Fish consumption rose from $12\frac{1}{2}$ pounds to $15\frac{1}{2}$ pounds.

$$\text{Increase} = 15\tfrac{1}{2} - 12\tfrac{1}{2} = 3$$

$$\frac{\text{increase}}{\text{original}} = \frac{x}{100}$$

$$\frac{3}{12.5} = \frac{x}{100}$$

$$12.5 \cdot x = 3 \cdot 100$$

$$\frac{12.5 \cdot x}{12.5} = \frac{300}{12.5}$$

$$x = 24$$

The percent of increase of 24%.

36. The number of manufacturing jobs fell from 41.1 to 40.9.

$$\text{decrease} = 41.1 - 40.9 = 0.2$$

$$\frac{\text{decrease}}{\text{original}} = \frac{x}{100}$$

$$\frac{0.2}{41.1} = \frac{x}{100}$$

$$41.1 \cdot x = 0.2 \cdot 100$$

$$\frac{41.1 \cdot x}{41.1} \approx \frac{20}{41.1}$$

$$x \approx 0.5$$

The percent of decrease was ≈ 0.5%.

38. *amount of discount = rate of discount · original price*

$$= 25\% \cdot 769$$

$$= 0.25 \cdot \$769$$

$$= \$192.25$$

The sale price of the dishwasher is $576.75 ($769 − $192.25).

40. *commission = rate of commission · sales*

$$= 3\% \cdot \$10,730$$

$$= 0.03 \cdot \$10,730$$

$$= \$321.90$$

Brown's commission is $321.90.

42. *commission = rate of commission · sales*

$$\$576.10 = r \cdot \$11,522$$

$$\frac{576.10}{11,522} = \frac{r \cdot 11,522}{11,522}$$

$$0.05 = r$$

$$0.05 = 5\%$$

The rate of commission for Washington is 5%.

44. *discount = rate of discount · original price*

$$= 17\% \cdot \$28,700$$

$$= 0.17 \cdot \$28,700$$

$$= \$4879$$

The discount is $4879 and the sale price is $23,821 ($28,700 − $4879).

46. The cost for generating electricity from the sun has been brought down from 24 cents per kilowatt hour to 8 cents.

$$\text{decrease} = 24 - 8 = 16 \text{ cents}$$

$$\frac{\text{decrease}}{\text{original}} = \frac{x}{100}$$

$$\frac{16}{24} = \frac{x}{100}$$

$$24 \cdot x = 16 \cdot 100$$

$$\frac{24 \cdot x}{24} = \frac{1600}{24}$$

$$x \approx 66.7$$

The percent of decrease is $\approx 66.7\%$.

48. *discount = rate of discount · original price*

$$= 8\% \cdot 698$$

$$= 0.08 \cdot \$698$$

$$= \$55.84$$

The sale price is $642.16 ($698 − $55.84).

sales tax = tax rate · cost of item

$$= 8\% \cdot \$642.16$$

$$= 0.08 \cdot \$642.16$$

$$\approx \$51.37$$

The cost of the computer and monitor machine is $693.53 ($642.16 + $51.37).

50. Member fee   is 6% of   selling price.

    ↑   ↑   ↑

    x is 6% of   8,680,000

Use the percent proportion.

$$\frac{\text{part}}{\text{whole}} = \frac{\text{percent}}{100}$$

$$\frac{x}{8,680,000} = \frac{6}{100}$$

$$100 \cdot x = 52,080,000$$

$$\frac{100 \cdot x}{100} = \frac{52,080,000}{100}$$

$$x = 520,800$$

Association fee   is 2% of   member fee.

    ↑   ↑   ↑

    part   is 2% of   520,800

$$\frac{x}{520,800} = \frac{2}{100}$$

$$100 \cdot x = 1,041,600$$

$$\frac{100 \cdot x}{100} = \frac{1,041,600}{100}$$

$$x = 10,416$$

The association will get $10,416.

52. *amount of discount = rate of discount · original price*

$$= 22\% \cdot \$10,800$$

$$= 0.22 \cdot \$10,800$$

$$= \$2376$$

The sale price is $8424 ($10,800 − $2376).

sales tax = rate of tax · cost of item

$$= 7\tfrac{1}{4}\% \cdot \$8424$$

$$= 0.0725 \cdot \$8424$$

$$= \$610.74$$

The total price is $9034.74 ($8424 + $610.74).

6.7 Simple Interest

2. $200 at 3% for 1 year

$$I = p \cdot r \cdot t$$

$$= 200 \cdot (0.03) \cdot 1$$

$$= 6$$

The interest is $6.

4. $900 at 4% for 4 years

$$I = p \cdot r \cdot t$$
$$= 900 \cdot (0.04) \cdot 4$$
$$= 144$$

The interest is $144.

6. $190 at 3% for 2 years

$$I = p \cdot r \cdot t$$
$$= 190 \cdot (0.03) \cdot 2$$
$$= 11.4$$

The interest is $11.40.

8. $4700 at $5\frac{1}{2}$% at $1\frac{1}{2}$ years.

$$I = p \cdot r \cdot t$$
$$= 4700 \cdot (0.055) \cdot 1.5$$
$$= 258.5 \cdot 1.5$$
$$= 387.75$$

The interest is $387.75.

10. $12,400 at $6\frac{1}{2}$ for $3\frac{3}{4}$ years.

$$I = p \cdot r \cdot t$$
$$= 12,400 \cdot (0.065) \cdot 3\frac{3}{4}$$
$$= 806 \cdot 3.75$$
$$= 3022.5$$

The interest is $3022.50.

12. $600 at 7% for 5 months

$$I = p \cdot r \cdot t$$
$$= 600 \cdot (0.07) \cdot \frac{5}{12}$$
$$= 42 \cdot \frac{5}{12}$$
$$= 17.5$$

The interest is $17.50.

14. $780 at 8% for 24 months

$$I = p \cdot r \cdot t$$
$$= 780 \cdot (0.08) \cdot \frac{24}{12}$$
$$= 62.4 \cdot 2$$
$$= 124.8$$

The interest is $124.80.

16. $178 at 4% for 12 months.

$$I = p \cdot r \cdot t$$
$$= 178 \cdot (0.04) \cdot \frac{12}{12}$$
$$= 7.12 \cdot 1$$
$$= 7.12$$

The interest is $7.12.

18. $2660 at $7\frac{1}{2}$% for 3 months.

$$I = p \cdot r \cdot t$$
$$= 2660 \cdot (0.075) \cdot \frac{3}{12}$$
$$= 199.5 \cdot \frac{1}{4}$$
$$\approx 49.88$$

The interest is $49.88.

20. $13,700 at $3\frac{3}{4}$% for 11 months.

$$I = p \cdot r \cdot t$$
$$= 13,700 \cdot (0.0375) \cdot \frac{11}{12}$$
$$= 513.75 \cdot \frac{11}{12}$$
$$\approx 470.94$$

The interest is $470.94.

22. $400 at 4% for 6 months.

$$I = p \cdot r \cdot t$$
$$= 400 \cdot (0.04) \cdot \frac{6}{12}$$
$$= 16 \cdot \frac{1}{2}$$
$$= \frac{16}{2} = 8$$

The interest is $8.

$$amount\ due = principal + interest$$
$$= \$400 + \$8 = \$408$$

The total amount due is $408.

24. $1180 at 3% for 2 years

$$I = p \cdot r \cdot t$$
$$= 1180 \cdot (0.03) \cdot 2$$
$$= 35.4 \cdot 2$$
$$= 70.8$$

$$amount\ due = principal + interest$$
$$= \$1180 + \$70.80$$
$$= \$1250.80$$

26. $9000 at 6% for 7 months.

$$I = p \cdot r \cdot t$$
$$= 9000 \cdot (0.06) \cdot \frac{7}{12}$$
$$= 540 \cdot \frac{7}{12}$$
$$= 315$$

The interest is $315.

$$amount\ due = principal + interest$$
$$= \$9000 + \$315$$
$$= \$9315$$

The total amount due is $9315.

28. $7600 at 5% for 1 year

$$I = p \cdot r \cdot t$$
$$= 7600 \cdot (0.05) \cdot 1$$
$$= 380$$

The interest is $380.

$$amount\ due = principal + interest$$
$$= \$7600 + \$380$$
$$= \$7980$$

The total amount due is $7980.

30. $19,450 at $5\frac{1}{2}$% for 6 months.

$$I = p \cdot r \cdot t$$
$$= 19,450 \cdot (0.055) \cdot \frac{6}{12}$$
$$= 1069.75 \cdot \frac{1}{2}$$
$$\approx 534.88$$

The interest is $534.88

$$amount\ due = principal + interest$$
$$= \$19,450 + \$534.88$$
$$= \$19,984.88$$

The total amount due is $19,984.88

32. When time is given in months, the number of months are placed over 12. This becomes a fraction of a year. For example,

$$6\ months = \frac{6}{12}\ year = \frac{1}{2}\ year = 0.5\ year.$$

34. $18,000 at 9% for 6 months

$$I = p \cdot r \cdot t$$
$$= 18,000 \cdot (0.09) \cdot \frac{6}{12}$$
$$= 1620 \cdot 0.5$$
$$= 810$$

The Jidobu family will receive $810 interest.

36. $80,000 at 7% for 3 years

$$I = p \cdot r \cdot t$$
$$= 80,000 \cdot (0.07) \cdot 3$$
$$= 16,800$$

The interest will be $16,800.

38. $2750 at 8% for 9 months

$$I = p \cdot r \cdot t$$
$$= 2750 \cdot (0.08) \cdot \frac{9}{12}$$
$$= 220 \cdot \frac{3}{4}$$
$$= 165$$

The interest is $165.

$$amount\ due = principal + interest$$
$$= \$2750 + \$165$$
$$= \$2915$$

The total amount due is $2915.

40. $27,000 at $7\frac{1}{4}$% for 24 months.

$$I = p \cdot r \cdot t$$
$$= 27,000 \cdot (0.0725) \cdot \frac{24}{12}$$
$$= 1957.5 \cdot 2 \quad Lowest\ terms$$
$$= 3915$$

Silvo will owe $3915 in interest.

42. $1900 at $12\frac{1}{4}$% for 6 months.

$$I = p \cdot r \cdot t$$
$$= 1900 \cdot (0.1225) \cdot \frac{6}{12}$$
$$= 232.75 \cdot 0.5$$
$$\approx 116.38$$

The interest is $116.38.

$$amount\ due = principal + interest$$
$$= \$1900 + \$116.38$$
$$= \$2016.38$$

The total amount is $2016.38.

44. $35,400 at 14.9% for $\frac{1}{2}$ year.

$$I = p \cdot r \cdot t$$
$$= 35,400 \cdot (0.149) \cdot \frac{1}{2}$$
$$= 5274.6 \cdot 0.5$$
$$= 2637.30$$

The interest will be $2637.30.

46. $4 \cdot \$87,500 = \$350,000$
80% of $350,000
$x = 0.8 \cdot 350,000$
$x = 280,000$
$280,000 at $11\frac{1}{2}$% for $1\frac{1}{2}$ years

$$I = p \cdot r \cdot t$$
$$= 280,000 \cdot (0.115) \cdot 1.5$$
$$= 48,300$$

The interest is $48,300.

$$amount\ due = principal + interest$$
$$= \$280,000 + \$48,300$$
$$= \$328,300$$

The total amount due is $328,300.

Summary Exercises on Percent

2. $380\% = 3.80$ or 3.8
Drop the percent sign and move the decimal point two places to the left.

4. $0.006 = 0.6\%$
Move the decimal point two places to the right and attach percent sign.

6. $160\% = \dfrac{160}{100} = \dfrac{160 \div 20}{100 \div 20} = \dfrac{8}{5} = 1\dfrac{3}{5}$

8.
$$\frac{1}{125} = \frac{p}{100}$$
$$125 \cdot p = 1 \cdot 100$$
$$\frac{125 \cdot p}{125} = \frac{100}{125}$$
$$p = 0.8$$
$$\frac{1}{125} = 0.8\%$$

10. part is 70; percent is 14
$$\frac{70}{x} = \frac{14}{100}$$
$$\frac{70}{x} = \frac{7}{50}$$
$$x \cdot 7 = 70 \cdot 50$$
$$\frac{x \cdot 7}{7} = \frac{3500}{7}$$
$$x = 500$$
70 rolls of film is 14% of 500 rolls of film.

12. percent is 0.8; whole is 3500
$$\frac{x}{3500} = \frac{0.8}{100}$$
$$x \cdot 100 = 3500 \cdot 0.8$$
$$\frac{x \cdot 100}{100} = \frac{2800}{100}$$
$$x = 28$$
0.8% of 3500 screening exams is 28 screening exams.

14. part is 18; whole is 658
$$\frac{18}{658} = \frac{x}{100}$$
$$\frac{9}{329} = \frac{x}{100}$$
$$329 \cdot x = 9 \cdot 100$$
$$\frac{329 \cdot x}{329} = \frac{900}{329}$$
$$x \approx 2.7$$
About 2.7% of 658 circuits is 18 circuits.

16. $sales\ tax = rate\ of\ tax \cdot cost\ of\ item$
$$64.82 = x \cdot 926$$
$$\frac{64.82}{926} = x$$
$$.07 = x$$
The tax rate is 7% and the total cost is $990.82 ($926 + $64.82).

18. $commission = rate\ of\ commission \cdot sales$
$$\$1461.33 = r \cdot \$22,482$$
$$\frac{\$1461.33}{\$22,482} = r$$
$$0.065 = r$$
$$0.065 = 6.5\%$$
The rate of commission is 6.5% or $6\frac{1}{2}$%.

20. $discount = rate\ of\ discount \cdot original\ price$
$$\$239.40 = r \cdot \$684$$
$$\frac{\$239.40}{\$684} = r$$
$$0.35 = r$$
$$0.35 = 35\%$$
The rate of discount is 35%, and the sale price is $444.60 ($684 − $239.40).

22. $I = p \cdot r \cdot t$
$$= 2380 \cdot 0.075 \cdot 3$$
$$= 535.5$$
The interest is $535.50 and the total amount due is $2915.50 ($2380 + $535.50).

24. $I = p \cdot r \cdot t$

$\qquad = 6820 \cdot 0.065 \cdot \dfrac{18}{12}$

$\qquad = 443.3 \cdot 1.5$

$\qquad = 664.95$

The interest is \$664.95 and the total amount due is \$7484.95 (\$6820 + \$664.95).

26. decrease = 3820 − 3419 = 401

$$\dfrac{401}{3820} = \dfrac{x}{100}$$

$$3820 \cdot x = 401 \cdot 100$$

$$\dfrac{3820 \cdot x}{3820} = \dfrac{40{,}100}{3820}$$

$$x \approx 10.5$$

The percent of decrease is ≈ 10.5%.

6.8   Compound Interest

2. \$1000 at 5% for 3 years

Year	Interest
1	$1000 · 0.05 · 1 = $50
	$1000 + $50 = $1050
	Compound amount
2	$1050 · 0.05 = $52.50
	$1050 + $52.50 = $1102.50
	Compound amount
3	$1102.50 · 0.05 ≈ $55.13
	$1102.50 + $55.13 = $1157.63

The compound amount is ≈ \$1157.63.

4. \$2000 at 8% for 3 years

Year	Interest
1	$2000 · 0.08 · 1 = $160
	$2000 + $160 = $2160
	Compound amount
2	$2160 · 0.08 · 1 = $172.80
	$2160 + $172.80 = $2332.80
	Compound amount
3	$2332.80 · 0.08 · 1 ≈ $186.62
	$2332.80 + $186.22 = $2519.42
	Compound amount

The compound amount is \$2519.42.

6. \$5500 at 6% for 4 years

Year	Interest
1	$5500 · 0.06 · 1 = $330
	$5500 + $330 = $5830
	Compound amount
2	$5830 · 0.06 · 1 = $349.80
	$5830 + $349.8 = $6179.80
	Compound amount
3	$6179.80 · 0.06 · 1 ≈ $370.79
	$6179.80 + $370.79 = $6550.59
	Compound amount
4	$6550.59 · 0.06 · 1 ≈ $393.04
	$6550.59 + $393.04 = $6943.63
	Compound amount

The compound amount is ≈ \$6943.63.

8. \$500 at 4% for 3 years
100% + 4% = 104% = 1.04
\$500 · 1.04 · 1.04 · 1.04 ≈ \$562.43
The compound amount is ≈ \$562.43

10. \$1800 at 8% for 4 years
100% + 8% = 108% = 1.08
\$1800 · 1.08 · 1.08 · 1.08 · 1.08 ≈ \$2448.88
The compound amount is ≈ \$2448.88

12. \$12,800 at 6% for 7 years
100% + 6% = 106% = 1.06
\$12,800 · 1.06 · 1.06 · 1.06 · 1.06 · 1.06 · 1.06 · 1.06 ≈ \$19,246.47.
The compound amount is ≈ \$19,246.47.

14. \$15,710 at 10% for 8 years
100% + 10% = 110% = 1.10
\$15,710 · 1.10 · 1.10 · 1.10 · 1.10 · 1.10 · 1.10 · 1.10 · 1.10 ≈ \$33,675.78
The compound interest is ≈ \$33,675.78

16. \$10,000 at 3% for 4 years
3% column, row 4 of the table gives 1.1255.
Multiply.
\$10,000 · 1.1255 = \$11,255 *compound amount*
\$11,255 − \$10,000 = \$1255 *interest*

18. $7800 at 5% for 8 years

   5% column, row 8 of the table gives 1.4775.
   Multiply.

   7800 · 1.4775 = $11,524.50 *compound amount*

   $11,524.50 − $7800 = $3724.50 *interest*

20. $10,472.88 at $5\frac{1}{2}$% for 12 years

   5.50% column, row 12 of the table gives
   1.9012.
   Multiply.

   $10,472.88 · 1.9012$
   $\approx \$19,911.04$ *compound amount*
   $\$19,911.04 - \$10,472.88$
   $= \$9438.16$ *interest*

22. Compound amount is the total amount, original
   deposit plus interest on deposit, at the end of
   the compound interest period.
   Compound interest is found by subtracting the
   original deposit from the compound amount.

24. $22,500 at 8% compounded annually for 5
   years

   8% column, row 5 of the table gives 1.4693
   Multiply.

   $22,500 · 1.4693 = \$33,059.25$

   John will repay $33,059.25.

26. (a) $28,500 at 5% compounded annually for 5
   years
   5% column, row 5 of the table gives
   1.2763.
   Multiply.

   $28,500 · 1.2763 = \$36,374.55$

   The total amount that she will have at the
   end of 5 years is $36,374.55.

   (b) The amount of interest earned is $7874.55
   ($36,374.55 − $28,500).

28. (a) $25,000 at 8% compounded annually for
   3 years
   8% column, row 3 from the table is
   1.2597.
   Multiply. 25,000 · 1.2597 = 31,492.5.
   After 3 years she will have $31,492.50.
   After the second $25,000 deposit, she will
   have $56,492.50.
   8% column, row 2 from the table is 1.1664

   $56,492.50 · 1.1664 \approx \$65,892.85$

   (b) The interest is ≈ $15,892.85
   (≈ $65,892.85 − $50,000).

Chapter 7

MEASUREMENT

7.1 Problem Solving with English Measurement

2. 1 ft = <u>12</u> in.

4. <u>4</u> qt = 1 gal

6. 1 wk = <u>7</u> days

8. <u>16</u> oz = 1 lb

10. 1 day = <u>24</u> hr

12. 180 min to hours

$$\frac{180 \text{ min}}{1} \cdot \frac{1 \text{ hr}}{60 \text{ min}} = \frac{180}{60} \text{ hr} = 3 \text{ hr}$$

14. 6 gal to quarts

$$\frac{6 \text{ gal}}{1} \cdot \frac{4 \text{ qt}}{1 \text{ gal}} = 6 \cdot 4 \text{ qt} = 24 \text{ qt}$$

16. 45 ft to yards

$$\frac{\overset{15}{\cancel{45} \text{ ft}}}{1} \cdot \frac{1 \text{ yd}}{\underset{1}{\cancel{3} \text{ ft}}} = 15 \text{ yd}$$

The largest meat-eating dinosaur may have been 15 yd.

18. 20,000 lb to tons

$$\frac{\overset{10}{\cancel{20,000} \text{ lb}}}{1} \cdot \frac{1 \text{ T}}{\underset{1}{\cancel{2000} \text{ lb}}} = 10 \text{ T}$$

20. 96 oz to pounds

$$\frac{\overset{6}{\cancel{96} \text{ oz}}}{1} \cdot \frac{1 \text{ lb}}{\underset{1}{\cancel{16} \text{ oz}}} = 6 \text{ lb}$$

22. 26 pt to quarts

$$\frac{\overset{13}{\cancel{26} \text{ pt}}}{1} \cdot \frac{1 \text{ qt}}{\underset{1}{\cancel{2} \text{ pt}}} = 13 \text{ qt}$$

24. 45 sec to minutes

$$\frac{45 \text{ sec}}{1} \cdot \frac{1 \text{ min}}{60 \text{ sec}} = \frac{45}{60} \text{ min} = \frac{3}{4} \text{ or } 0.75 \text{ min}$$

26. 30 in. to feet

$$\frac{30 \text{ in.}}{1} \cdot \frac{1 \text{ ft}}{12 \text{ in.}} = \frac{30}{12} \text{ ft} = 2\frac{1}{2} \text{ or } 2.5 \text{ ft}$$

28. 36 oz to pounds

$$= \frac{36 \text{ oz}}{1} \cdot \frac{1 \text{ lb}}{16 \text{ oz}} = \frac{36}{16} \text{ lb} = 2\frac{1}{4} \text{ or } 2.25 \text{ lb}$$

30. 15 qt to gallons

$$= \frac{15 \text{ qt}}{1} \cdot \frac{1 \text{ gal}}{4 \text{ qt}} = \frac{15}{4} \text{ gal} = 3\frac{3}{4} \text{ or } 3.75 \text{ gal}$$

32. 4 oz to pounds

$$= \frac{4 \text{ oz}}{1} \cdot \frac{1 \text{ lb}}{16 \text{ oz}} = \frac{4}{16} \text{ lb} = \frac{1}{4} \text{ or } 0.25 \text{ lb}$$

34. $4\frac{1}{2}$ pt to cups

$$= \frac{4\frac{1}{2} \text{ pt}}{1} \cdot \frac{2 \text{ c}}{1 \text{ pt}} = 4\frac{1}{2} \cdot 2 \text{ c} = \frac{9}{\underset{1}{\cancel{2}}} \cdot \frac{\overset{1}{\cancel{2}}}{1} = 9 \text{ c}$$

36. $2\frac{1}{4}$ hr to min

$$= \frac{2\frac{1}{4} \text{ hr}}{1} \cdot \frac{60 \text{ min}}{1 \text{ hr}} = 2\frac{1}{4} \cdot 60 \text{ min} = 135 \text{ min}$$

38. $7\frac{2}{3}$ ft to inches.

$$\frac{7\frac{2}{3} \text{ ft}}{1} \cdot \frac{12 \text{ in.}}{1 \text{ ft}} = \frac{23}{\underset{1}{\cancel{3}}} \cdot \frac{\overset{4}{\cancel{12}}}{1} \text{ in.} = 92 \text{ in.}$$

His height is 92 in.

40. 2 T to ounces

$$\frac{2 \text{ T}}{1} \cdot \frac{2000 \text{ lb}}{1 \text{ T}} \cdot \frac{16 \text{ oz}}{1 \text{ lb}} = 2 \cdot 2000 \cdot 16 \text{ oz}$$
$$= 64,000 \text{ oz}$$

42. 336 hr to weeks

$$\frac{\overset{\overset{2}{\cancel{14}}}{\cancel{336} \text{ hr}}}{1} \cdot \frac{1 \text{ day}}{\underset{1}{\cancel{24} \text{ hr}}} \cdot \frac{1 \text{ wk}}{\underset{1}{\cancel{7} \text{ days}}} = 2 \text{ wk}$$

44. 5 gal to cups

$$\frac{5 \text{ gal}}{1} \cdot \frac{4 \text{ qt}}{1 \text{ gal}} \cdot \frac{2 \text{ pt}}{1 \text{ qt}} \cdot \frac{2 \text{ c}}{1 \text{ pt}} = 5 \cdot 4 \cdot 2 \cdot 2 \text{ c}$$
$$= 80 \text{ c}$$

46. $3\frac{1}{2}$ yd to inches

$$\frac{3\frac{1}{2}\text{ yd}}{1}\cdot\frac{3\text{ ft}}{1\text{ yd}}\cdot\frac{12\text{ in.}}{1\text{ ft}}=\frac{10}{\overset{1}{\cancel{3}}}\cdot\frac{\overset{1}{\cancel{3}}}{1}\cdot\frac{12}{1}\text{ in.}=120\text{ in.}$$

48. Feet and inches both measure length, so you can add them once you've changed 2 feet into inches. But pounds measure weight and cannot be added to a length measurement.

50. $5\frac{3}{4}$ T to ounces

$$\frac{5\frac{3}{4}\text{ T}}{1}\cdot\frac{2000\text{ lb}}{1\text{ T}}\cdot\frac{16\text{ oz}}{1\text{ lb}}=\frac{23}{\underset{1}{4}}\cdot\overset{500}{\cancel{2000}}\cdot16\text{ oz}$$
$$=184{,}000\text{ oz}$$

52. $3\frac{1}{2}$ days to seconds

$$\frac{3\frac{1}{2}\text{ days}}{1}\cdot\frac{24\text{ hr}}{1\text{ day}}\cdot\frac{60\text{ min}}{1\text{ hr}}\cdot\frac{60\text{ sec}}{1\text{ min}}$$
$$=\frac{7}{2}\cdot\overset{12}{\cancel{24}}\cdot60\cdot60$$
$$=302{,}400\text{ sec}$$

54. 57,024 in. to miles

$$\frac{57{,}024\text{ in.}}{1}\cdot\frac{1\text{ ft}}{12\text{ in.}}\cdot\frac{1\text{ mi}}{5280\text{ ft}}=\frac{\overset{4752}{\cancel{57{,}024}}}{1}\cdot\frac{1}{\underset{1}{\cancel{12}}}\cdot\frac{1\text{ mi}}{5280}$$
$$=0.9\text{ or }\frac{9}{10}\text{ mi}$$

For Exercises 56–62, the six problem-solving steps should be used, but are only shown for Exercise 56.

56. *Step 1*
The problem asks for the cost per pound.
Step 2
Convert ounces to pounds. Then divide the cost by the pounds.
Step 3
To estimate, round $0.79 to $0.8
Then, there are 16 oz in a pound, so 1.6 oz is $\frac{1}{10}$ lb of 0.1 lb. So, $0.8 ÷ 0.1 = $8 per pound is our estimate.
Step 4

$$\frac{1.6\text{ oz}}{1}\cdot\frac{1\text{ lb}}{16\text{ oz}}=\frac{1.6}{16}\text{ lb}=0.1\text{ lb}$$

$$\frac{\$0.79}{0.1\text{ lb}}=\$7.90$$

Step 5
The candy bar costs $7.90 per pound.
Step 6
The answer, $7.90, is close to our estimate of $8.

58. Find the difference in inches, then convert to feet.
136 in. − 14 in. = 122 in.

$$\frac{\overset{61}{\cancel{122}}\text{ in.}}{1}\cdot\frac{1\text{ ft}}{\underset{6}{\cancel{12}}\text{ in.}}=\frac{61}{6}\text{ ft}\approx10.2\text{ ft}$$

The difference in snowfall between the two cities is about 10.2 ft.

60. (a) Convert minutes per feet to hours per mile.

$$\frac{3\text{ min}}{\underset{1}{\cancel{2}}\text{ ft}}\cdot\frac{\overset{44}{\cancel{\underset{}{5280}}}\text{ ft}}{1\text{ mi}}\cdot\frac{1\text{ hr}}{\underset{1}{\cancel{60}}\text{ min}}=3\cdot44\text{ hr per mi}$$

$$=132\text{ hr per mi}$$
It will take the snail 132 hr to travel 1 mi.

(b) Convert 132 hr to days.

$$\frac{\overset{11}{\cancel{132}}\text{ hr}}{1}\cdot\frac{1\text{ day}}{\underset{2}{\cancel{24}}\text{ hr}}=\frac{11}{2}\text{ days}$$
$$=5\frac{1}{2}\text{ days}$$

It will take the snail $5\frac{1}{2}$ or 5.5 days to travel 1 mi.

62. (a) Multiply to find the ounces of gold, then convert ounces to pounds.
$301\cdot0.2=60.2$ ounces of gold

$$\frac{60.2\text{ oz}}{1}\cdot\frac{1\text{ lb}}{16\text{ oz}}=\frac{60.2}{16}\text{ lb}\approx3.8\text{ lb}$$

There were about 3.8 lb of gold used to make the medals.

(b) There is 7 oz − 0.2 oz = 6.8 oz of silver per medal. Multiply to find the ounces of silver, then convert ounces to pounds.
$301\cdot6.8=2046.8$ ounces of silver

$$\frac{2046.8\text{ oz}}{1}\cdot\frac{1\text{ lb}}{16\text{ oz}}=\frac{2046.8}{16}\text{ lb}\approx127.9\text{ lb}$$

There were about 127.9 lb of silver used to make the medals.

7.2   The Metric System—Length

2. *Deka* means <u>10</u> so 1 dam = <u>10</u> m.

4. *Deci* means $\frac{1}{10}$ or 0.1 so 1 dm = $\frac{1}{10}$ or <u>0.1</u> m.

6. *Hecto* means <u>100</u> so 1 hm = <u>100</u> m.

8. The width of your hand in millimeters
10 times the number of cm measured in
Exercise 7 or about 80 mm

10. The width of your thumb in centimeters
The number of mm measured in Exercise 9
divided by 10 or about 2 cm

12. The cardboard was 3 mm thick.

14. The bookcase is 75 cm wide.

16. The door is 2 m high.

18. Lamard jogs 4 km every morning.

20. My pen is 145 mm long.

22. Wheelchairs need doorways that are at least
80 cm wide.

24. Conversions can be done using decimals
instead of fractions which means fewer
conversion relationships to memorize.

26. 18 m to cm

$$\frac{18 \ \cancel{m}}{1} \cdot \frac{100 \ cm}{1 \ \cancel{m}} = 18 \cdot 100 \ cm = 1800 \ cm$$

28. 6 mm to m
Count 3 places to the left on the metric
conversion line.
6 mm = 0.006 m

30. 0.7 km to m

$$\frac{0.7 \ \cancel{km}}{1} \cdot \frac{1000 \ m}{1 \ \cancel{km}} = 0.7 \cdot 1000 \ m = 700 \ m$$

32. 30 cm to m

$$\frac{30 \ \cancel{cm}}{1} \cdot \frac{1 \ m}{100 \ \cancel{cm}} = \frac{30}{100} \ m = 0.3 \ m$$

34. 25 mm to cm
Count 1 place to the left on the metric
conversion line.
25 mm = 2.5 cm

36. 4 m to mm

$$4 \ \cancel{m} \cdot \frac{1000 \ mm}{1 \ \cancel{m}} = 4000 \ mm$$

38. There are 1000 meters in 1 kilometer, so 1022
m is *greater* than 1 km.
The difference is
   1022 m − 1000 m = 22 m
or 1.022 km − 1 km = 0.022 km.

40. 3 mm to cm
Count 1 place to the left on the metric
conversion line.
—   3 mm = 0.3 cm
5 mm to cm
Count 1 place to the left on the metric
conversion line.
—   5 mm = 0.5 cm
10 mm to cm
Count 1 place to the left on the metric
conversion line.
——   10 mm = 1 cm

42. 60,000 km to m
Count 3 places to the right on the metric
conversion line.
60,000 km = 60,000,000 m
There are 60,000,000 m of blood vessels.

44. 16.5 km to mm

$$16.5 \ \cancel{km} \cdot \frac{1000 \ \cancel{m}}{1 \ \cancel{km}} \cdot \frac{1000 \ mm}{1 \ \cancel{m}} = 16,500,000 \ mm$$

7.3 The Metric System— Capacity and Weight (Mass)

2. Hiromi used 20 *L* of water to wash the kitchen
floor.

4. Jay gave 2 *mL* of vitamin drops to the baby.

6. A small safety pin weighs 750 *mg*.

8. One dime weighs 2 *g*.

10. Barbara bought the large 2 *L* bottle of soda.

12. The 8 people on the elevator weighed a total
of 500 *kg*.

14. Kevin poured 10 *mL* of vanilla into the bowl.

16. One grain of salt weighs 2 *mg*.

18. This is reasonable because 1 milliliter would
be about $\frac{1}{4}$ teaspoon.

20. This is unreasonable (too much) because 0.5
liter would be a little more than half of a
quart.

22. Taking 200 milligrams of vitamin C daily is
reasonable.

24. A tube of ointment weighing 0.002 gram is
unreasonable (too little). This weight is equal
to 2 mg, about the weight of a grain of salt.

26. A box measuring 1 cm on each side holds 1 mL of water and the water weighs 1 g. Also, a box measuring 10 cm on every side holds exactly 1 L.

28. From mg to g is three places to the left on the metric conversion line, so move the decimal point three places left.
$_\wedge$020.   20 mg = 0.02 g

30. 6 L to mL
Count 3 places to the right on the metric conversion line.
6.000$_\wedge$ = 6000 mL

32. 18,000 mL to L
Count 3 places to the left on the metric conversion line.
18$_\wedge$000 mL = 18 L

34. 200 mL to L

$$\frac{200 \text{ mL}}{1} \cdot \frac{1 \text{ L}}{1000 \text{ mL}} = \frac{2}{10} = 0.2 \text{ L}$$

36. 25 mL to L
Count 3 places to the left on the metric conversion line.
$_\wedge$025. mL = 0.025 L

38. 11.7 L to mL

$$\frac{11.7 \text{ L}}{1} \cdot \frac{1000 \text{ mL}}{1 \text{ L}} = 11.7 \cdot 1000 \text{ mL} = 11,700 \text{ mL}$$

40. 25,000 g to kg
Count 3 places to the left on the metric conversion line.
25$_\wedge$000. g = 25 kg

42. 12.42 kg to g
Count 3 places to the right on the metric conversion line.
12.420$_\wedge$ kg = 12,420 g

44. 0.2 g to mg

$$\frac{0.2 \text{ g}}{1} \cdot \frac{1000 \text{ mg}}{1 \text{ g}} = 200 \text{ mg}$$

46. 7500 mg to g

$$\frac{\overset{7.5}{7500} \text{ mg}}{1} \cdot \frac{1 \text{ g}}{\underset{1}{1000} \text{ mg}} = 7.5 \text{ g}$$

48. 900 mg to g
Count 3 places to the left on the metric conversion line.
$_\wedge$900. mg = 0.9 g

50. 6.007 kg to g
Count 3 places to the right on the metric conversion line.
6.007$_\wedge$ kg = 6007 g

52. 12 mg to g
Count 3 places to the left on the metric conversion line.
$_\wedge$012. mg = 0.012 g

54. 13,700 mL to L

$$\frac{\overset{13.7}{13,700} \text{ mL}}{1} \cdot \frac{1 \text{ L}}{\underset{1}{1000} \text{ mL}} = 13.7 \text{ L}$$

56. The roll of tape has 55 m of tape on it.

58. One onion weighs 200 g.

60. Add 2 L of windshield washer fluid to your car.

62. The hallway is 10 m long.

64. 3.5 L to mL

$$\frac{3.5 \text{ L}}{1} \cdot \frac{1000 \text{ mL}}{1 \text{ L}} = 3500 \text{ mL}$$

66. 1907 g to kg

$$\frac{\overset{1.907}{1907} \text{ g}}{1} \cdot \frac{1 \text{ kg}}{\underset{1}{1000} \text{ g}} = 1.907 \text{ kg}$$

68. 900 mL to L

$$\frac{\overset{0.9}{900} \text{ mL}}{1} \cdot \frac{1 \text{ L}}{\underset{1}{1000} \text{ mL}} = 0.9 \text{ L}$$

70. 29 g to kilograms

$$\frac{29 \text{ g}}{1} \cdot \frac{1 \text{ kg}}{1000 \text{ g}} = \frac{29}{1000} \text{ kg} = 0.029 \text{ kg}$$

72. There are 1000 milliliters in 1 liter, so 990 mL is less than 1 L. The difference is
1000 mL − 990 mL = 10 mL
or 1 L − 0.99 mL = 0.01 L.

74. Because 3.5 g are contained in 1000 mL and 1 liter = 1000 mL, there are 3.5 g of salt in 1 liter.

7.4 Problem Solving with Metric Measurement

2. Convert centimeters to meters.
3 m 15 cm = 3.15 m

$$\frac{\$4.75}{1 \text{ m}} \cdot \frac{3.15 \text{ m}}{1} = \$14.9625$$

Lanh will pay $14.96 (rounded to the nearest cent).

4. Convert 33 cm to mm.

$$\frac{33 \text{ cm}}{1} \cdot \frac{10 \text{ mm}}{1 \text{ cm}} = 330 \text{ mm}$$

Find the difference.
330 mm − 0.2 mm = 329.8 mm
The giant stick insect is 329.8 mm longer than the fairy fly.

6. Convert grams to kilograms.
185 g = 0.185 kg
Multiply by the number of tiles.
0.185 kg · 24 = 4.44 kg
The carton of 24 tiles weighs 4.44 kg.
Multiply by the number of stacks.
4.44 kg · 5 = 22.2
Five stacks would weigh 22.2 kg.

8. Convert 750 mL to L

$$\frac{750 \text{ mL}}{1} \cdot \frac{1 \text{ L}}{1000 \text{ mL}} = 0.75 \text{ L}$$

Multiply by 30 to find the liters for a one-month supply.
0.75 L · 30 = 22.5 L
The caretaker should order 22.5 L.
Divide to find the number of containers.

$$\frac{22.5 \text{ L}}{42} = 5.625 \text{ containers}$$

The caretaker should order 6 containers, because you cannot buy part of a container. 0.625 of the 6th container will be used, so 1 − 0.625 = 0.325 of the container will be left over.
(0.325)(4 L) = 1.5 L
1.5 L will be left over.

10. Convert centimeters to meters.
10 m 30 cm = 10.3 m
Divide by the number of windows.

$$\frac{10.3 \text{ m}}{3 \text{ windows}} \approx 3.43 \text{ m / windows}$$

There are about 3.43 m of fabric for each window.

12. Convert centimeters to meters.
3 m 80 cm = 3.8 m
Multiply by the price per meter.

$$\frac{\$5.89}{1 \text{ m}} \cdot \frac{3.8 \text{ m}}{1} = \$22.382$$

Sales tax:
$22.382 · 0.07 = $1.56674
Total cost:
$22.382 + $1.56674 = $23.9487
James will pay $23.95 (rounded to the nearest cent).

14. $16 case:
Capacity = 12 · 1 L = 12 L

$$\text{Cost per liter} = \frac{\$16}{12 \text{ L}} \approx \$1.33 \text{ per L}$$

$18 case:
400 mL = 0.4 L
Capacity = 36 · 0.4 L = 14.4 L

$$\text{Cost per liter} = \frac{\$18}{14.4 \text{ L}} = \$1.25 \text{ per L}$$

The $18 case is the better buy.

7.5 Metric–English Conversions and Temperature

2. 8 km to miles

$$\frac{8 \text{ km}}{1} \cdot \frac{0.62 \text{ mi}}{1 \text{ km}} \approx 5.0 \text{ mi}$$

4. 85 cm to inches

$$\frac{85 \text{ cm}}{1} \cdot \frac{0.39 \text{ in.}}{1 \text{ cm}} \approx 33.2 \text{ in.}$$

6. 3.2 yd to meters

$$\frac{3.2 \text{ yd}}{1} \cdot \frac{0.91 \text{ m}}{1 \text{ yd}} \approx 2.9 \text{ m}$$

8. 2.5 oz to grams

$$\frac{2.5 \text{ oz}}{1} \cdot \frac{28.35 \text{ g}}{1 \text{ oz}} \approx 70.9 \text{ g}$$

10. 7.68 kg to pounds

$$\frac{7.68 \text{ kg}}{1} \cdot \frac{2.20 \text{ lb}}{1 \text{ kg}} \approx 16.9 \text{ lb}$$

12. 15.75 L to gallons

$$\frac{15.75 \text{ L}}{1} \cdot \frac{0.26 \text{ gal}}{1 \text{ L}} \approx 4.1 \text{ gal}$$

14. Convert 120 m to feet

$$\frac{120 \text{ m}}{1} \cdot \frac{3.28 \text{ ft}}{1 \text{ m}} = 393.6 \text{ ft}$$

The signals travel about 393.6 ft per sec.

16. Convert 4.5 L to gallons.

$$\frac{4.5 \text{ L}}{1} \cdot \frac{0.26 \text{ gal}}{1 \text{ L}} = 1.17 \text{ gal}$$

The dishwasher uses about 1.2 gal.

18. Convert 4.4 lb to kilograms.

$$\frac{4.4 \text{ lb}}{1} \cdot \frac{0.45 \text{ kg}}{1 \text{ lb}} = 1.98 \text{ kg}$$

The laptop weighs about 2.0 kg.

20. Brewing coffee
80°C is reasonable. 80°F is warm enough for a nice summer day, but not for brewing coffee.

22. Swimming pool water
78°F is reasonable. 78°C would be a very hot water temperature.

24. Light jacket weather
10°C is reasonable. 10°F is below freezing and most of us would prefer a heavier coat for winter weather.

26. Advantage: the rest of the world uses the Celsius scale. Disadvantage: people would have to buy new thermometers and get used to a new system.

28. 80°F

$$C = \frac{5(80 - 32)}{9} = \frac{5(48)}{9} = \frac{240}{9} \approx 26.7$$

80°F ≈ 27°C

30. 36°F

$$C = \frac{5(36 - 32)}{9} = \frac{20}{9} \approx 2.2$$

36°F ≈ 2°C

32. 18°C

$$F = \frac{9 \cdot 18}{5} + 32 = 32.4 + 32 \approx 64.4$$

18°C ≈ 64°F

34. 0°C

$$F = \frac{9 \cdot 0}{5} + 32 = 0 + 32 = 32$$

0°C ≈ 32°F

36. 107°F

$$C = \frac{5(107 - 32)}{9} = \frac{5(75)}{9} = \frac{375}{9} \approx 42$$

39°F

$$C = \frac{5(39 - 32)}{9} = \frac{5(7)}{9} = \frac{35}{9} \approx 4$$

These temperature are about 42° C and 4° C.

38. (a) Pour boiling water over the tea bag and leave it in the water for 4 minutes.

(b) 100°C

$$F = \frac{9 \cdot 100}{5} + 32 = \frac{900}{5} + 32 = 180 + 32$$
$$= 212$$

212°F would give the same result as 100°C.

Chapter 8

GEOMETRY

8.1 Basic Geometric Terms

2. The figure is a *ray* because it is a part of a line that has only one endpoint and goes on forever in one direction.
   The ray is named $\overrightarrow{AB}$.

4. The figure has two endpoints so it is a line segment. The *line segment* is named $\overline{EF}$ or $\overline{FE}$.

6. This figure is a straight row of points that go on forever in both directions, so it is a *line*.
   The line is named $\overleftrightarrow{ST}$ or $\overleftrightarrow{TS}$.

8. The lines intersect so they are not parallel. At the intersection they do not form a right angle so they are not perpendicular. The lines are *intersecting*.

10. The lines are *parallel* because they are in the same plane and will never intersect (cross).

12. The lines intersect to form a right angle, so they are *perpendicular*.

14. The vertex is at O so the angle is named $\angle BOD$ or $\angle DOB$.

16. The vertex is at R so the angle is named $\angle CRB$ or $\angle BRC$.

18. The vertex is at Q so the angle is named $\angle FQB$ or $\angle BQF$.

20. The measure of the angle is between 90° and 180° so it is an *obtuse* angle.

22. The measure of the angle is between 90° and 180° so it is an *obtuse* angle.

24. The measure of the angle is between 0° and 90° so it is an *acute* angle.

26. There are many possibilities. Some examples are: a corner of a room, a street corner, corners of a window, a corner of a piece of paper.

8.2 Angles and Their Relationships

2. The pairs of complementary angles are:
   $\angle COQ$ and $\angle COP$ because $45° + 45° = 90°$;
   $\angle SOR$ and $\angle SOP$ because $31° + 59° = 90°$.

4. The pairs of supplementary angles are:
   $\angle AQB$ and $\angle AQD$ because $140° + 40° = 180°$;
   $\angle BQC$ and $\angle CQD$ because $40° + 140° = 180°$;
   $\angle AQB$ and $\angle BQC$ because $140° + 40° = 180°$;
   $\angle CQD$ and $\angle AQD$ because $140° + 40° = 180°$;

6. The complement of 35° is 55° because $90° - 35° = 55°$.

8. The complement of 59° is 31° because $90° - 59° = 31°$.

10. The supplement of 75° is 105° because $180° - 75° = 105°$.

12. The supplement of 5° is 175° because $180° - 5° = 175°$.

14. $\angle AOB \cong \angle COD$ because the angles each measure 135°.
    $\angle AOD \cong \angle BOC$ because the angles each measure 45°.

16. $\angle ROS$ measures 105° because $\angle ROS$ and $\angle POU$ are vertical angles, so they are congruent.
    Since $\angle UOT$ and $\angle POU$ share their vertex and have a side in common, then the measure of $\angle TOP$ equals the sum of the measures of $\angle UOT$ and $\angle POU$, that is, $40° + 105° = 145°$ is the measure of $\angle TOP$. Since $\angle TOP$ and $\angle POQ$ are supplementary angles, then the measure of $\angle POQ = 180° - 145° = 35°$.
    $\angle TOS$ measures 35° because $\angle TOS$ and $\angle POQ$ are vertical angles, so they are congruent.
    $\angle QOR$ measures 40° because $\angle QOR$ and $\angle UOT$ are vertical angles, so they are congruent.

18. There are many possibilities. One example is:

Find the number of degrees in $\angle AOD$ and $\angle DOC$. $\angle AOD$ measures $115°$ and $\angle DOC$ measures $65°$.

20. $\angle ABC$ and $\angle BCD$ are congruent because they both measure $133°$, so $\angle ABC \cong \angle BCD$.
Because $\angle ABC$ and $\angle EBA$ are supplementary,
$\angle EBA = 180° - 133° = 47°$.
$\angle DCG$ and $\angle BCD$ are also supplementary.
$\angle DCG = 180° - 133° = 47°$
$\angle DCG$ and $\angle EBA$ are congruent because they both measure $47°$ so
$\angle DCG \cong \angle EBA$.

22. Yes, because acute angles are $< 90°$ so their sum could equal $90°$.

8.3 Rectangles and Squares

2. $P = 2 \cdot length + 2 \cdot width$
   $= 2 \cdot 18 \text{ in.} + 2 \cdot 7 \text{ in.}$
   $= 36 \text{ in.} + 14 \text{ in.}$
   $= 50 \text{ in.}$
$A = length \cdot width$
   $= 18 \text{ in.} \cdot 7 \text{ in.}$
   $= 126 \text{ in.}^2$

4. $P = 4 \cdot s$
   $= 4 \cdot 7.5 \text{ m}$
   $= 30 \text{ m}$
$A = s \cdot s$
   $= 7.5 \text{ m} \cdot 7.5 \text{ m}$
   $= 56.25 \text{ m}^2$

6. 8 cm by 17 cm
$P = 2 \cdot length + 2 \cdot width$
   $= 2 \cdot 17 \text{ cm} + 2 \cdot 8 \text{ cm}$
   $= 34 \text{ cm} + 16 \text{ cm}$
   $= 50 \text{ cm}$
$A = length \cdot width$
   $= 17 \text{ cm} \cdot 8 \text{ cm}$
   $= 136 \text{ cm}^2$

8. 2.35 km by 8.4 km
$P = 2 \cdot length + 2 \cdot width$
   $= 2 \cdot 8.4 \text{ km} + 2 \cdot 2.35 \text{ km}$
   $= 4.7 \text{ km} + 16.8 \text{ km}$
   $= 21.5 \text{ km}$
$A = length \cdot width$
   $= 8.4 \text{ km} \cdot 2.35 \text{ km}$
   $= 19.74 \text{ km}^2$

10. 12 m by 12 m
$P = 4 \cdot s$
   $= 4 \cdot 12 \text{ m}$
   $= 48 \text{ m}$
$A = s \cdot s$
   $= 12 \text{ m} \cdot 12 \text{ m}$
   $= 144 \text{ m}^2$

12. A square 20.3 cm on a side
$P = 4 \cdot s$
   $= 4 \cdot 20.3 \text{ cm}$
   $= 81.2 \text{ cm}$
$A = s \cdot s$
   $= 20.3 \text{ cm} \cdot 20.3 \text{ cm}$
   $= 412.09 \text{ cm}^2$

14. $P = 4 \text{ ft} + 12 \text{ ft} + 12 \text{ ft} + 3 \text{ ft} + 8 \text{ ft} + 9 \text{ ft} = 48 \text{ ft}$
Draw a horizontal line and break up the figure into two rectangles.

rectangle with	rectangle with
length: 9 ft	length: 12 ft
width: 4 ft	width: 3 ft
$A = 9 \text{ ft} \cdot 4 \text{ ft}$	$A = 12 \text{ ft} \cdot 3 \text{ ft}$
$= 36 \text{ ft}^2$	$= 36 \text{ ft}^2$

Total area $= 36 \text{ ft}^2 + 36 \text{ ft}^2 = 72 \text{ ft}^2$

16. $P = 3.5 \text{ cm} + 3 \text{ cm} + 1.5 \text{ cm} + 5 \text{ cm} + 5 \text{ cm}$
    $+ 8 \text{ cm} = 26 \text{ cm}$
Draw a horizontal line and break up the figure into two rectangles.

rectangle with	square with
length: 3.5 cm	side: 5 cm
width: 3 cm	
$A = 3.5 \text{ cm} \cdot 3 \text{ cm}$	$A = 5 \text{ cm} \cdot 5 \text{ cm}$
$= 10.5 \text{ cm}^2$	$= 25 \text{ cm}^2$

Total area $= 10.5 \text{ cm}^2 + 25 \text{ cm}^2 = 35.5 \text{ cm}^2$

18. To find the measurement for the bottom line, add the horizontal segments from the top line.
$12 \text{ ft} + 16 \text{ ft} + 20 \text{ ft} = 48 \text{ ft}$
The unlabeled side = 48 ft.
$P = 12 \text{ ft} + 18 \text{ ft} + 16 \text{ ft} + 10 \text{ ft} + 20 \text{ ft} + 32 \text{ ft}$
$\qquad + 48 \text{ ft} + 40 \text{ ft} = 196 \text{ ft}$
To find the area break up the figure into 3 rectangles.
rectangle with length 18 ft, width 12 ft:
$A = 18 \text{ ft} \cdot 12 \text{ ft}$
$\quad = 216 \text{ ft}^2$
rectangle with length 48 ft, width 22 ft:
$A = 48 \text{ ft} \cdot 22 \text{ ft}$
$\quad = 1056 \text{ ft}^2$
rectangle with length 20 ft, width 10 ft:
$A = 20 \text{ ft} \cdot 10 \text{ ft}$
$\quad = 200 \text{ ft}^2$
Total area $= 216 \text{ ft}^2 + 1056 \text{ ft}^2 + 200 \text{ ft}^2$
$\qquad\qquad = 1472 \text{ ft}^2$

20. length of the page = 27.5 cm
width of the page = 20.5 cm
$P = 2 \cdot length + 2 \cdot width$
$\quad = 2 \cdot 27.5 \text{ cm} + 2 \cdot 20.5 \text{ cm}$
$\quad = 55 \text{ cm} + 41 \text{ cm}$
$\quad = 96 \text{ cm}$
$A = length \cdot width$
$\quad = 27.5 \text{ cm} \cdot 20.5 \text{ cm}$
$\quad = 563.75 \text{ cm}^2$

22. Find the area of the room.
$A = s \cdot s$
$\quad = 5 \text{ yd} \cdot 5 \text{ yd}$
$\quad = 25 \text{ yd}^2$
Cost of carpet
$$\frac{25 \text{ yd}^2}{1} \cdot \frac{\$23}{\text{yd}^2} = \$575$$
Cost of padding and installation
$$\frac{25 \text{ yd}^2}{1} \cdot \frac{\$6}{\text{yd}^2} = \$150$$
Total cost
$\$575 + \$150 = \$725$

24. $P = 2 \cdot 54 \text{ ft} + 2 \cdot 15 \text{ ft}$
$\quad = 108 \text{ ft} + 30 \text{ ft}$
$\quad = 138 \text{ ft}$
$A = 54 \text{ ft} \cdot 15 \text{ ft}$
$\quad = 810 \text{ ft}^2$
The perimeter is 138 ft and the area is 810 ft^2.

26. $\qquad A = length \cdot width$
$14,790 \text{ ft}^2 = length \cdot 85 \text{ ft}$
$$\frac{14,790 \text{ ft}^2}{85 \text{ ft}} = length$$
$\qquad 174 \text{ ft} = length$

28. length of sides along country road
$\quad = 126 \text{ ft} + 82 \text{ ft} = 208 \text{ ft}$
cost for sides along country road
$$\frac{208 \text{ ft}}{1} \cdot \frac{\$4.25}{1 \text{ ft}} = \$884$$
length of the other two sides
$\quad = 82 \text{ ft} + 126 \text{ ft} = 208 \text{ ft}$
Cost for the other two sides
$$\frac{208 \text{ ft}}{1} \cdot \frac{\$2.75}{1 \text{ ft}} = \$572$$
Total cost $= \$884 + \$572 = \$1456$

8.4 Parallelograms and Trapezoids

2. $P = 2 \cdot length + 2 \cdot width$
$\quad = 2 \cdot 1240 \text{ ft} + 2 \cdot 1000 \text{ ft}$
$\quad = 2480 \text{ ft} + 2000 \text{ ft}$
$\quad = 4480 \text{ ft}$

4. $P = 12.6 \text{ in.} + 24.8 \text{ in.} + 11.9 \text{ in.} + 14.7 \text{ in.}$
$\quad = 64 \text{ in.}$

6. $P = 7.33 \text{ cm} + 2.8 \text{ cm} + 4.17 \text{ cm} + 4.3 \text{ cm}$
$\quad = 18.6 \text{ cm}$

8. $A = b \cdot h$
$\quad = 21.4 \text{ m} \cdot 13.2 \text{ m}$
$\quad = 282.48 \text{ m}^2$

10. $A = \dfrac{1}{2} \cdot h \cdot (b + B)$
$\quad = \dfrac{1}{2} \cdot 8 \text{ in.} \cdot \left(9\frac{1}{4} \text{ in.} + 15\frac{3}{4} \text{ in.}\right)$
$\quad = \dfrac{1}{2} \cdot 8 \text{ in.} \cdot (25 \text{ in.})$
$\quad = 100 \text{ in.}^2$

12. $A = 0.5 \cdot h \cdot (b + B)$
$\quad = 0.5 \cdot 0.6 \text{ km} \cdot (0.4 \text{ km} + 1.2 \text{ km})$
$\quad = 0.5 \cdot 0.6 \text{ km} \cdot (1.6 \text{ km})$
$\quad = 0.48 \text{ km}^2$

14. base: 12.4 m, height: 9.6 m, cost per square meter: \$4.92

$A = b \cdot h$

$= 12.4 \text{ m} \cdot 9.6 \text{ m}$

$= 119.04 \text{ m}^2$

$$\text{Cost} = \frac{119.04 \text{ m}^2}{1} \cdot \frac{\$4.92}{1 \text{ m}^2}$$

$$\approx \$585.68$$

16. Find the area.

$A = \frac{1}{2} \cdot h \cdot (b + B)$

$= \frac{1}{2} \cdot 20 \text{ ft} \cdot (20 \text{ ft} + 32 \text{ ft})$

$= 10 \text{ ft}(52 \text{ ft})$

$= 520 \text{ ft}^2$

$$\frac{\$832}{520 \text{ ft}^2} = \$1.60 / \text{ft}^2$$

She is paying \$1.60 per ft^2

18. The short base and long base are parallel lines. The short base should be 13 ft and the long base 22 ft. Area is measured in square units.

$A = 0.5 \cdot h \cdot (b + B)$

$= 0.5 \cdot 11.5 \text{ ft} \cdot (22 \text{ ft} + 13 \text{ ft})$

$= 0.5 \cdot 11.5 \text{ ft} \cdot (35 \text{ ft})$

$= 201.25 \text{ ft}^2$

20. Break up the figure into 2 trapezoids.
trapezoid with height: 46.2 cm, short base: 61.7 cm, long base: 87.3 cm

$A = \frac{1}{2} \cdot 46.2 \text{ cm} \cdot (61.7 \text{ cm} + 87.3 \text{ cm})$

$= \frac{1}{2} \cdot 46.2 \text{ cm} \cdot (149 \text{ cm})$

$= 3441.9 \text{ cm}^2$

trapezoid with height: 32 cm, short base: 61.7 cm, long base: 92.3 cm

$A = \frac{1}{2} \cdot 32 \text{ cm} \cdot (61.7 \text{ cm} + 92.3 \text{ cm})$

$= \frac{1}{2} \cdot 32 \text{ cm} \cdot (154 \text{ cm})$

$= 2464 \text{ cm}^2$

Total area $= 3441.9 \text{ cm}^2 + 2464 \text{ cm}^2$

$= 5905.9 \text{ cm}^2$

8.5 Triangles

2. $P = 13 \text{ yd} + 9 \text{ yd} + 12 \text{ yd} = 34 \text{ yd}$

$A = \frac{1}{2} \cdot b \cdot h$

$= \frac{1}{2} \cdot 13 \text{ yd} \cdot 8 \text{ yd}$

$= 52 \text{ yd}^2$

4. $P = 22.6 \text{ in.} + 16 \text{ in.} + 16 \text{ in.} = 54.6 \text{ in.}$

$A = \frac{1}{2} \cdot b \cdot h$

$= \frac{1}{2} \cdot 16 \text{ in.} \cdot 16 \text{ in.}$

$= 128 \text{ in.}^2$

6. $P = 10 \text{ ft} + 18 \text{ ft} + 9 \text{ ft} = 37 \text{ ft}$

$A = \frac{1}{2} \cdot b \cdot h$

$= \frac{1}{2} \cdot 9 \text{ ft} \cdot 6\frac{1}{4} \text{ ft}$

$= 28.125 \text{ ft}^2 \text{ or } 28\frac{1}{8} \text{ ft}^2$

8. $P = 7.2 \text{ ft} + 7.2 \text{ ft} + 7.2 \text{ ft} = 21.6 \text{ ft}$

$A = \frac{1}{2} \cdot b \cdot h$

$= \frac{1}{2} \cdot 7.2 \text{ ft} \cdot 6.2 \text{ ft}$

$= 22.32 \text{ ft}^2$

10. Find the area of each part.
the parallelogram:

$A = b \cdot h$

$= 20 \text{ m} \cdot 19 \text{ m}$

$= 380 \text{ m}^2$

the triangle:

$A = \frac{1}{2} \cdot b \cdot h$

$= \frac{1}{2} \cdot 27 \text{ m} \cdot 20 \text{ m}$

$= 270 \text{ m}^2$

Shaded area $= 380 \text{ m}^2 + 270 \text{ m}^2$

$= 650 \text{ m}^2$

12. Find the area of the triangle.

$A = \dfrac{1}{2} \cdot b \cdot h$

$ = \dfrac{1}{2} \cdot 18 \text{ ft} \cdot 7 \text{ ft}$

$ = 63 \text{ ft}^2$

Now find the area of the unshaded square.

$A = s \cdot s$

$ = 3 \text{ ft} \cdot 3 \text{ ft}$

$ = 9 \text{ ft}^2$

Shaded area $= 63 \text{ ft}^2 - 9 \text{ ft}^2$

$\phantom{\text{Shaded area }} = 54 \text{ ft}^2$

14. *Step 1* $46° + 67° = 113°$
Step 2 $180° - 113° = 67°$
The unlabeled angle measures $67°$.

16. *Step 1* $20° + 15° = 35°$
Step 2 $180° - 35° = 145°$
The unlabeled angle measures $145°$.

18. Two identical triangles form a parallelogram. The area of a parallelogram is base times height, so the area of one of the triangles is $\frac{1}{2} \cdot base \cdot height$. Sketches will vary.

20. Use the formula for the area of a triangle.

$A = 0.5 \cdot b \cdot h$

$ = 0.5 \cdot 1.5 \text{ m} \cdot 1.2 \text{ m}$

$ = 0.9 \text{ m}^2$

The sign has a surface area of 0.9 m^2.

22. Find the area for one gable end of the house. Use the formula for the area of a triangle.

$A = 0.5 \cdot b \cdot h$

$ = 0.5 \cdot 36 \text{ ft} \cdot 9.5 \text{ ft}$

$ = 171 \text{ ft}^2$

The area for both gable ends is
$171 \text{ ft}^2 + 171 \text{ ft}^2 = 342 \text{ ft}^2$.

24. Find the total area.

$A = length \cdot width$

$ = 65 \text{ yd} \cdot 50 \text{ yd}$

$ = 3250 \text{ yd}^2$

Now find the area of the triangular building.

$A = \dfrac{1}{2} \cdot b \cdot h$

$ = \dfrac{1}{2} \cdot 40 \text{ yd} \cdot 38 \text{ yd}$

$ = 760 \text{ yd}^2$

Shaded area $= 3250 \text{ yd}^2 - 760 \text{ yd}^2$

$\phantom{\text{Shaded area }} = 2490 \text{ yd}^2$

Total cost $= \dfrac{2490 \text{ yd}^2}{1} \cdot \dfrac{\$28}{\text{yd}^2} = \$69,720$

8.6   Circles

2. The radius is 15 mi so
$d = 2 \cdot r$
$ = 2 \cdot 15 \text{ mi} = 30 \text{ mi.}$

4. The diameter is 6.1 cm so
$r = \dfrac{d}{2} = \dfrac{6.1}{2} \text{ cm} = 3.05 \text{ cm}$

6. $r = 41$ cm
$C = 2 \cdot \pi \cdot r$
$ \approx 2 \cdot 3.14 \cdot 41 \text{ cm}$
$ \approx 257.5 \text{ cm}$
$A = \pi \cdot r \cdot r$
$ \approx 3.14 \cdot 41 \text{ cm} \cdot 41 \text{ cm}$
$ \approx 5278.3 \text{ cm}^2$

8. $d = 3$ inches so $r = \dfrac{3}{2} = 1\frac{1}{2}$ inches.
$C = \pi \cdot d$
$ \approx 3.14 \cdot 3 \text{ in.}$
$ \approx 9.4 \text{ in.}$
$A = \pi \cdot r \cdot r$
$ \approx 3.14 \cdot 1.5 \text{ in.} \cdot 1.5 \text{ in.}$
$ \approx 7.1 \text{ in.}^2$

10. $d = 39$ ft; $r = \dfrac{39 \text{ ft}}{2} = 19.5 \text{ ft}$
$C = \pi \cdot d$
$ \approx 3.14 \cdot 39 \text{ ft}$
$ \approx 122.5 \text{ ft}$
$A = \pi \cdot r \cdot r$
$ \approx 3.14 \cdot 19.5 \text{ ft} \cdot 19.5 \text{ ft}$
$ \approx 1194.0 \text{ ft}^2$

12. $d = 4\frac{1}{2}$ yd; $r = 2\frac{1}{4}$ yd
$C = \pi \cdot d$
$ \approx 3.14 \cdot 4.5 \text{ yd}$
$ \approx 14.1 \text{ yd}$
$A = \pi \cdot r \cdot r$
$ \approx 3.14 \cdot 2.25 \text{ yd} \cdot 2.25 \text{ yd}$
$ \approx 15.9 \text{ yd}^2$

14. $d = 19.5$ mm; $r = \dfrac{19.5}{2} = 9.75$ mm

$C = \pi \cdot d$

$\quad \approx 3.14 \cdot 19.5$ mm

$\quad \approx 61.2$ mm

$A = \pi \cdot r \cdot r$

$\quad \approx 3.14 \cdot 9.75$ mm $\cdot 9.75$ mm

$\quad \approx 298.5$ mm^2

16. area of the square

$A = s \cdot s$

$\quad = 8$ ft $\cdot 8$ ft

$\quad = 64$ ft^2

$r = \dfrac{8 \text{ ft}}{2} = 4$ ft

$A = \pi \cdot r \cdot r$

$\quad = 3.14 \cdot 4$ ft $\cdot 4$ ft

$\quad = 50.24$ ft^2

The shaded area is

64 ft$^2 - 50.24$ ft$^2 = 13.8$ ft^2.

18. area of the rectangle

$A = length \cdot width$

$\quad = 20$ in. $\cdot 18$ in.

$\quad = 360$ in.^{2}

area of the circle

$d = 18$ in. so $r = 9$ in.

$A = \pi \cdot r \cdot r$

$\quad = 3.14 \cdot 9$ in. $\cdot 9$ in.

$\quad = 254.34$ in.^{2}

area of the semicircle

$\quad = \dfrac{254.34 \text{ in.}^2}{2} \approx 127.17$ in.^{2}

The shaded area is

$= 360$ in.$^2 - 127.17$ in.$^2 \approx 232.8$ in.^{2}.

20. Circumference and perimeter are both the distance around a shape and are both measured in linear units like ft, yd, cm, or m. However, circumference applies *only* to circles. Perimeter can apply to many shapes such as squares, rectangles, triangles, and so on. Your circumference problem should use the formula $C = 2\pi r$ or $C = \pi d$. To find perimeter, add up the lengths of the sides of the shape.

22. Find the circumference of the circle that the ball travels.

$r = 2$ m

$C = 2 \cdot \pi \cdot r$

$\quad \approx 2 \cdot 3.14 \cdot 2$ m

$\quad \approx 12.6$ m

The ball will travel ≈ 12.6 m on each turn.

24. $A = \pi \cdot r \cdot r$

$\quad \approx 3.14 \cdot 125$ ft $\cdot 125$ ft

$\quad \approx 49,062.5$ ft^2

26. The radius is 900 km.

$A = \pi \cdot r \cdot r$

$\quad \approx 3.14 \cdot 900$ km $\cdot 900$ km

$\quad = 2,543,400$ km^2

The earthquake affected $\approx 2,543,400$ km^2.

28. 9 in. $= \dfrac{9}{12}$ ft $= \dfrac{3}{4}$ ft

12 ft 9 in. $= 12$ ft $+ \dfrac{3}{4}$ ft $= 12\frac{3}{4}$ ft

$C = \pi \cdot 12\frac{3}{4}$ ft

$\quad \approx 3.14 \cdot 12\frac{3}{4}$ ft

$\quad \approx 40$ ft

The sign is correct.

30. (a) $\quad C = 62.8$ mi

$\quad\quad C = \pi \cdot d$

62.8 mi $= \pi \cdot d$

62.8 mi $\approx 3.14 \cdot d$

$\dfrac{62.8 \text{ mi}}{3.14} \approx d$

$\quad d \approx 20$ mi

The diameter is ≈ 20 mi.

(b) $r = \dfrac{20}{2}$ mi $= 10$ mi

$A = \pi \cdot r \cdot r$

$\quad \approx 3.14 \cdot 10$ mi $\cdot 10$ mi

$\quad = 314$ mi^2

The area is ≈ 314 mi^2.

32. Find the area of the rectangle.

$A = length \cdot width$

$\quad = 60$ ft $\cdot 25$ ft

$\quad = 1500$ ft^2

Find the area of the circle.

radius: 25 ft

$A = \pi \cdot r \cdot r$

$\quad \approx 3.14 \cdot 25$ ft $\cdot 25$ ft

$\quad = 1962.50$ ft^2

$A =$ Because only $\frac{3}{4}$ of the circle is shown, multiply $\frac{3}{4}$ and the area of the circle.

$\dfrac{3}{4} \cdot 1962.50$ ft$^2 = 0.75 \cdot 1962.50$ ft^2

$\quad\quad\quad \approx 1471.9$ ft^2

The total area is approximately
$1500 \text{ ft}^2 + 1471.9 \text{ ft}^2 = 2971.9 \text{ ft}^2$.

34. The *par* prefix means beside, so parallel lines are beside each other. (Perpendicular lines cross so that they form a right angle.)

36. The diameter is 13 in., so the radius is

$\dfrac{13 \text{ in.}}{2} = 6\frac{1}{2}$ in. or 6.5 in.

$\begin{aligned} Area &= \pi \cdot r \cdot r \\ &\approx 3.14 \cdot 6.5 \cdot 6.5 \\ &\approx 132.665 \text{ in.}^2 \\ &\approx 132.7 \text{ in.}^2 \end{aligned}$

The area of a medium pizza is ≈ 132.7 in.^{2}.

38.

Size	Cost per square inch	
small	$\dfrac{\$2.80}{44.2 \text{ in.}^2}$	$\approx \$0.063$
medium	$\dfrac{\$6.50}{132.7 \text{ in.}^2}$	$\approx \$0.049$
large	$\dfrac{\$9.30}{201.0 \text{ in.}^2}$	$\approx \$0.046$

The best buy is the large pizza.

40.

Size	Cost per square inch	
small	$\dfrac{\$3.40}{44.2 \text{ in.}^2}$	$\approx \$0.077$
medium	$\dfrac{\$10.95}{132.7 \text{ in.}^2}$	$\approx \$0.083$
large	$\dfrac{\$15.65}{201.0 \text{ in.}^2}$	$\approx \$0.078$

The best buy is the small pizza.

Summary Exercises on Perimeter, Circumference, and Area

2. (a) circle showing radius

(b) circle showing diameter

(c) The diameter is twice the radius, or the radius is half the diameter.

4. Perimeter is the total distance around the outside edges of a shape. Area is the number of square units needed to cover the space inside the shape.

6. (a) $C = 2 \cdot \pi \cdot r$

(b) $C = \pi \cdot d$

(c) Divide the diameter by 2 to find the radius.

8. (a) $A = 12 \text{ cm}^2$

(b) $P = 6\frac{1}{2}$ ft

(c) $C \approx 28.5$ m

(d) $A = 307 \text{ in.}^2$

10. $\begin{aligned} P &= 4 \cdot s \\ &= 4 \cdot 12 \text{ yd} \\ &= 48 \text{ yd} \end{aligned}$

$\begin{aligned} P &= s^2 \\ &= (12 \text{ yd})^2 \\ &= 144 \text{ yd}^2 \end{aligned}$

12. $\begin{aligned} P &= 6 \text{ mm} + 8.5 \text{ mm} + 10 \text{ mm} + 9 \text{ mm} \\ &= 33.5 \text{ mm} \end{aligned}$

$\begin{aligned} A &= \frac{1}{2} \cdot h \cdot (b + B) \\ &= \frac{1}{2} \cdot 8 \text{ mm} \cdot (6 \text{ mm} + 10 \text{ mm}) \\ &= 4 \text{ mm} \cdot (16 \text{ mm}) \\ &= 64 \text{ mm}^2 \end{aligned}$

14. (a) $d = 30 \text{ mi}; \ r = \dfrac{30 \text{ mi}}{2} = 15 \text{ mi}$

(b) $\begin{aligned} C &= 2 \cdot \pi \cdot r \\ &\approx 2 \cdot 3.14 \cdot 15 \text{ mi} \\ &= 94.2 \text{ mi} \end{aligned}$

(c) $\begin{aligned} A &= \pi \cdot r \cdot r \\ &\approx 3.14 \cdot 15 \text{ mi} \cdot 15 \text{ mi} \\ &= 706.5 \text{ mi}^2 \end{aligned}$

16. Find the area of the square and the rectangle. Then add the areas.

Square: $A = s^2 = (1.6 \text{ m})^2 = 2.56 \text{ m}^2$

Rectangle: $A = l \cdot w = (3.8 \text{ m})(0.5 \text{ m}) = 1.9 \text{ m}^2$

Shaded area $= 2.56 \text{ m}^2 + 1.9 \text{ m}^2 = 4.46 \text{ m}^2$

The area is $\approx 4.5 \text{ m}^2$.

18. Subtract the area of the circle from the area of the square.

Circle: $A = \pi \cdot r \cdot r \approx 3.14 \cdot 10 \text{ in.} \cdot 10 \text{ in.}$

$\qquad = 314 \text{ in.}^2$

Square: $A = s^2 = (20 \text{ in.})^2 = 400 \text{ in.}^2$

Shaded area $\approx 400 \text{ in.}^2 - 314 \text{ in.}^2 = 86 \text{ in.}^2$

20. $P = 2 \cdot l + 2 \cdot w$

$\qquad = 2 \cdot 2 \text{ m} + 2 \cdot 0.9 \text{ m}$

$\qquad = 4 \text{ m} + 1.8 \text{ m}$

$\qquad = 5.8 \text{ m}$

Cost $= 5.8 \text{ m} \cdot \$0.77 / \text{m} \approx \$4.47$

The total cost is $4.47.

8.7 Volume

2. Volume of a cube

$V = length \cdot width \cdot height$

$\qquad = 4\frac{1}{2} \text{ ft} \cdot 4\frac{1}{2} \text{ ft} \cdot 4\frac{1}{2} \text{ ft}$

$\qquad = \frac{9}{2} \text{ ft} \cdot \frac{9}{2} \text{ ft} \cdot \frac{9}{2} \text{ ft}$

$\qquad = \frac{729}{8} \text{ ft}^3$

$\qquad = 91\frac{1}{8} \text{ ft}^3$

$\qquad = 91.125 \text{ ft}^3$

$\qquad \approx 91.1 \text{ ft}^3$

4. Volume of a sphere

$V = \frac{4}{3} \cdot \pi \cdot r^3$

$\qquad \approx \dfrac{4 \cdot 3.14 \cdot 1.53 \text{ m} \cdot 1.53 \text{ m} \cdot 1.53 \text{ m}}{3}$

$\qquad \approx \dfrac{44.984607}{3} \text{ m}^3$

$\qquad \approx 14.994869 \text{ m}^3$

$\qquad \approx 15.0 \text{ m}^3$

6. Volume of a hemisphere

$V = \dfrac{2 \cdot \pi \cdot r^3}{3}$

$\qquad \approx \dfrac{2 \cdot 3.14 \cdot 7.4 \text{ in.} \cdot 7.4 \text{ in.} \cdot 7.4 \text{ in.}}{3}$

$\qquad \approx \dfrac{2544.8067}{3} \text{ in.}^3$

$\qquad \approx 848.26891 \text{ in.}^3$

$\qquad \approx 848.3 \text{ in.}^3$

8. Volume of a cylinder

$V = \pi \cdot r^2 \cdot h$

$\qquad \approx 3.14 \cdot 12 \text{ in.} \cdot 12 \text{ in.} \cdot 21 \text{ in.}$

$\qquad = 9495.36 \text{ in.}^3$

$\qquad \approx 9495.4 \text{ in.}^3$

10. Volume of a cylinder

$V = \dfrac{\pi \cdot r^2 \cdot h}{3}$

$\qquad \approx \dfrac{3.14 \cdot 40 \text{ cm} \cdot 40 \text{ cm} \cdot 28 \text{ cm}}{3}$

$\qquad = \dfrac{140,672 \text{ cm}^3}{3}$

$\qquad \approx 46,890.667 \text{ cm}^3$

$\qquad \approx 46,890.7 \text{ cm}^3$

12. Volume of a pyramid

$B = length \cdot width$

$\qquad = 7 \text{ m} \cdot 5 \text{ m}$

$\qquad = 35 \text{ m}^2$

$V = \dfrac{B \cdot h}{3}$

$\qquad = \dfrac{35 \text{ m}^2 \cdot 15 \text{ m}}{3}$

$\qquad = \dfrac{525}{3} \text{ m}^3$

$\qquad = 175 \text{ m}^3$

14. Use the formula for the volume of a cube.

$V = l \cdot w \cdot h$

$\qquad = 6 \text{ m} \cdot 3.4 \text{ m} \cdot 2 \text{ m}$

$\qquad = 40.8 \text{ m}^3$

Each crate needs 40.8 m^3 of space.

16. Volume of a sphere

radius $= \dfrac{6\frac{1}{2}}{2} = 3\frac{1}{4} \text{ ft or } 3.25 \text{ ft}$

$V = \dfrac{4}{3} \cdot \pi \cdot r^3$

$\qquad \approx \dfrac{4 \cdot 3.14 \cdot 3.25 \text{ ft} \cdot 3.25 \text{ ft} \cdot 3.25 \text{ ft}}{3}$

$\qquad = \dfrac{431.16125}{3} \text{ ft}^3$

$\qquad \approx 143.7 \text{ ft}^3$

18. Volume of a cylinder

radius $= \dfrac{11}{2}$ cm $= 5\frac{1}{2}$ cm $= 5.5$ cm

$V = \pi \cdot r^2 \cdot h$
$\approx 3.14 \cdot 5.5$ cm $\cdot 5.5$ cm $\cdot 8$ cm
$= 759.88$ cm^3
≈ 759.9 cm^3

20. First find the area of the circular base.

radius $= \dfrac{2 \text{ inches}}{2} = 1$ inch

$B = \pi \cdot r^2$
$\approx 3.14 \cdot 1$ inch $\cdot 1$ inch
$= 3.14$ in^2

$V = \dfrac{B \cdot h}{3}$

$\approx \dfrac{3.14 \text{ in.}^2 \cdot 4 \text{ in.}}{3}$

$= \dfrac{12.56}{3}$ in.^{3}

≈ 4.1866667 in.^{3}

≈ 4.2 in.^{3}

The volume of the ice cream cone is
≈ 4.2 in.^{3}.

22. Both involve finding the area of a circular base and multiplying by the height. To find the volume of the cone, divide the volume of the cylinder by 3.

24. A cube with length 14 cm, width 14 cm, and height is 15 cm
Volume of the entire cube
$V = length \cdot width \cdot height$
$= 14$ cm $\cdot 14$ cm $\cdot 15$ cm
$= 2940$ cm^3
Unshaded cube with length 8 cm, width 8 cm, height 15 cm
Volume of unshaded part
$V = 8$ cm $\cdot 8$ cm $\cdot 15$ cm
$= 960$ cm^3
Volume of the unshaded part
2940 cm$^3 - 960$ cm$^3 = 1980$ cm^3

8.8 Pythagorean Theorem

2. $\sqrt{4} = 2$ because $2 \cdot 2 = 4$.

4. $\sqrt{81} = 9$ because $9 \cdot 9 = 81$.

6. $\sqrt{23}$
Calculator shows 4.7958315.
$\sqrt{23} \approx 4.796$

8. $\sqrt{2}$
Calculator shows 1.4142136.
$\sqrt{2} \approx 1.414$

10. $\sqrt{80}$
Calculator shows 8.9442719.
$\sqrt{80} \approx 8.944$

12. $\sqrt{125}$
Calculator shows 11.18034.
$\sqrt{125} \approx 11.180$

14. $\sqrt{160}$
Calculator shows 12.649111.
$\sqrt{160} \approx 12.649$

16. $\sqrt{2000}$
Calculator shows 44.72136.
$\sqrt{2000} \approx 44.721$

18. Squaring a number is multiplying the number times itself.
Finding the square root of a number is the opposite operation and "undoes" squaring.
Examples will vary;
one possibility is $7^2 = 7 \cdot 7 = 49$
so $\sqrt{49} = 7$.

20. legs: 12 cm and 9 cm
$hypotenuse = \sqrt{(leg)^2 + (leg)^2}$
$= \sqrt{(12)^2 + (9)^2}$
$= \sqrt{144 + 81}$
$= \sqrt{225}$
$= 15$ cm

22. legs: 30 in. and 72 in.

$$hypotenuse = \sqrt{(leg)^2 + (leg)^2}$$
$$= \sqrt{(72)^2 + (30)^2}$$
$$= \sqrt{5184 + 900}$$
$$= \sqrt{6084}$$
$$= 78 \text{ in.}$$

24. hypotenuse: 13 m, leg: 5 m

$$leg = \sqrt{(hypotenuse)^2 - (leg)^2}$$
$$= \sqrt{(13)^2 - (5)^2}$$
$$= \sqrt{169 - 25}$$
$$= \sqrt{144}$$
$$= 12 \text{ m}$$

26. legs: 11 cm and 5 cm

$$hypotenuse = \sqrt{(leg)^2 + (leg)^2}$$
$$= \sqrt{(11)^2 + (5)^2}$$
$$= \sqrt{121 + 25}$$
$$= \sqrt{146}$$
$$\approx 12.083046$$
$$\approx 12.1 \text{ cm}$$

28. hypotenuse: 10 km, leg: 7 km

$$leg = \sqrt{(hypotenuse)^2 - (leg)^2}$$
$$= \sqrt{(10)^2 - (7)^2}$$
$$= \sqrt{100 - 49}$$
$$= \sqrt{51}$$
$$\approx 7.1414284$$
$$\approx 7.1 \text{ km}$$

30. hypotenuse: 16 cm, leg: 9 cm

$$leg = \sqrt{(hypotenuse)^2 - (leg)^2}$$
$$= \sqrt{(16)^2 - (9)^2}$$
$$= \sqrt{256 - 81}$$
$$= \sqrt{175}$$
$$\approx 13.228757$$
$$\approx 13.2 \text{ cm}$$

32. legs: 4.2 mi and 4.2 mi

$$hypotenuse = \sqrt{(leg)^2 + (leg)^2}$$
$$= \sqrt{(4.2)^2 + (4.2)^2}$$
$$= \sqrt{17.64 + 17.64}$$
$$= \sqrt{35.28}$$
$$\approx 5.939697$$
$$\approx 5.9 \text{ mi}$$

34. hypotenuse: 10.8 mm, leg: 9.1 mm

$$leg = \sqrt{(hypotenuse)^2 - (leg)^2}$$
$$= \sqrt{(10.8)^2 - (9.1)^2}$$
$$= \sqrt{116.64 - 82.81}$$
$$= \sqrt{33.83}$$
$$\approx 5.8163562$$
$$\approx 5.8 \text{ mm}$$

36. hypotenuse: 37.4 ft, leg: 26.5 ft

$$leg = \sqrt{(hypotenuse)^2 - (leg)^2}$$
$$= \sqrt{(37.4)^2 - (26.5)^2}$$
$$= \sqrt{1398.76 - 702.25}$$
$$= \sqrt{696.51}$$
$$\approx 26.391476$$
$$\approx 26.4 \text{ ft}$$

38. legs: 9 ft and 3 ft

$$hypotenuse = \sqrt{(leg)^2 + (leg)^2}$$
$$= \sqrt{(9)^2 + (3)^2}$$
$$= \sqrt{81 + 9}$$
$$= \sqrt{90}$$
$$\approx 9.486833$$
$$\approx 9.5 \text{ ft}$$

40. hypotenuse: 54 ft, leg: 35 ft

$$leg = \sqrt{(hypotenuse)^2 - (leg)^2}$$
$$= \sqrt{(54)^2 - (35)^2}$$
$$= \sqrt{2916 - 1225}$$
$$= \sqrt{1691}$$
$$\approx 41.12177$$
$$\approx 41.1 \text{ ft}$$

The height of the farm silo is ≈ 41.1 ft.

42.

legs: 15 miles and 7 miles

$$hypotenuse = \sqrt{(15)^2 + (7)^2}$$
$$= \sqrt{225 + 49}$$
$$= \sqrt{274}$$
$$\approx 16.552945$$
$$\approx 16.6 \text{ mi}$$

William is ≈ 16.6 mi from his starting point.

44. The student used the formula for finding the hypotenuse, but the unknown side is a leg, so $? = \sqrt{(20)^2 - (13)^2}$. Also, the final answer should be m, not m^2. The correct answer is $\sqrt{231} \approx 15.2$ m.

8.9 Similar Triangles

2. The triangles have the same shape so they are similar.

4. The triangles do not have the same shape so they are not similar.

6. The triangles do not have the same shape so they are not similar.

8. The corresponding angles are
$\angle 1$ and $\angle 5$
$\angle 2$ and $\angle 4$
$\angle 3$ and $\angle 6$
The corresponding sides are
$\overline{SR}$ and $\overline{YX}$, $\overline{ST}$ and $\overline{YZ}$, $\overline{RT}$ and $\overline{XZ}$.

10. The corresponding angles are
$\angle 1$ and $\angle 5$
$\angle 2$ and $\angle 6$
$\angle 3$ and $\angle 4$
The corresponding sides are
$\overline{FG}$ and $\overline{MN}$, $\overline{FE}$ and $\overline{ML}$, $\overline{EG}$ and $\overline{LN}$.

12. $\dfrac{AB}{PQ} = \dfrac{22 \text{ cm}}{33 \text{ cm}} = \dfrac{22}{33} = \dfrac{2}{3}$

$\dfrac{AC}{PR} = \dfrac{30 \text{ cm}}{45 \text{ cm}} = \dfrac{30}{45} = \dfrac{2}{3}$

$\dfrac{BC}{QR} = \dfrac{16 \text{ cm}}{24 \text{ cm}} = \dfrac{16}{24} = \dfrac{2}{3}$

14. Set up a ratio of corresponding sides.
$\dfrac{75 \text{ m}}{25 \text{ m}} = \dfrac{75}{25} = \dfrac{3}{1}$
Write a proportion to find a.
$\dfrac{3}{1} = \dfrac{a}{10}$
$1 \cdot a = 3 \cdot 10$
$a = 30$ m
Write a proportion to find b.
$\dfrac{3}{1} = \dfrac{b}{20}$
$1 \cdot b = 3 \cdot 20$
$b = 60$ m

16. Set up a ratio of corresponding sides.
$\dfrac{9 \text{ ft}}{3 \text{ ft}} = \dfrac{9}{3} = \dfrac{3}{1}$
Write a proportion to find a.
$\dfrac{3}{1} = \dfrac{6}{a}$
$3 \cdot a = 1 \cdot 6$
$a = 2$ ft
Write a proportion to find b.
$\dfrac{3}{1} = \dfrac{b}{2}$
$b \cdot 1 = 2 \cdot 3$
$b = 6$ ft

18. Set up a ratio of corresponding sides.
$\dfrac{11.6 \text{ yd}}{17.4 \text{ yd}} = \dfrac{11.6 \div 5.8}{17.4 \div 5.8} = \dfrac{2}{3}$
Write a proportion to find x.
$\dfrac{8}{x} = \dfrac{2}{3}$
$2 \cdot x = 8 \cdot 3$
$2 \cdot x = 24$
$\dfrac{2 \cdot x}{2} = \dfrac{24}{2}$
$x = 12$ yd
$P = 12 \text{ yd} + 15.3 \text{ yd} + 17.4 \text{ yd}$
$\quad = 44.7$ yd
Write a proportion to find y.
$\dfrac{y}{15.3} = \dfrac{2}{3}$
$y \cdot 3 = 15.3 \cdot 2$
$y \cdot 3 = 30.6$
$\dfrac{y \cdot 3}{3} = \dfrac{30.6}{3}$
$y = 10.2$ yd
$P = 8 \text{ yd} + 11.6 \text{ yd} + 10.2 \text{ yd}$
$\quad = 29.8$ yd

20. Write a proportion to find the length of $\overline{MO}$.

$$\frac{10}{8} = \frac{13.2}{x}$$

$$10 \cdot x = 13.2 \cdot 8$$

$$\frac{10 \cdot x}{10} = \frac{105.6}{10}$$

$$x = 10.56 \text{ m}$$

$\overline{MO}$ is 10.56 m.

Perimeter of triangle MNO

$= 11.2 \text{ m} + 10.56 \text{ m} + 8 \text{ m}$

$= 29.76 \text{ m}$

Write a proportion to find the height of triangle MNO.

$$\frac{h}{9} = \frac{8}{10}$$

$$10 \cdot h = 9 \cdot 8$$

$$\frac{10 \cdot h}{10} = \frac{72}{10}$$

$$h = 7.2 \text{ m}$$

Area of triangle MNO

$= 0.5 \cdot 11.2 \text{ m} \cdot 7.2 \text{ m}$

$= 40.32 \text{ m}^2$

22. Set up a ratio of corresponding sides.

$$\frac{56 \text{ m}}{3.5 \text{ m}} = \frac{16}{1}$$

Write a proportion to find the height of the tower.

$$\frac{16}{1} = \frac{h}{2}$$

$$h = 32$$

The tower is 32 m high.

24. (a) $56 \text{ m} - 3.5 \text{ m} = 52.5 \text{ m}$ from the tower.

(b) $\quad \frac{x}{1} = \frac{56}{32}$ Use the answer from Exercise 22.

$$x \cdot 32 = 1 \cdot 56$$

$$\frac{x \cdot 32}{32} = \frac{56}{32}$$

$$x = 1.75$$

$56 \text{ m} - 1.75 \text{ m} = 54.25 \text{ m}$ from the tower.

26.

Congruent triangles

Examples of congruent objects include two matching chairs, two contact lenses, and two pieces of notebook paper.

28. Write a proportion to find c.

$$\frac{c}{50} = \frac{5 + 45}{45}$$

$$\frac{c}{50} = \frac{50}{45}$$

$$45 \cdot c = 50 \cdot 50$$

$$45 \cdot c = 2500$$

$$\frac{45 \cdot c}{45} = \frac{2500}{45}$$

$$c \approx 55.55555$$

$$c \approx 55.6 \text{ in.}$$

30. Write a proportion to find y.

$$\frac{y}{1} = \frac{45}{1.5}$$

$$y \cdot 1.5 = 45 \cdot 1$$

$$y \cdot 1.5 = 45$$

$$\frac{y \cdot 1.5}{1.5} = \frac{45}{1.5}$$

$$y = 30 \text{ ft}$$

Add the distance from the ground to eye level.

$30 \text{ ft} + 5\frac{1}{2} \text{ ft} = 35\frac{1}{2} \text{ ft}$ or 35.5 ft

Chapter 9

BASIC ALGEBRA

9.1   Signed Numbers

2. She made a profit of $920.

$$+\,920$$

4. His checking account is overdrawn by $30.79.

$$-30.79$$

6. The river is 20 ft above flood stage.

$$+\,20 \text{ or } 20$$

8. The bottom of Lake Baykal is 5315 ft below the surface of the water.

$$-5315$$

10. $-2, 1, -3, 5, 0$

12. $-4, -\dfrac{3}{4}, 1, -1\dfrac{1}{4}, \dfrac{5}{2}$

14. $3.25, -1, -4.5, 1.25, 2$

16. $6 < 11$

Because 6 is to the left of 11 on a number line, 6 is less than 11.

18. $0 < 2$

Because 0 is to the left of 2 on a number line, 0 is less than 2.

20. $-9 < 9$

Because -9 is to the left of 9 on a number line, -9 is less than 9.

22. $-1 < 0$

Because -1 is to the left of 0 on a number line, -1 is less than 0.

24. $-5 < -1$

Because -5 is to the left of -1 on a number line, -5 is less than -1.

26. $-50 > -60$

Because -50 is to the right of -60 on a number line, -50 is greater than -60.

32. $|9| = 9$

The distance from 0 to 9 is 9.

34. $|-2| = 2$

The distance from 0 to -2 is 2.

36. $\left|-\dfrac{1}{2}\right| = \dfrac{1}{2}$

The distance from 0 to $-\dfrac{1}{2}$ is $\dfrac{1}{2}$.

38. $-|-5| = -(5) = -5$

This is a two-step problem. First $|-5| = 5$. Then $-(5) = -5$.

40. $-|20| = -(20) = -20$

Because the negative sign is outside the absolute value bars, the answer is negative.

42. The opposite of 1 is -1.

44. The opposite of -5 is $-(-5) = 5$.

46. The opposite of 0 is 0.

48. The opposite of 0.2 is -0.2.

50. The opposite of $-\dfrac{3}{10}$ is $\left(-\dfrac{3}{10}\right) = \dfrac{3}{10}$.

52. $|-12| > |-15| = 12 > 15$

12 is less than 15 so, $|-12| > |-15|$ is false.

54. $-9 < -(-9)$

$-(-9) = 9$

-9 is less than 9, so $-9 < -(-9)$ is true.

56. $-|-0| > 0$

$\quad -(0) > 0$

$\qquad 0 > 0$

False

9.2   Adding and Subtracting Signed Numbers

2. $-3 + 4 = 1$

4. $-2 + (-2) = -4$

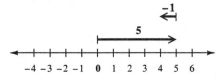

6. $5 + (-1) = 4$

8. $-3 + 2$

The signs are different, so subtract the absolute values.

$$|-3| = 3; \ |2| = 2$$
$$3 - 2 = 1$$

The negative number, -3, has the larger absolute value, so the answer is negative.

$$-3 + 2 = -1$$

10. $-4 + 10$

The signs are different, so subtract the absolute values.

$$|-4| = 4; \ |10| = 10$$
$$10 - 4 = 6$$

The positive number, 10, has the larger absolute value, so the answer is positive.
$-4 + 10 = 6$

12. $-7 + (-3)$

Add the absolute values.

$$|-7| = 7; \ |-3| = 3$$
$$7 + 3 = 10$$

Write a negative sign in front of the sum because both numbers are negative.
$-7 + (-3) = -10$

14. $11 + (-3)$

Subtract the absolute values because the signs are different.

$$|11| = 11; \ |-3| = 3$$
$$11 - 3 = 8$$

The positive number, 11, has the larger absolute value, so the answer is positive.
$11 + (-3) = 8$

16. $9 + (-10) = -1$

The signs are different, so subtract the absolute values.

$$|9| = 9; \ |-10| = 10$$
$$10 - 9 = 1$$

The negative number, -10, has the larger absolute value, so the answer is negative.
$9 + (-10) = -1$

18. $-5 + (-20)$

Add the absolute values.

$$|-5| = 5; \ |-20| = 20$$
$$5 + 20 = 25$$

Write a negative sign in front of the sum because both numbers are negative.
$-5 + (-20) = -25$

20. -15 degrees below zero and a drop in temperature of another $60°$

$$-15 + (-60) = -75° \text{ C}$$

22. A negative $48.40 plus a positive $30
$-\$48.40 + \$30 = -\$18.40$

24. Rose (positive); Fell (negative)
Red River: $8 + (-3) + (-5) = 0$ ft
Mississippi: $4 + 7 + (-13) = -2$ ft

26. $4.9 + (-8.1)$

The signs are different, so subtract the absolute values.

$$|4.9| = 4.9; \ |-8.1| = 8.1$$
$$8.1 - 4.9 = 3.2$$

The negative number, -8.1, has the larger absolute value, so the answer is negative.

$$4.9 + (-8.1) = -3.2$$

28. $-\dfrac{2}{3} + \dfrac{5}{6}$

Subtract the absolute values because the signs are different.

$$\left|-\frac{2}{3}\right| = \frac{2}{3}; \ \left|\frac{5}{6}\right| = \frac{5}{6}$$

$$\frac{5}{6} - \frac{2}{3} = \frac{5}{6} - \frac{4}{6} = \frac{1}{6}$$

The positive number, $\frac{5}{6}$, has the larger absolute value so the answer is positive.

$$-\frac{2}{3} + \frac{5}{6} = \frac{1}{6}$$

30. $-\dfrac{3}{4} + \dfrac{3}{8}$

Subtract the absolute values.

$$\left|-\frac{3}{4}\right| = \frac{3}{4}; \ \left|\frac{3}{8}\right| = \frac{3}{8}$$

$$\frac{3}{4} - \frac{3}{8} = \frac{6}{8} - \frac{3}{8} = \frac{3}{8}$$

The negative number, $-\frac{3}{4}$, has the larger absolute value, so the answer is negative.

$$-\frac{3}{4} + \frac{3}{8} = -\frac{3}{8}$$

32. $-\dfrac{8}{5}+\left(-\dfrac{3}{10}\right)$

Add the absolute values.

$$\left|-\dfrac{8}{5}\right|=\dfrac{8}{5};\ \left|-\dfrac{3}{10}\right|=\dfrac{3}{10}$$

$$\dfrac{8}{5}+\dfrac{3}{10}=\dfrac{16}{10}+\dfrac{3}{10}=\dfrac{19}{10}$$

Write a negative sign in front of the sum because both numbers are negative.

$$-\dfrac{8}{5}+\left(-\dfrac{3}{10}\right)=-\dfrac{19}{10}$$

34. The additive inverse of 4 is –4.

36. The additive inverse of –14 is 14.

38. The additive inverse of $\dfrac{7}{8}$ is $-\dfrac{7}{8}$.

40. The additive inverse of –0.5 is 0.5.

42. $24-11=24+(-11)=13$

44. $1-8=1+(-8)=-7$

46. $2-17=2+(-17)=-15$

48. $-10-4=-10+(-4)=-14$

50. $-3-11=-3+(-11)=-14$

52. $-1-(-4)=-1+(+4)=3$

54. $8-(-1)=8+(+1)=9$

56. $6-(-1)=6+(+1)=7$

58. $-25-25=-25+(-25)=-50$

60. $-20-(-20)=-20+(+20)=0$

62. $-\dfrac{8}{15}-\dfrac{3}{10}=-\dfrac{8}{15}+\left(-\dfrac{3}{10}\right)$

$$=-\dfrac{16}{30}+\left(-\dfrac{9}{30}\right)$$

$$=-\dfrac{25}{30}=-\dfrac{5}{6}$$

64. $\dfrac{2}{3}-\dfrac{11}{12}=\dfrac{8}{12}-\dfrac{11}{12}$

$$=\dfrac{8}{12}+\left(-\dfrac{11}{12}\right)$$

$$=-\dfrac{3}{12}=-\dfrac{1}{4}$$

66. $-2-(-3.9)=-2+(+3.9)=1.9$

72. (a) $6-9$
6 minus 9

(b) (-9)
negative 9

(c) $-(-2)$
The opposite of negative 2

74. $-5-(-2)+(-6)$
$=-5+(+2)+(-6)$
$=-3+(-6)=-9$

76. $6-(-1)+(-10)$
$=6+(+1)+(-10)$
$=7+(-10)=-3$

78. $-1-(-7)-(-4)$
$=-1+(+7)-(-4)$
$=+6+(+4)=10$

80. $5-(-2)-8$
$=5+(+2)-8$
$=7-(8)=-1$

82. $\dfrac{2}{5}-\dfrac{7}{10}+\left(-\dfrac{3}{2}\right)=\dfrac{2}{5}+\left(-\dfrac{7}{10}\right)+\left(-\dfrac{3}{2}\right)$

$$=\dfrac{4}{10}+\left(-\dfrac{7}{10}\right)+\left(-\dfrac{15}{10}\right)$$

$$=-\dfrac{3}{10}+\left(-\dfrac{15}{10}\right)$$

$$=-\dfrac{18}{10}=-\dfrac{9}{5}$$

84. $-6.5-(-11.2)-1.4$
$=-6.5+(+11.2)-1.4$
$=4.7-1.4=3.3$

86. $|-7+2|+(-2)+4$
$=|-5|+(-2)+4$
$=5+(-2)+4$
$=3+4=7$

88. $5-8-(6-7)+1$
$=5-8-(-1)+1$
$=5+(-8)-(-1)+1$
$=-3-(-1)+1$
$=-3+1+1$
$=-2+1=-1$

90. $\dfrac{5}{8} - \left(-\dfrac{1}{2} - \dfrac{3}{4}\right) = \dfrac{5}{8} - \left(-\dfrac{2}{4} - \dfrac{3}{4}\right)$

$\qquad = \dfrac{5}{8} - \left(-\dfrac{5}{4}\right)$

$\qquad = \dfrac{5}{8} + \dfrac{5}{4}$

$\qquad = \dfrac{5}{8} + \dfrac{10}{8} = \dfrac{15}{8}$

92. $478 + $212 - $89 - 605
$= $478 + $212 + (-$89) + (-$605)$
$= $690 + (-$89) + (-$605)$
$= $601 + (-$605)$
$= -$4$
The balance is $-$4.

94. $-$23.77 - $16 + $583.29 - 50
$= -$23.77 + (-$16) + $583.29 + (-$50)$
$= -$39.77 + $583.29 + (-$50)$
$= $543.52 + -$50$
$= 493.52
The balance is $493.52.

9.3 Multiplying and Dividing Signed Numbers

2. $-10 \cdot 2 = -20$
The numbers have different signs, so the product is negative.

4. $(-9)(4) = -36$
The numbers have different signs, so the product is negative.

6. $8 \cdot (-6) = -48$

8. $5 \cdot (-11) = -55$

10. $(75)(-1) = -75$

12. $-3 \cdot (-9) = 27$
The numbers have the same sign, so the product is positive.

14. $4 \cdot 25 = 100$

16. $-21 \cdot (-3) = 63$
The numbers have the same sign, so the product is positive.

18. $-1 \cdot (-31) = 31$

20. $(-50)(0) = 0$

22. $\dfrac{1}{3} \cdot (-15) = \dfrac{-15}{3} = -5$

24. $-25 \cdot \left(-\dfrac{7}{10}\right) = -\dfrac{\overset{5}{\cancel{25}}}{1} \cdot \left(-\dfrac{7}{\underset{2}{\cancel{10}}}\right) = \dfrac{35}{2}$

26. $\left(-\dfrac{7}{9}\right)\left(-\dfrac{3}{4}\right) = -\dfrac{7}{\underset{3}{\cancel{9}}} \cdot \left(-\dfrac{\overset{1}{\cancel{3}}}{4}\right) = \dfrac{7}{12}$

28. $-\dfrac{9}{10} \cdot \dfrac{5}{4} = -\dfrac{9}{\underset{2}{\cancel{10}}} \cdot \dfrac{\overset{1}{\cancel{5}}}{4} = -\dfrac{9}{8}$

30. $-\dfrac{5}{9} \cdot \dfrac{18}{25} = -\dfrac{\overset{1}{\cancel{5}}}{\underset{1}{\cancel{9}}} \cdot \dfrac{\overset{2}{\cancel{18}}}{\underset{5}{\cancel{25}}} = -\dfrac{2}{5}$

32. $-\dfrac{8}{5} \cdot \left(-\dfrac{15}{16}\right) = -\dfrac{\overset{1}{\cancel{8}}}{\underset{1}{\cancel{5}}} \cdot \left(-\dfrac{\overset{3}{\cancel{15}}}{\underset{2}{\cancel{16}}}\right) = \dfrac{3}{2}$

34. $15 \cdot (-6.3) = -94.5$

36. $(-3.15)(-5) = 15.75$

38. $-4.3 \cdot (9.7) = -41.71$

40. $6.33 \cdot 0.2 = 1.266$

42. $(-1)(-0.69) = 0.69$

44. $-91.3 \cdot 0 = 0$

46. $\dfrac{-8}{2} = -4$
The numbers have different signs, so the answer is negative.

48. $\dfrac{21}{-7} = -3$

50. $\dfrac{-40}{0}$ is undefined.

52. $\dfrac{25}{-1} = -25$

54. $\dfrac{-80}{-4} = 20$
The numbers have the same sign, so the answer is positive.

56. $\dfrac{-30}{-15} = 2$

58. $\dfrac{50}{-50} = -1$

60. $\dfrac{-580}{-5} = 116$

62. $\dfrac{0}{-4} = 0$

64. $\dfrac{-25}{-25} = 1$

66. $\dfrac{-\frac{3}{4}}{-\frac{9}{16}} = -\dfrac{3}{4} \div -\dfrac{9}{16} = \dfrac{\cancel{3}^{1}}{\cancel{4}_{1}} \cdot \dfrac{\cancel{16}^{4}}{\cancel{9}_{3}} = \dfrac{4}{3}$

68. $-\dfrac{3}{4} \div (-9) = -\dfrac{\cancel{3}^{1}}{4} \cdot \left(-\dfrac{1}{\cancel{9}_{3}}\right) = \dfrac{1}{12}$

70. $7 \div \left(-\dfrac{14}{15}\right) = \dfrac{\cancel{7}^{1}}{1} \cdot \left(-\dfrac{15}{\cancel{14}_{2}}\right) = -\dfrac{15}{2}$

72. $-\dfrac{4}{9} \div \dfrac{8}{3} = -\dfrac{\cancel{4}^{1}}{\cancel{9}_{3}} \cdot \dfrac{\cancel{3}^{1}}{\cancel{8}_{2}} = -\dfrac{1}{6}$

74. $\dfrac{-22.75}{-7} = 3.25$

$$\begin{array}{r} 3.25 \\ 7\overline{)22.75} \\ \underline{21} \\ 1\,7 \\ \underline{1\,4} \\ 35 \\ \underline{35} \\ 0 \end{array}$$

76. $\dfrac{-17.02}{7.4} = -2.3$

$$\begin{array}{r} 2.3 \\ 7.4_\wedge\overline{)17.0_\wedge 2} \\ \underline{14\,8} \\ 2\,2\,2 \\ \underline{2\,2\,2} \\ 0 \end{array}$$

78. $\dfrac{6.27}{-0.3} = -20.9$

$$\begin{array}{r} 2\,0.9 \\ 0.3_\wedge\overline{)6.2_\wedge 7} \\ \underline{6} \\ 0\,2 \\ \underline{0} \\ 2\,7 \\ \underline{2\,7} \\ 0 \end{array}$$

80. $(-9)\cdot(-3)\cdot\dfrac{2}{3} = \dfrac{\cancel{27}^{9}}{1}\cdot\dfrac{2}{\cancel{3}_{1}} = 18$

82. $(-4)(-1.2)(-0.7)$
$= (4.8)(-0.7) = -3.36$

84. $\left(\dfrac{3}{4}\right)\cdot\left(-\dfrac{5}{6}\right)\cdot\left(\dfrac{2}{3}\right) = \left(\dfrac{\cancel{3}^{1}}{\cancel{4}_{2}}\right)\cdot\left(-\dfrac{5}{\cancel{6}_{2}}\right)\cdot\left(\dfrac{\cancel{2}^{1}}{3}\right)$
$$= -\dfrac{5}{12}$$

86. $-48 \div (-8) \cdot (-4) \div (-4) \div (-3)$
$= 6 \cdot (-4) \div (-4) \div (-3)$
$= -24 \div (-4) \div (-3)$
$= 6 \div (-3) = -2$

88. $-6\cdot|-3|\div|9|\cdot(-2)$
$= -6\cdot 3 \div 9 \cdot (-2)$
$= -18 \div 9 \cdot (-2)$
$= -2(-2) = 4$

90. $\dfrac{-3245}{11} = -295$
The average drop was −295 students each year.

92. $12(17) = 204$
Pat ate 204 calories.

94. $(-95)(52) = -4940$
It will lose −4940 customers.

96. $-150 - 15(25) = -150 - 375$
$ = -525$
Its depth is −525 ft.

9.4 Order of Operations

2. $10 - 30 \div 2$
$= 10 - 15$
$= 10 + (-15)$
$= -5$

4. $9 + (-5) + 2 \cdot (-2)$
$= 9 + (-5) + (-4)$
$= 4 + (-4)$
$= 0$

6. $3^2 + 8^2$
$= 9 + 64$
$= 73$

8. $5 - 5^2$

$= 5 - 25$

$= 5 + (-25)$

$= -20$

10. $(-2)^4 - 7$

$= 16 - 7$

$= 9$

12. $5^2 + 2^2 + (-12)$

$= 25 + 4 + (-12)$

$= 29 + (-12)$

$= 17$

14. $6 - (-9) + 2^3$

$= 6 - (-9) + 8$

$= 6 + (+9) + 8$

$= 15 + 8$

$= 23$

16. $(-5)^2 + (-6)^2 + 12$

$= 25 + 36 + 12$

$= 61 + 12$

$= 73$

18. $4 + 3 \cdot (8 - 3)$

$= 4 + 3 \cdot 5$

$= 4 + 15$

$= 19$

20. $-3 + 5 \cdot (9 - 12)$

$= -3 + 5 \cdot (-3)$

$= -3 + (-15)$

$= -18$

22. $-5 + (-3) \cdot (6 - 7)$

$= -5 + (-3) \cdot (-1)$

$= -5 + 3$

$= -2$

24. $(-4) \cdot (9 - 17) \div (-8)$

$= (-4) \cdot (-8) \div (-8)$

$= 32 \div (-8)$

$= -4$

26. $-48 \div (-4)^2 + 3$

$= -48 \div 16 + 3$

$= -3 + 3$

$= 0$

28. $1 - (-10) \cdot (-2)^3$

$= 1 - (-10) \cdot (-8)$

$= 1 - 80$

$= 1 + (-80)$

$= -79$

30. $4 \cdot (-2) + (-3) \cdot (-5)$

$= -8 + (-3) \cdot (-5)$

$= -8 + 15$

$= 7$

32. $8 \div (-4) - 42 \div (-7)$

$= -2 - 42 \div (-7)$

$= -2 + 6$

$= 4$

34. $9 \cdot 3 - 6 \cdot 4 + 3 \cdot 7$

$= 27 - 6 \cdot 4 + 3 \cdot 7$

$= 27 - 24 + 3 \cdot 7$

$= 27 - 24 + 21$

$= 3 + 21$

$= 24$

36. $5 \cdot 4^2 - 6 \cdot (1 + 4) - (-3)$

$= 5 \cdot 4^2 - 6 \cdot 5 - (-3)$

$= 5 \cdot 16 - 6 \cdot 5 - (-3)$

$= 80 - 6 \cdot 5 - (-3)$

$= 80 - 30 - (-3)$

$= 50 - (-3)$

$= 50 + (+3)$

$= 53$

38. $\dfrac{-6 + 3^2 - (-7)}{7 - 9 - 3}$

Numerator:

$$-6 + 3^2 - (-7)$$

$$= -6 + 9 - (-7)$$

$$= -6 + 9 + (+7)$$

$$= 3 + (+7)$$

$$= 10$$

Denominator:

$$7 - 9 - 3$$

$$= 7 + (-9) + (-3)$$

$$= -2 + (-3)$$

$$= -5$$

Divide. $\dfrac{10}{-5} = -2$

40. $\dfrac{3 \cdot 3^2 - 5 \cdot (9 - 2)}{8 \cdot (6 - 9) \div (-3)}$

Numerator:

$$3 \cdot 3^2 - 5 \cdot (9 - 2)$$

$$= 3 \cdot 3^2 - 5 \cdot 7$$

$$= 3 \cdot 9 - 5 \cdot 7$$

$$= 27 - 35$$

$$= 27 + (-35)$$

$$= -8$$

Denominator:

$$8 \cdot (6 - 9) \div (-3)$$
$$= 8 \cdot (-3) \div (-3)$$
$$= 8 \cdot 1$$
$$= 8$$

Divide. $\dfrac{-8}{8} = -1$

42. $\dfrac{3^3 + (-1 - 2) \cdot 4 - 25}{-4 + 4 \cdot (3 \cdot 5) + (-6 \cdot 9)}$

Numerator:

$$3^3 + (-1 - 2) \cdot 4 - 25$$
$$= 3^3 + (-3) \cdot 4 - 25$$
$$= 27 + (-3) \cdot 4 - 25$$
$$= 27 + (-12) - 25$$
$$= 15 - 25$$
$$= 15 + (-25)$$
$$= -10$$

Denominator:

$$-4 + 4 \cdot (3 \cdot 5) + (-6 \cdot 9)$$
$$= -4 + 4 \cdot 15 + (-54)$$
$$= -4 + 60 + (-54)$$
$$= 56 + (-54)$$
$$= 2$$

Divide. $\dfrac{-10}{2} = -5$

44. $(-5)^2 \cdot (9 - 17)^2 \div (-10)^2$
$$= (-5)^2 \cdot (-8)^2 \div (-10)^2$$
$$= 25 \cdot 64 \div 100$$
$$= 1600 \div 100$$
$$= 16$$

46. $(0.2)^3 - (-0.4)^2 + 3.02$
$$= 0.008 - (0.16) + 3.02$$
$$= -0.152 + 3.02$$
$$= 2.868$$

48. $(-0.3) \cdot (4 - 6.8)^2$
$$= (-0.3) \cdot (-2.8)^2$$
$$= (-0.3) \cdot (7.84)$$
$$= -2.352$$

50. $(0.3)^3 \cdot (-5) - (-2.8)$
$$= 0.027 \cdot (-5) - (-2.8)$$
$$= -0.135 - (-2.8)$$
$$= -0.135 + (+2.8)$$
$$= 2.665$$

52. $\dfrac{5}{8} \div \left(-\dfrac{10}{3} \right) - \dfrac{3}{4}$

$$= \dfrac{\overset{1}{\cancel{5}}}{8} \cdot \left(-\dfrac{3}{\underset{2}{\cancel{10}}} \right) - \dfrac{3}{4}$$

$$= -\dfrac{3}{16} - \dfrac{12}{16}$$

$$= -\dfrac{3}{16} + \left(-\dfrac{12}{16} \right)$$

$$= -\dfrac{15}{16}$$

54. $\left(-\dfrac{2}{3} \right)^2 - \left(\dfrac{1}{6} - \dfrac{11}{6} \right)$

$$= \left(-\dfrac{2}{3} \right)^2 - \left(-\dfrac{10}{6} \right)$$

$$= \dfrac{4}{9} - \left(-\dfrac{5}{3} \right)$$

$$= \dfrac{4}{9} + \left(+\dfrac{15}{9} \right)$$

$$= \dfrac{19}{9}$$

56. $\dfrac{2}{7} \cdot \left(-\dfrac{14}{5} \right) - \left(\dfrac{4}{3} - \dfrac{13}{9} \right)$

$$= \dfrac{2}{7} \cdot \left(-\dfrac{14}{5} \right) - \left(\dfrac{12}{9} - \dfrac{13}{9} \right)$$

$$= \dfrac{2}{\underset{1}{\cancel{7}}} \cdot \left(-\dfrac{\overset{2}{\cancel{14}}}{5} \right) - \left(-\dfrac{1}{9} \right)$$

$$= -\dfrac{4}{5} + \left(+\dfrac{1}{9} \right)$$

$$= -\dfrac{36}{45} + \dfrac{5}{45}$$

$$= -\dfrac{31}{45}$$

58. $4^2 \cdot (13 - 17) \cdot (-2) \cdot (-3)^2$
$$= 4^2 \cdot (-4) \cdot (-2) \cdot (-3)^2$$
$$= 16 \cdot (-4) \cdot (-2) \cdot 9$$
$$= -64 \cdot (-2) \cdot 9$$
$$= 128 \cdot 9$$
$$= 1152$$

60. $6.5 \cdot (-4.8) \div (-0.3) \div (-2)^3$
$= 6.5 \cdot (-4.8) \div (-0.3) \div (-8)$
$= -31.2 \div (-0.3) \div (-8)$
$= 104 \div (-8)$
$= -13$

62. -5^2 is the opposite of 5^2 or $-(5 \cdot 5) = -25$. The parentheses in $(-5)^2$ mean that -5 is multiplied times itself. So $(-5)^2 = (-5)(-5) = 25$. One answer is negative and the other is positive.

64. $\dfrac{-20 - 15 \cdot (-4) - (-40)}{4 + 27 \div 3 \cdot (-2) - 6}$

Numerator:
$$-20 - 15 \cdot (-4) - (-40)$$
$$= -20 + 60 - (-40)$$
$$= 40 + (+40)$$
$$= 80$$

Denominator:
$$4 + 27 \div 3 \cdot (-2) - 6$$
$$= 4 + 9 \cdot (-2) - 6$$
$$= 4 + (-18) - 6$$
$$= -14 + (-6)$$
$$= -20$$

Divide. $\dfrac{80}{-20} = -4$

66. $(-0.3)^2 \cdot (-5 \cdot 3) + (6 \div 2 \cdot 0.4)$
$= (-0.3)^2 \cdot (-5 \cdot 3) + (3 \cdot 0.4)$
$= (-0.3)^2 \cdot (-15) + 1.2$
$= 0.09 \cdot (-15) + 1.2$
$= -1.35 + 1.2$
$= -0.15$

68. $6 - (2 - 3 \cdot 4) + 5^2 \div \left(-2 \cdot \dfrac{5}{2}\right) + (2)^2$

$= 6 - (-10) + 5^2 \div (-5) + 2^2$
$= 6 - (-10) + 25 \div (-5) + 4$
$= 6 - (-10) + (-5) + 4$
$= 6 + (+10) + (-5) + 4$
$= 16 + (-5) + 4$
$= 11 + 4$
$= 15$

Summary Exercises on Operations with Signed Numbers

2. $(-16)(0) = 0$

4. $\dfrac{-42}{6} = -7$

6. $\dfrac{-12}{12} = -1$

8. $1 + (-23) = -22$

10. $-\dfrac{8}{3} \div \left(-\dfrac{4}{9}\right) = -\dfrac{\overset{2}{\cancel{8}}}{\cancel{3}_1} \cdot \left(-\dfrac{\overset{3}{\cancel{9}}}{\cancel{4}_1}\right) = 6$

12. $\dfrac{0}{-10} = 0$

14. $-17 + 0 = -17$

16. $-\dfrac{1}{10} - \dfrac{9}{10} = \dfrac{-1 - 9}{10} = \dfrac{-10}{10} = -1$

18. $\dfrac{30}{0}$ is undefined.

20. $\dfrac{1.8}{-3} = -0.6$

22. $-2 + (-12) + (-5) = -14 + (-5) = -19$

24. $-8 - 4 - 8 = -8 + (-4) + (-8) = -12 + (-8)$
$= -20$

26. $2 - (-5) + 3^2 = 2 - (-5) + 9$
$= 2 + (+5) + 9$
$= 7 + 9$
$= 16$

28. $(-6)(-2)(-3) = (12)(-3) = -36$

30. $-72 \div (-9) \div (-4) = 8 \div (-4) = -2$

32. $9 - 6 - 3 - 5 = 9 + (-6) + (-3) + (-5)$
$= 3 + (-3) + (-5)$
$= 0 + (-5)$
$= -5$

34. $-1 \cdot 9732 \cdot (-1) \cdot (-1) = -9732 \cdot (-1) \cdot (-1)$
$= 9732 \cdot (-1)$
$= -9732$

36. $-10 - 4 + 0 + 18 = -10 + (-4) + 0 + 18$
$$= -14 + 0 + 18$$
$$= -14 + 18$$
$$= 4$$

38. $5 - |-3| + 3 = 5 - 3 + 3$
$$= 5 + (-3) + 3$$
$$= 2 + 3$$
$$= 5$$

40. $-3 - (-2 + 4) - 5 = -3 - (2) - 5$
$$= -3 + (-2) - 5$$
$$= -5 - 5$$
$$= -5 + (-5)$$
$$= -10$$

42. $(-4)^2 \cdot (7 - 9)^2 \div 2^3 = (-4)^2 \cdot (-2)^2 \div 2^3$
$$= 16 \cdot 4 \div 8$$
$$= 64 \div 8$$
$$= 8$$

44. $\dfrac{-9 + 24 \div (-4) \cdot (-6)}{32 - 4 \cdot (12) \div 3 \cdot 2} = \dfrac{-9 + (-6) \cdot (-6)}{32 - 48 \div 3 \cdot 2}$
$$= \dfrac{-9 + 36}{32 - 16 \cdot 2}$$
$$= \dfrac{27}{32 - 32}$$
$$= \dfrac{27}{0} \text{ is undefined.}$$

46. $-\$238 + \$450 = \$212$
Her balance is \$212.

48. $-102 + 37 + 52 = -65 + 52 = -13$
The final temperature was -13 degrees.

50. $-48 + 191 = 143$
They gained 143 yd.

52. Jan. $\$2400 - \$3100 = -\$700$
Feb. $\$1900 - \$2000 = -\$100$
March $\$2500 - \$1800 = \$700$
April $\$2300 - \$1400 = \$900$
May $\$1600 - \$1600 = \$0$
June $\$1900 - \$1200 = \$700$

54. $\dfrac{\$2400 + \$1900 + \$2500 + \$2300 + \$1600 + \$1900}{6}$
$$= \dfrac{\$12,600}{6} = \$2100$$
Her average monthly income was \$2100.

56. Subtract the smaller absolute value from the larger absolute value. The answer has the same sign as the addend with the larger absolute value. Examples: $-6 + 2 = -4$ and $6 + (-2) = 4$

9.5 Evaluating Expressions and Formulas

2. $r = 6, s = 1$
Replace r with 6. Replace s with 1.
$$2r + 4s$$
$$= 2(6) + 4(1)$$
$$= 12 + 4$$
$$= 16$$

4. $r = 7, s = -2$
Replace r with 7. Replace s with -2.
$$2r + 4s$$
$$= 2(7) + 4(-2)$$
$$= 14 + (-8)$$
$$= 6$$

6. $r = -3, s = 5$
Replace r with -3. Replace s with 5.
$$2r + 4s$$
$$= 2(-3) + 4(5)$$
$$= -6 + (20)$$
$$= 14$$

8. $r = -3, s = -5$
Replace r with -3. Replace s with -5.
$$2r + 4s$$
$$= 2(-3) + 4(-5)$$
$$= -6 + (-20)$$
$$= -26$$

10. $r = -7, s = 0$
Replace r with -7. Replace s with 0.
$$2r + 4s$$
$$= 2(-7) + 4(0)$$
$$= -14 + 0$$
$$= -14$$

12. $a - 5b, a = 10, b = 2$
Replace a with 10. Replace b with 2.
$$a - 5b$$
$$= 10 - 5(2)$$
$$= 10 - 10$$
$$= 0$$

14. $7p + 7q; p = -4, q = 1$
Replace p with -4. Replace q with 1.
$$7p + 7q$$
$$= 7(-4) + 7(1)$$
$$= -28 + 7$$
$$= -21$$

16. $\dfrac{2y-z}{x-2}$; $y = 0$, $z = 5$, $x = 1$

Replace y with 0, z with 5, and x with 1.

$$\dfrac{2y-z}{x-2} = \dfrac{2(0)-5}{1-2}$$
$$= \dfrac{-5}{-1}$$
$$= 5$$

18. $7k - 3r$; $k = \dfrac{2}{3}$, $r = \dfrac{1}{3}$

Replace k with $\frac{2}{3}$ and r with $\frac{1}{3}$.

$$7k - 3r = 7\left(\dfrac{2}{3}\right) - 3\left(\dfrac{1}{3}\right)$$
$$= \dfrac{14}{3} + \left(-\dfrac{3}{3}\right)$$
$$= \dfrac{11}{3}$$

20. $-c - 5b$; $c = -1$, $b = -2$

Replace c with -1. Replace b with -2.

$$-c - 5b$$
$$= -(-1) - 5(-2)$$
$$= +1 + (+10)$$
$$= 11$$

22. $-4x - y$; $x = 3$, $y = -8$

Replace x with 3. Replace y with -8.

$$-4x - y$$
$$= -4(3) - (-8)$$
$$= -12 + (+8)$$
$$= -4$$

24. $-k - m - 8n$; $k = 0$, $m = -7$, $n = -1$

Replace k with 0, m with -7, n with -1.

$$-k - m - 8n$$
$$= -(0) - (-7) - 8(-1)$$
$$= +(+7) + (+8)$$
$$= 15$$

26. $\dfrac{-3s - t - 4}{-s - 20 - t}$; $s = -3$, $t = -6$

Numerator:

$$-3s - t - 4$$
$$= -3(-3) - (-6) - 4$$
$$= 9 + (+6) - 4$$
$$= 15 - 4$$
$$= 11$$

Denominator:

$$-s - 20 - t$$
$$= -(-3) - 20 - (-6)$$
$$= +(+3) - 20 + (+6)$$
$$= -17 + 6$$
$$= -11$$

Divide: $\dfrac{11}{-11} = -1$

28. $P = 4s$, $s = 0.8$

Replace s with 0.8.

$$P = 4s$$
$$= 4 \cdot 0.8$$
$$= 3.2$$

30. $P = 2l + 2w$; $l = 12$, $w = 2$

Replace l with 12 and w with 2.

$$P = 2l + 2w$$
$$= 2(12) + 2(2)$$
$$= 24 + 4$$
$$= 28$$

32. $A = \pi r^2$; $\pi \approx 3.14$, $r = 10$

Replace π with 3.14. Replace r with 10.

$$A = \pi r^2$$
$$\approx 3.14 \cdot 10 \cdot 10$$
$$= 314$$

34. $A = \dfrac{1}{2}bh$; $b = 5$, $h = 11$

Replace b with 5 and h with 11.

$$A = \dfrac{1}{2}bh$$
$$= \dfrac{1}{2}(5)(11)$$
$$= \left(\dfrac{5}{2}\right)(11)$$
$$= \dfrac{55}{2} \text{ or } 27\tfrac{1}{2}$$

36. $V = \dfrac{1}{3}Bh$; $B = 105$, $h = 5$

Replace B with 105 and h with 5.

$$V = \dfrac{1}{3}Bh$$
$$= \dfrac{1}{\cancel{3}} \cdot \overset{35}{\cancel{105}} \cdot 5$$
$$= 175$$

38. $d = rt$; $r = 180$, $t = 5$
Replace r with 180 and t with 5.
$$d = rt$$
$$= 180 \cdot 5$$
$$= 900$$

40. $C = 2\pi r$; $\pi \approx 3.14$, $r = 18$
Replace π with 3.14 and r with 18.
$$C = 2\pi r$$
$$\approx 2 \cdot 3.14 \cdot 18$$
$$= 6.28 \cdot 18$$
$$= 113.04$$

42. (a) $P = 5s$; $s = 25$
$P = 5(25) = 125$
The perimeter is 125 cm.

(b) $P = 5s$; $s = 8$
$P = 5(8) = 40$
The perimeter is 40 in.

44. (a) $\dfrac{p}{b}$; $p = 176$, $b = 44$
$$\frac{p}{b} = \frac{176}{44} = 4$$
buses needed = 4

(b) $\dfrac{p}{b}$; $p = 72$, $b = 36$
$$\frac{p}{b} = \frac{72}{36} = 2$$
buses needed = 2

46. (a) Area of trapezoid $= \dfrac{1}{2}h(b + B)$
Selected values will vary. One possible answer:
If $h = 12$, $b = 6$, and $B = 10$, then
$$A = \frac{1}{2}(12)(6 + 10)$$
$$A = 6(16)$$
$$A = 96$$

(b) Volume of rectangular solid $= lwh$
Selected values will vary. One possibility is:
If $l = 5$, $w = 3$, and $h = 4$, then
$$V = (5)(3)(4)$$
$$V = 60$$

9.6 Solving Equations

2. $k - 2 = 7$; 9
Replace k with 9.
$$9 - 2 = 7$$
$$7 = 7$$
9 is a solution.

4. $5p = 30$; 6
Replace p with 6.
$$5(6) = 30$$
$$30 = 30$$
6 is a solution.

6. $6r - 3 = -14$; -2
Replace r with -2.
$$6(-2) - 3 = -14$$
$$-15 = -14$$
-14 is not a solution.

8. $a + 3 = 12$
Subtract 3 from both sides.
$$a + 3 - 3 = 12 - 3$$
$$a = 9$$
Check: $9 + 3 = 12$
$\qquad\quad 12 = 12$ *True*
The solution is 9.

10. $y + 6 = 0$
Subtract 6 from both sides.
$$y + 6 - 6 = 0 - 6$$
$$y = -6$$
Check: $-6 + 6 = 0$
$\qquad\quad 0 = 0$ True
The solution is -6.

12. $x - 9 = 4$
Add 9 to both sides.
$$x - 9 + 9 = 4 + 9$$
$$x = 13$$
Check: $13 - 9 = 4$
$\qquad\quad 4 = 4$ *True*
The solution is 13.

14. $3 = b - 5$
Add 5 to both sides.
$$3 + 5 = b - 5 + 5$$
$$8 = b$$
Check: $3 = 8 - 5$
$\qquad\quad 3 = 3$ *True*
The solution is 8.

16. $-1 = a + 8$
Subtract 8 from both sides.
$$-1 + (-8) = a + 8 - 8$$
$$-9 = a$$
Check: $-1 = -9 + 8$
$-1 = -1$ *True*

The solution is -9.

18. $12 = z + 7$
Subtract 7 from both sides.
$$12 - 7 = z + 7 - 7$$
$$5 = z$$
Check: $12 = 5 + 7$
$12 = 12$ *True*

The solution is 5.

20. $-9 + y = 7$
Add 9 to both sides.
$$-9 + y + 9 = 7 + 9$$
$$y = 16$$
Check: $-9 + 16 = 7$
$7 = 7$ *True*
The solution is 16.

22. $-3 + m = -9$
$$3 - 3 + m = -9 + 3$$
$$m = -6$$
Check: $-3 + (-6) = -9$
$-9 = -9$ *True*

The solution is -6.

24. $-1 = -10 + y$
$$10 - 1 = -10 + 10 + y$$
$$9 = y$$
Check: $-1 = -10 + 9$
$-1 = -1$ *True*

The solution is 9.

26. $x + \dfrac{1}{2} = 4$
$$x + \frac{1}{2} - \frac{1}{2} = 4 - \frac{1}{2}$$
$$x = \frac{8}{2} - \frac{1}{2}$$
$$x = \frac{7}{2} \text{ or } 3\tfrac{1}{2}$$
Check: $3\tfrac{1}{2} + \dfrac{1}{2} = 4$
$4 = 4$ *True*
The solution is $\dfrac{7}{2}$ or $3\tfrac{1}{2}$.

28. $m - \dfrac{3}{4} = 6$
$$m - \frac{3}{4} + \frac{3}{4} = 6 + \frac{3}{4}$$
$$m = \frac{24}{4} + \frac{3}{4}$$
$$= \frac{27}{4} \text{ or } 6\tfrac{3}{4}$$
Check: $\dfrac{27}{4} - \dfrac{3}{4} = 6$
$$\frac{24}{4} = 6$$
$6 = 6$ *True*

The solution is $\dfrac{27}{4}$ or $6\tfrac{3}{4}$.

30. $\dfrac{3}{5} = t - 1$
$$\frac{3}{5} + 1 = t - 1 + 1$$
$$\frac{3}{5} + \frac{5}{5} = t$$
$$\frac{8}{5} = t$$
Check: $\dfrac{3}{5} = \dfrac{8}{5} - 1$
$$\frac{3}{5} = \frac{8}{5} - \frac{5}{5}$$
$$\frac{3}{5} = \frac{3}{5}$$ *True*
The solution is $\dfrac{8}{5}$ or $1\tfrac{3}{5}$.

32. $z - \dfrac{7}{3} = \dfrac{32}{9}$
$$z - \frac{7}{3} + \frac{7}{3} = \frac{32}{9} + \frac{7}{3}$$
$$z = \frac{32}{9} + \frac{21}{9}$$
$$= \frac{53}{9}$$
Check: $\dfrac{53}{9} - \dfrac{7}{3} = \dfrac{32}{9}$
$$\frac{53}{9} - \frac{21}{9} = \frac{32}{9}$$
$$\frac{32}{9} = \frac{32}{9}$$ *True*
The solution is $\dfrac{53}{9}$.

34.
$$a - 3.82 = 7.9$$
$$a - 3.82 + 3.82 = 7.9 + 3.82$$
$$a = 11.72$$
Check: $11.72 - 3.82 = 7.9$
$$7.9 = 7.9 \quad \textit{True}$$
The solution is 11.72.

36.
$$8.9 = 10.5 + b$$
$$8.9 - 10.5 = 10.5 - 10.5 + b$$
$$-1.6 = b$$
Check: $8.9 = 10.5 + (-1.6)$
$$8.9 = 8.9 \quad \textit{True}$$
The solution is -1.6.

38. $8k = 24$
$$\frac{8k}{8} = \frac{24}{8}$$
$$k = 3$$
Check: $8(3) = 24$
$$24 = 24 \quad \textit{True}$$
The solution is 3.

40. $99 = 11m$
$$\frac{99}{11} = \frac{11m}{11}$$
$$9 = m$$
Check: $99 = 11(9)$
$$99 = 99 \quad \textit{True}$$
The solution is 9.

42. $5a = 0 \setminus$
$$\frac{5 \cdot a}{5} = \frac{0}{5}$$
$$a = 0$$
Check: $5 \cdot 0 = 0$
$$0 = 0 \quad \textit{True}$$
The solution is 0.

44. $-7y = 70$
$$\frac{-7y}{-7} = \frac{70}{-7}$$
$$y = -10$$
Check: $-7(-10) = 70$
$$70 = 70 \quad \textit{True}$$
The solution is -10.

46. $-54 = -9r$
$$\frac{-54}{-9} = \frac{-9r}{-9}$$
$$6 = r$$
Check: $-54 = -9(6)$
$$-54 = -54 \quad \textit{True}$$
The solution is 6.

48. $-5.4z = 27$
$$\frac{-5.4z}{-5.4} = \frac{27}{-5.4}$$
$$z = -5$$
Check: $-5.4(-5) = 27$
$$27 = 27 \quad \textit{True}$$
The solution is -5.

50. $-3.2y = -16.64$
$$\frac{-3.2y}{-3.2} = \frac{-16.64}{-3.2}$$
$$y = 5.2$$
Check: $-3.2(5.2) = -16.64$
$$-16.64 = -16.64 \quad \textit{True}$$
The solution is 5.2.

52.
$$\frac{y}{3} = 5$$
$$\frac{1}{3}y = 5$$
$$\frac{\overset{1}{\cancel{3}}}{1} \cdot \frac{1}{\underset{1}{\cancel{3}}}y = 5 \cdot 3$$
$$y = 15$$
Check: $\dfrac{15}{3} = 5$
$$5 = 5 \quad \textit{True}$$
The solution is 15.

54.
$$5 = \frac{m}{8}$$
$$5 = \frac{1}{8}m$$
$$8 \cdot 5 = \frac{1}{\underset{1}{\cancel{8}}}m \cdot \frac{\overset{1}{\cancel{8}}}{1}$$
$$40 = m$$
Check: $5 = \dfrac{40}{8}$
$$5 = 5 \quad \textit{True}$$
The solution is 40.

56.
$$\frac{z}{9} = -3$$

$$\frac{1}{9}z = -3$$

$$\frac{\cancel{9}^{1}}{1} \cdot \frac{1}{\cancel{9}_{1}}z = -3 \cdot 9$$

$$z = -27$$

Check: $\dfrac{-27}{9} = -3$

$\qquad -3 = -3 \quad$ *True*

The solution is –27.

58.
$$-\frac{5}{6}k = 15$$

$$\left(-\frac{\cancel{6}^{1}}{\cancel{5}_{1}}\right) \cdot \left(-\frac{\cancel{5}^{1}}{\cancel{6}_{1}}\right)k = \frac{\cancel{15}^{3}}{1} \cdot \left(-\frac{6}{\cancel{5}_{1}}\right)$$

$$k = -18$$

Check: $-\dfrac{5}{6} \cdot (-18) = 15$

$\qquad\qquad 15 = 15 \quad$ *True*

The solution is –18.

60.
$$-\frac{9}{10}b = -18$$

$$\left(-\frac{\cancel{10}^{1}}{\cancel{9}_{1}}\right) \left(-\frac{\cancel{9}^{1}}{\cancel{10}_{1}}\right)b = -\frac{\cancel{18}^{2}}{1} \cdot \left(-\frac{10}{\cancel{9}_{1}}\right)$$

$$b = 20$$

Check: $\left(-\dfrac{9}{10}\right) \cdot 20 = -18$

$\qquad\qquad -18 = -18 \quad$ *True*

The solution is 20.

62.
$$4 = \frac{2}{3}a$$

$$\frac{\cancel{4}^{2}}{1} \cdot \frac{3}{\cancel{2}_{1}} = \frac{\cancel{3}^{1}}{\cancel{2}_{1}} \cdot \frac{\cancel{2}^{1}}{\cancel{3}_{1}}a$$

$$6 = a$$

Check: $4 = \dfrac{2}{3} \cdot 6$

$\qquad\quad 4 = 4 \quad$ *True*

The solution is 6.

64.
$$\frac{k}{0.7} = 3.2$$

$$\frac{0.7}{1} \cdot \left(\frac{k}{0.7}\right) = 3.2 \cdot 0.7$$

$$k = 2.24$$

Check: $\dfrac{2.24}{0.7} = 3.2$

$\qquad\qquad 3.2 = 3.2 \quad$ *True*

The solution is 2.24.

66.
$$\frac{m}{-5.2} = 2.1$$

$$\frac{-5.2}{1} \cdot \left(\frac{m}{-5.2}\right) = -5.2 \cdot 2.1$$

$$m = -10.92$$

Check: $\dfrac{-10.92}{-5.2} = 2.1$

$\qquad\qquad 2.1 = 2.1 \quad$ *True*

The solution is –10.92.

68. You may multiply or divide both sides of an equation by the same number (except you cannot divide by zero). Many different equations could have +6 as the solution. One possibility is:

$$8r = 48$$

$$\frac{\cancel{8}^{1} \cdot r}{\cancel{8}_{1}} = \frac{48}{8}$$

$$r = 6.$$

70.
$$y + 4 = 10 - 9$$
$$y + 4 = 1$$
$$y + 4 - 4 = 1 - 4$$
$$y = -3$$
The solution is –3.

72.
$$-1 = y + 7 - 9$$
$$-1 = y - 2$$
$$-1 + 2 = y - 2 + 2$$
$$1 = y$$
The solution is 1.

74.
$$\frac{3}{4}x = \frac{5}{3}$$

$$\frac{4}{3} \cdot \frac{3}{4}x = \frac{5}{3} \cdot \frac{4}{3}$$

$$x = \frac{20}{9}$$

The solution is $\dfrac{20}{9}$.

76. $\dfrac{2}{3} - \dfrac{8}{9} = \dfrac{c}{6}$

$\dfrac{6}{9} - \dfrac{8}{9} = \dfrac{c}{6}$

$-\dfrac{2}{9} = \dfrac{c}{6}$

$\dfrac{6}{1} \cdot -\dfrac{2}{9} = \dfrac{c}{6} \cdot \dfrac{6}{1}$

$-\dfrac{12}{9} = c$

$-\dfrac{4}{3} = c$

The solution is $-\dfrac{4}{3}$.

78. $10 - |0 - 8| = n + 1 - 4$

$10 - |-8| = n - 3$

$10 - 8 = n - 3$

$2 = n - 3$

$2 + 3 = n - 3 + 3$

$5 = n$

The solution is 5.

9.7   Solving Equations with Several Steps

2. $6k + 3 = 15$

$6k + 3 - 3 = 15 - 3$

$6k = 12$

$\dfrac{\overset{1}{\cancel{6}}k}{\underset{1}{\cancel{6}}} = \dfrac{12}{6}$

$k = 2$

Check: Replace k with 2.

$6(2) + 3 = 15$

$12 + 3 = 15$ *True*

The solution is 2.

4. $10 = 11p - 12$

$10 + 12 = 11p - 12 + 12$

$22 = 11p$

$\dfrac{22}{11} = \dfrac{\overset{1}{\cancel{11}}p}{\underset{1}{\cancel{11}}}$

Check: Replace p with 2.

$10 = 11 \cdot 2 - 12$

$10 = 22 - 12$

$10 = 10$ *True*

The solution is 2.

6. $-4k + 5 = 5$

$-4k + 5 - 5 = 5 - 5$

$-4k = 0$

$\dfrac{-4k}{-4} = \dfrac{0}{-4}$

$k = 0$

Check: Replace k with 0.

$-4(0) + 5 = 5$

$0 + 5 = 5$

$5 = 5$ *True*

The solution is 0.

8. $5 = -10p + 25$

$5 - 25 = -10p + 25 - 25$

$-20 = -10p$

$\dfrac{-20}{-10} = \dfrac{\overset{1}{\cancel{-10}}\,p}{\underset{1}{\cancel{-10}}}$

$2 = p$

Check: Replace p with 2.

$5 = -10(2) + 25$

$5 = -20 + 25$

$5 = 5$ *True*

The solution is 2.

10. $-12a - 3 = 21$

$-12a - 3 + 3 = 21 + 3$

$-12a = 24$

$\dfrac{\overset{1}{\cancel{-12}}\,a}{\underset{1}{\cancel{-12}}} = \dfrac{24}{-12}$

$a = -2$

Check: Replace a with -2.

$-12(-2) - 3 = 21$

$24 - 3 = 21$

$21 = 21$ *True*

The solution is -2.

12. $-\dfrac{5}{8}r + 4 = -6$

$-\dfrac{5}{8}r + 4 - 4 = -6 - 4$

$-\dfrac{5}{8}r = -10$

$-\dfrac{\overset{1}{\cancel{8}}}{\underset{1}{\cancel{5}}}\left(-\dfrac{\overset{1}{\cancel{5}}}{\underset{1}{\cancel{8}}}r\right) = -\dfrac{8}{\underset{1}{\cancel{5}}}\left(-\overset{2}{\cancel{10}}\right)$

$r = 16$

Check: Replace r with 16.

$$-\frac{5}{\cancel{8}}\cdot \cancel{16}^{\,2}+4=-6$$

$$-10+4=-6$$
$$-6=-6 \quad True$$

The solution is 16.

14.
$$0.25 = -3c + 0.85$$
$$0.25 - 0.85 = -3c + 0.85 - 0.85$$
$$-0.6 = -3c$$
$$\frac{-0.6}{-3} = \frac{-3c}{-3}$$
$$0.2 = c$$

Check: Replace c with 0.2
$$0.25 = -3(0.2) + 0.85$$
$$0.25 = -0.6 + 0.85$$
$$0.25 = 0.25 \quad True$$

The solution is 0.2.

16. $8(k + 5) = 8 \cdot k + 8 \cdot 5 = 8k + 40$

18. $9(t - 4) = 9 \cdot t + 9(-4) = 9t - 36$

20. $-5(a + 2) = -5 \cdot a + (-5) \cdot 2 = -5a - 10$

22. $-4(r - 7) = -4 \cdot r - (-4) \cdot 7$
$$= -4r - (-28)$$
$$= -4r + 28$$

24. $-6(n + 5) = -6 \cdot n + (-6) \cdot 5 = -6n - 30$

26. $-11(x - 11) = -11 \cdot x - (-11) \cdot 11 = -11x + 121$

28. $2m + 5m = (2 + 5)m = 7m$

30. $10x - 2x = (10 - 2)x = 8x$

32. $-10a + a = (-10 + 1)a = -9a$

34. $3y - y - 4y = (3 - 1 - 4)y = -2y$

36. $-6c - c + 7c = (-6 - 1 + 7)c = 0c = 0$

38. $\dfrac{3}{8}d - \dfrac{9}{8}d = \left(\dfrac{3}{8} - \dfrac{9}{8}\right)d = -\dfrac{6}{8}d = -\dfrac{3}{4}d$

40. $3a + 2a = 15$
$$5a = 15$$
$$\frac{\cancel{5}^{\,1} a}{\cancel{5}} = \frac{15}{5}$$
$$a = 3$$

Check: Replace a with 3.
$$3(3) + 2(3) = 15$$
$$9 + 6 = 15$$
$$15 = 15 \quad True$$

The solution is 3.

42. $28 = x + 6x$
$$28 = 7x$$
$$\frac{28}{7} = \frac{\cancel{7}}{\cancel{7}}^{\,1}$$
$$4 = x$$

Check: Replace x with 4.
$$28 = 4 + 6(4)$$
$$28 = 4 + 24$$
$$28 = 28 \quad True$$

The solution is 4.

44. $3r - 9r = 18$
$$(3 - 9)r = 18$$
$$-6r = 18$$
$$\frac{-\cancel{6}^{\,1} r}{-\cancel{6}}_{\,1} = \frac{18}{-6}$$
$$r = -3$$

Check: Replace r with –3.
$$3(-3) - 9(-3) = 18$$
$$-9 + 27 = 18$$
$$18 = 18 \quad True$$

The solution is –3.

46. $-5 = 10z - 15z$
$$-5 = (10 - 15)z$$
$$-5 = (-5)z$$
$$-5 = -5z$$
$$\frac{-5}{-5} = \frac{-\cancel{5}^{\,1} z}{-\cancel{5}}_{\,1}$$
$$1 = z$$

Check: Replace z with 1.
$$-5 = 10(1) - 15(1)$$
$$-5 = 10 - 15$$
$$-5 = -5 \quad True$$

The solution is 1.

48.
$$5y - 5 = 2y + 10$$
$$5y - 5 - 2y = 2y + 10 - 2y$$
$$3y - 5 = 10$$
$$3y - 5 + 5 = 10 + 5$$
$$3y = 15$$
$$\frac{\overset{1}{\cancel{3}}y}{\underset{1}{\cancel{3}}} = \frac{15}{3}$$
$$y = 5$$

Check: Replace y with 5.
$$5 \cdot 5 - 5 = 2 \cdot 5 + 10$$
$$25 - 5 = 10 + 10$$
$$20 = 20 \quad True$$

The solution is 5.

50.
$$8 + 4a = 2a + 2$$
$$8 + 4a - 2a = 2a + 2 - 2a$$
$$8 + 2a = 2$$
$$8 + 2a - 8 = 2 - 8$$
$$2a = -6$$
$$\frac{\overset{1}{\cancel{2}}a}{\underset{1}{\cancel{2}}} = \frac{-6}{2}$$
$$a = -3$$

Check: Replace a with -3.
$$8 + 4(-3) = 2(-3) + 2$$
$$8 + (-12) = -6 + 2$$
$$-4 = -4 \quad True$$

The solution is -3.

52.
$$5x - 4 = -3x + 4$$
$$5x - 4 + 3x = -3x + 4 + 3x$$
$$8x - 4 = 4$$
$$8x - 4 + 4 = 4 + 4$$
$$8x = 8$$
$$\frac{\overset{1}{\cancel{8}}x}{\underset{1}{\cancel{8}}} = \frac{8}{8}$$
$$x = 1$$

Check: Replace x with 1.
$$5(1) - 4 = -3(1) + 4$$
$$5 - 4 = -3 + 4$$
$$1 = 1 \quad True$$

The solution is 1.

54.
$$t + 0.8 = -1.7$$
$$t + 0.8 - 0.8 = -1.7 - 0.8$$
$$t = -2.5$$

Check: Replace t with -2.5.
$$-2.5 + 0.8 = -1.7$$
$$-1.7 = -1.7 \quad True$$

The solution is -2.5.

56.
$$0.5x - 6 = 2$$
$$0.5x - 6 + 6 = 2 + 6$$
$$0.5x = 8$$
$$\frac{\overset{1}{\cancel{0.5}}x}{\underset{1}{\cancel{0.5}}} = \frac{8}{0.5}$$
$$x = 16$$

Check: Replace x with 16.
$$0.5(16) - 6 = 2$$
$$8 - 6 = 2$$
$$2 = 2 \quad True$$

The solution is 16.

58.
$$-3 = 3(x + 6)$$
$$-3 = 3x + 18$$
$$-3 - 18 = 3x + 18 - 18$$
$$-21 = 3x$$
$$\frac{-21}{3} = \frac{\overset{1}{\cancel{3}}x}{\underset{1}{\cancel{3}}}$$
$$-7 = x$$

Check: Replace x with -7.
$$-3 = 3(-7 + 6)$$
$$-3 = 3(-1)$$
$$-3 = -3 \quad True$$

The solution is -7.

60.
$$-5(k + 3) = 25$$
$$(-5) \cdot k + (-5) \cdot 3 = 25$$
$$-5k + (-15) = 25$$
$$-5k + (-15) + 15 = 25 + 15$$
$$-5k = 40$$
$$\frac{-\overset{1}{\cancel{5}}k}{-\underset{1}{\cancel{5}}} = \frac{40}{-5}$$
$$k = -8$$

Check: Replace k with -8.
$$-5(-8 + 3) = 25$$
$$-5(-5) = 25$$
$$25 = 25 \quad True$$

The solution is -8.

62.
$$7(r-5) = -35$$
$$7r - 35 = -35$$
$$7r - 35 + 35 = -35 + 35$$
$$7r = 0$$
$$\frac{\overset{1}{\cancel{7}}r}{\cancel{7}} = \frac{0}{7}$$
$$\underset{1}{}$$
$$r = 0$$

Check: Replace r with 0.
$$7(0-5) = -35$$
$$7(-5) = -35$$
$$-35 = -35$$

The solution is 0.

64. Check:
$$3[2(-2)+5] = -7$$
$$3(-4+5) = -7$$
$$3(1) = -7$$
$$3 = -7 \quad \textit{False}$$

The first step on the left side should have been
$$3(2x+5) = -7$$
$$6x + 15 = -7$$
$$6x + 15 - 15 = -7 - 15$$
$$6x = -22$$
$$\frac{6x}{6} = \frac{-22}{6}$$
$$x = -\frac{11}{3}$$

The correct solution is $x = -\dfrac{11}{3}$.

66.
$$-6 - 5 + 14 = -50a + 51a$$
$$-11 + 14 = (-50 + 51)a$$
$$3 = a$$

The solution is 3.

68.
$$0 = -9(b-1)$$
$$0 = (-9) \cdot b + (-9) \cdot (-1)$$
$$0 = -9b + 9$$
$$0 + 9b = -9b + 9 + 9b$$
$$9b = 9$$
$$\frac{\overset{1}{\cancel{9}}b}{\cancel{9}} = \frac{9}{9}$$
$$\underset{1}{}$$
$$b = 1$$

The solution is 1.

70. $\dfrac{z}{3} + 1 = \dfrac{z}{2} - 3$

Multiply both sides of the equation by the LCD, 6, to clear the fractions.
$$6\left(\frac{z}{3} + 1\right) = 6\left(\frac{z}{2} - 3\right)$$
$$\frac{\overset{2}{\cancel{6}}}{1} \cdot \frac{z}{\cancel{3}} + 6(1) = \frac{\overset{3}{\cancel{6}}}{1} \cdot \frac{z}{\cancel{2}} + 6(-3)$$
$$\underset{1}{} \qquad\qquad \underset{1}{}$$
$$2z + 6 = 3z - 18$$
$$2z - 2z + 6 = 3z - 2z - 18$$
$$6 = z - 18$$
$$6 + 18 = z - 18 + 18$$
$$24 = z$$

The solution is 24.

72.
$$-5b - |47 - 7| = -8(b+8)$$
$$-5b - |40| = -8(b+8)$$
$$-5b - 40 = -8(b+8)$$
$$-5b - 40 = -8b - 64$$
$$-5b - 40 + 40 = -8b - 64 + 40$$
$$-5b = -8b - 24$$
$$-5b + 8b = -8b - 24 + 8b$$
$$3b = -24$$
$$\frac{3b}{3} = -\frac{24}{3}$$
$$b = -8$$

The solution is -8.

74.
$$-0.5(c-4) = -3(c-2.5)$$
$$-0.5c + 2 = -3c + 7.5$$
$$-0.5c + 2 - 2 = -3c + 7.5 - 2$$
$$-0.5c = -3c + 5.5$$
$$-0.5c + 3c = -3c + 5.5 + 3c$$
$$2.5c = 5.5$$
$$\frac{2.5c}{2.5} = \frac{5.5}{2.5}$$
$$c = 2.2$$

The solution is 2.2.

9.8 Using Equations to Solve Application Problems

2. The sum of a number and -8

$x + (-8)$ or $-8 + x$

4. 16 more than a number

$x + 16$ or $16 + x$

6. A number decreased by 25

$x - 25$

8. A number subtracted from -7

$-7 - x$

10. 3 fewer than a number

$x - 3$

12. The product of -3 and a number

$-3x$

14. Half a number

$\dfrac{1}{2}x$ or $\dfrac{x}{2}$

16. 4 divided by a number

$\dfrac{4}{x}$

18. Five times a number plus five

$5x + 5$ or $5 + 5x$

20. 12 less than six times a number

$6x - 12$

22. Triple a number subtracted from the number

$x - 3x$

24. True. Choose any letter you like, although it may help to choose a letter which reminds you of what it represents, such as w for an unknown width.

26. Let n = the unknown number.

The sum of 8	and	five times a number	is	53.
↓	↓	↓	↓	↓
8	+	$5n$	=	53

$$8 + 5n = 53$$
$$8 + 5n - 8 = 53 - 8$$
$$5n = 45$$
$$\frac{\overset{1}{\cancel{5}} n}{\underset{1}{\cancel{5}}} = \frac{45}{5}$$
$$n = 9$$

The number is 9.

Check:
$$8 + 5 \cdot 9 = 53$$
$$8 + 45 = 53$$
$$53 = 53 \quad \textit{True}$$

28. Let n = the unknown number.

Three times a number	less	a number	is	-8.
↓	↓	↓	↓	↓
$3n$	$-$	n	=	-8

$$3n - n = -8$$
$$2n = -8$$
$$\frac{2n}{2} = \frac{-8}{2}$$
$$n = -4$$

The number is -4.

Check:
$$3(-4) - (-4) = -8$$
$$-12 + 4 = -8$$
$$-8 = -8 \quad \textit{True}$$

30. Let n = the unknown number.

Eleven times a number	subtract	eight times a number	the result is	-9
↓	↓	↓	↓	↓
$11n$	$-$	$8n$	=	-9

$$11n - 8n = -9$$
$$3n = -9$$
$$\frac{\overset{1}{\cancel{3}} n}{\underset{1}{\cancel{3}}} = \frac{-9}{3}$$
$$n = -3$$

The number is -3.

Check: $11(-3) - 8(-3) = -9$
$$-33 + 24 = -9$$
$$-9 = -9 \quad \textit{True}$$

32. Let n = the unknown number.

Twice a number $\downarrow$ / decreased by $\downarrow$ / 8 $\downarrow$ / is $\downarrow$

$$2n \quad - \quad 8 \quad =$$

the number $\downarrow$ / increased by $\downarrow$ / 7 $\downarrow$

$$n \quad + \quad 7$$

$$2n - 8 = n + 7$$
$$2n - 8 + 8 = n + 7 + 8$$
$$2n = n + 15$$
$$2n - n = n + 15 - n$$
$$n = 15$$

The number is 15.

Check: $2(15) - 8 = 15 + 7$
$$30 - 8 = 22$$
$$22 = 22 \quad \textit{True}$$

34. Let n = the number.

$\frac{1}{3}$ of a number $\downarrow$ / added to $\downarrow$ / 3 times a number $\downarrow$ / is $\downarrow$ / 30. $\downarrow$

$$\frac{1}{3}n \quad + \quad 3n \quad = \quad 30$$

$$\frac{1}{3}n + 3n = 30$$

$$\left(\frac{1}{3} + 3\right)n = 30$$

$$\left(\frac{1}{3} + \frac{9}{3}\right)n = 30$$

$$\frac{10}{3}n = 30$$

$$\frac{\cancel{3}}{\cancel{10}} \cdot \frac{\cancel{10}}{\cancel{3}} n = \frac{3}{\cancel{10}} \cdot \cancel{30}$$

$$n = 9$$

Check:

$$\frac{1}{3}(9) + 3(9) = 30$$

$$3 + 27 = 30$$

$$30 = 30 \quad \textit{True}$$

For Exercises 36–48, use the six problem-solving steps. The steps are not labeled here.

36. Let a = Linda's age.

Three times Linda's age $\downarrow$ / is $\downarrow$ / decreased by 36; $\downarrow$ / the result is $\downarrow$ / twice Linda's age. $\downarrow$

$$3a \quad - \quad 36 \quad = \quad 2a$$

$$3a - 36 = 2a$$
$$3a - 36 + 36 = 2a + 36$$
$$3a = 2a + 36$$
$$3a - 2a = 2a + 36 - 2a$$
$$a = 36$$

Linda is 36 years old.

Check: $3(36) - 36 = 2(36)$
$$108 - 36 = 72$$
$$72 = 72 \quad \textit{True}$$

38. Let w = weight of child.

Dennis' weight (184 lb) $\downarrow$ / is $\downarrow$ / 6 times his child's weight $\downarrow$ / less $\downarrow$ / 2 lb $\downarrow$

$$184 \quad = \quad 6w \quad - \quad 2$$

$$184 = 6w - 2$$
$$184 + 2 = 6w - 2 + 2$$
$$186 = 6w$$
$$\frac{186}{6} = \frac{6w}{6}$$
$$31 = w$$

The child weighs 31 lb.

Check: $184 = 6(31) - 2$
$$184 = 186 - 2$$
$$184 = 184 \quad \textit{True}$$

40. Let v = the number of votes received.

Then $v + 93$ = the number of votes received by Marge.

Ed's votes	plus	Marge's votes	was	the total.
↓	↓	↓	↓	↓
v	$+$	$v + 93$	$=$	587

$$v + v + 93 = 587$$
$$2v + 93 - 93 = 587 - 93$$
$$2v = 494$$
$$\frac{\overset{1}{\cancel{2}}v}{\underset{1}{\cancel{2}}} = \frac{494}{2}$$
$$v = 247$$

Ed received 247 votes.
Marge received $247 + 93 = 340$ votes.

Check: $247 + 247 + 93 = 587$
$$494 + 93 = 587$$
$$587 = 587 \quad True$$

42. Let x = amount one charity receives.
Then $x - 18,000$ = amount other charity receives.

The sum of the amounts	is	$149,000
↓	↓	↓
$x + (x - 18,000)$	$=$	$149,000$

$$x + x - 18,000 = 149,000$$
$$2x - 18,000 = 149,000$$
$$2x - 18,000 + 18,000 = 149,000 + 18,000$$
$$2x = 167,000$$
$$\frac{2x}{2} = \frac{167,000}{2}$$
$$x = 83,500$$
$$x - 18,000 = 65,500$$

The charities will receive $83,500 and $65,500.

Check:
$$83,500 + 83,500 - 18,000 = 149,000$$
$$149,000 = 149,000 \quad True$$

44. Let a = attendance at Sunday's game.
Then $3a$ = attendance at Saturday's game.

In all (add)		56,000 fans attended
↓	↓	↓
$a + 3a$	$=$	$56,000$

$$a + 3a = 56,000$$
$$4a = 56,000$$
$$\frac{4a}{4} = \frac{56,000}{4}$$
$$a = 14,000$$
$$3a = 42,000$$

Saturday's game had 42,000 fans and Sunday's game had 14,000 fans.

Check: $14,000 + 3(14,000) = 56,000$
$$14,000 + 42,000 = 56,000$$
$$56,000 = 56,000 \quad True$$

46. Let x = length of shorter piece.
Then $x + 8$ = length of longer piece.

The rope (add the lengths)	is	50 ft.
↓	↓	↓
$x + (x + 8)$	$=$	50

$$x + x + 8 = 50$$
$$2x + 8 = 50$$
$$2x + 8 - 8 = 50 - 8$$
$$2x = 42$$
$$\frac{2x}{2} = \frac{42}{2}$$
$$x = 21$$
$$x + 8 = 29$$

The lengths are 21 ft. and 29 ft.

Check: $21 + 21 + 8 = 50$
$$50 = 50 \quad True$$

48. Let x = length of longer piece.
Then $x - 6$ = length of shorter piece.

$$\text{The pipe (add the length)} \quad \text{is} \quad 90 \text{ cm}$$
$$\downarrow \qquad\qquad \downarrow \quad \downarrow$$
$$x + (x - 6) \qquad\quad = \qquad 90$$

$$x + x - 6 = 90$$
$$2x - 6 = 90$$
$$2x - 6 + 6 = 90 + 6$$
$$2x = 96$$
$$\frac{2x}{2} = \frac{96}{2}$$
$$x = 48$$
$$x - 6 = 42$$

The lengths are 42 cm and 48 cm.

Check: $48 + 48 - 6 = 90$
$$90 = 90 \quad \textit{True}$$

50. Let w = the width of the rectangle.

Use $P = 2 \cdot l + 2 \cdot w$ with $P = 74$, and $l = 27$.
$$74 = 2(27) + 2w$$
$$74 = 54 + 2w$$
$$74 - 54 = 54 + 2w - 54$$
$$\frac{20}{2} = \frac{\overset{1}{\cancel{2}} w}{\cancel{2}_{1}}$$
$$10 = w$$

The width is 10 cm.

Check: $74 = 2(27) + 2(10)$
$$74 = 54 + 20$$
$$74 = 74 \quad \textit{True}$$

52. Let w = the width and
$3w$ = the length.

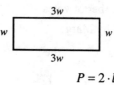

$$P = 2 \cdot l + 2 \cdot w$$
$$240 = 2 \cdot 3w + 2 \cdot w$$
$$240 = 6w + 2w$$
$$240 = 8w$$
$$\frac{240}{8} = \frac{\overset{1}{\cancel{8}} w}{\cancel{8}_{1}}$$
$$30 = w$$

The width is 30 yd and the length is
$3 \cdot 30 = 90$ yd.

Check: $2(30) + 2(90) = 240$
$$60 + 180 = 240$$
$$240 = 240 \quad \textit{True}$$

For Exercises 36–48, use the six problem-solving steps. The steps are not labeled here.

54. Let x = the length and
$x - 5$ = the width.

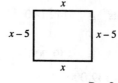

$$P = 2 \cdot l + 2 \cdot w$$
$$122 = 2 \cdot x + 2 \cdot (x - 5)$$
$$122 = 2x + 2x - 10$$
$$122 = 4x - 10$$
$$122 + 10 = 4x - 10 + 10$$
$$132 = 4x$$
$$\frac{132}{4} = \frac{4x}{4}$$
$$33 = x$$
$$28 = x - 5$$

The length is 33 ft. and the width is 28 ft.

Check: $122 = 2(33) + 2(28)$
$$122 = 66 + 56$$
$$122 = 122 \quad \textit{True}$$

Chapter 10

STATISTICS

10.1 Circle Graphs

2. The largest expense is carpentry at $12,100.

4. Total cost $= \$12,100 + \$9800 + \$2000$
$\qquad\qquad + \$900 + \$1800 + \$3000 + \$2400$
$\qquad\quad = \$32,000$

Cost of painting $= \$1800$

$$\frac{\text{Painting}}{\text{Total}} = \frac{\$1800}{\$32,000} = \frac{1800}{32,000} = \frac{9}{160}$$

6. $\dfrac{\text{Cost of windows}}{\text{Cost of floor}} = \dfrac{\$3000}{\$2400} = \dfrac{3000}{2400} = \dfrac{5}{4}$

8. The second largest number and the second largest sector represent the reason "Atmosphere."

10. "Enjoy eating out" to total

Total $= 1740 + 1200 + 1140 + 180 + 1020$
$+ 720 = 6000$

$$\frac{1140}{6000} = \frac{19}{100}$$

12. "Don't know" to "Quicker"

$$\frac{180}{720} = \frac{1}{4}$$

14. "Atmosphere" to "Enjoy eating out"

$$\frac{1200}{1140} = \frac{20}{19}$$

16. Ramps and handrails are 25% of $1,740,000.

$$x = 0.25 \cdot \$1,740,000$$
$$= \$435,000$$

18. Parking is 10% of $1,740,000.

$$x = 0.10 \cdot \$1,740,000$$
$$= \$174,000$$

20. Other is 10% of $1,740,000.

$$x = 0.10 \cdot \$1,740,000$$
$$= \$174,000$$

22. Checks and personal accounting software are 23% of 10,860 people.

$$x = 0.23 \cdot 10,860$$
$$\approx 2498 \text{ people}$$

24. Electronically/No paper is 31% of 10,860 people.

$$x = 0.31 \cdot 10,860$$
$$\approx 3367 \text{ people}$$

26. Face-to-face (4%) and Checks and personal accounting software (23%) combined are 27% of 10,860 people.

$$x = 0.27 \cdot 10,860$$
$$\approx 2932 \text{ people}$$

28. A protractor is used to measure the number of degrees in a sector. First, you must draw a line from the center of the circle to the left edge. Next, place the hole of the protractor at the center of the circle, making sure that the zero on the protractor is on the line. Finally, make a mark at the desired number of degrees, this gives you the size of the sector.

30. Percent for food $= \dfrac{72°}{360°}$
$\qquad\qquad\qquad = 0.20 = 20\%$

32. Degrees for books $= 10\%$ of $360°$
$\qquad\qquad\qquad\quad = 0.10 \times 360°$
$\qquad\qquad\qquad\quad = 36°$

34. Percent for savings $= \dfrac{\$273}{\$5460}$
$\qquad\qquad\qquad\quad = 0.05 = 5\%$

Degrees of circle $= 5\%$ of $360°$
$\qquad\qquad\qquad = 0.05 \times 360°$
$\qquad\qquad\qquad = 18°$

36.

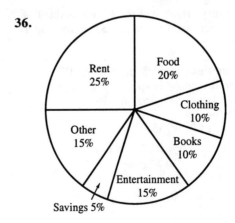

38. (a)   Mysteries $= 25\%$ of $360°$
$$= 0.25 \times 360°$$
$$= 90°$$

Biographies $= 10\%$ of $360°$
$$= 0.10 \times 360°$$
$$= 36°$$

Cookbooks $= 15\%$ of $360°$
$$= 0.15 \times 360°$$
$$= 54°$$

Romance Novels $= 15\%$ of $360°$
$$= 0.15 \times 360°$$
$$= 54°$$

Science $= 20\%$ of $360°$
$$= 0.20 \times 360°$$
$$= 72°$$

Business $= 15\%$ of $360°$
$$= 0.15 \times 360°$$
$$= 54°$$

(b)

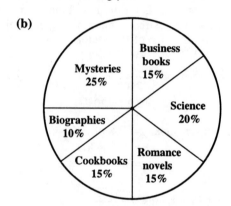

10.2   Bar Graphs and Line Graphs

2. The country which had the lowest percent of income spent on food was USA, which spent 10.9%.

4. The countries in which more than 20% of household income is spent, on average, for food are Israel, Mexico, and India.

6. What is 21.0% of 365 days?
$$x = 0.21 \cdot 365 \text{ days}$$
$$\approx 77 \text{ days}$$

8. In January of 2001, 4500 workers were unemployed.

10. In March of 2001, 6000 workers were unemployed.

In March of 2002, 8500 workers were unemployed.

There were 2500 fewer employed workers in March of 2001.

12. In January of 2002, 4000 workers were unemployed.

In June of 2002, 9000 workers were employed.

The increase from January to June, 2002 was 5000 workers.

14. In 2001, 650,000 ($650 \cdot 1000$) gallons of super unleaded gasoline were sold.

16. In 2002, the sales of supreme unleaded gasoline surpassed the sales of super unleaded gasoline.

18. In 1998, the sales were 400,000 ($400 \cdot 1000$) gallons.

In 2002, the sales were 600,000 ($600 \cdot 1000$) gallons.

$$\text{Increase} = 600,000 - 400,000$$
$$= 200,000 \text{ gallons}$$

20. The cost of a 3-minute phone call from New York to London in 1970 was $32.33.

22. Cost in 1980 = $7.61
Cost in 1998 = $2.25

Difference = $7.61 − $2.25 = $5.36

The cost in 1998 was $5.36 less than the cost in 1980.

24. Answers will vary. Some possibilities are: Less competition among long-distance companies; inflation resulting in overall higher prices.

26. In 2001, Chain Store A sold 2,500,000 ($2500 \cdot 1000$) compact discs.

28. In 2002, Chain Store B sold 4,000,000 ($4000 \cdot 1000$) compact discs.

30. In 2000, Chain Store B sold 2,000,000 ($2000 \cdot 1000$) compact discs.

32. Some possible explanations are that Store B may have started to: do more advertising; keep longer store hours; give better training to their staff; employ more help; or give better service than Store A.

34. You would use a set of bars or a set of lines for each set of data.

One example is the number of miles driven by two salespeople over a three-year period.

36. In 2001, total sales were $30,000 (30 · 1000).

38. In 2002, the profit was $15,000 (15 · 1000).

40. In 2000, the profit was $5000 (5 · 1000).

42. As sales increase or decrease, so do profits.

10.3 Frequency Distributions and Histograms

2. The least number of members is in the 16–20 years age group. There are 1000 members in this group.

4. The number of members 61 years of age and older is 40,000 (16,000 + 12,000 + 7000 + 5000) members.

6. The number of members that are 46 to 55 years of age is 26,000 (15,000 + 11,000) members.

8. The least number of employees is in the $100 to $1000 and the $2100 to $3000 salary groups.

There are 6 employees in both of these salary groups.

10. There are 10 employees in the $1100 to $2000 range.

12. The number of employees who earn $6100 or more is 32 (13 + 12 + 7) employees.

14. If too few class intervals were used, the class frequencies would be high and any differences in the data might not be observable.

If too many class intervals were used, interpretation might become impossible because class frequencies would be very low or nonexistent.

16. 150–159: 4 tally marks and a class frequency of 4

18. 170–179: 3 tally marks and a class frequency of 3

20. 190–199: 5 tally marks and a class frequency of 5

22. 25–49: 3 tally marks and a class frequency of 3

24. 75–99: 3 tally marks and a class frequency of 3

26. 125–149: 8 tally marks and a class frequency of 8

28. Construct a histogram by using the data in Exercises 21–27.

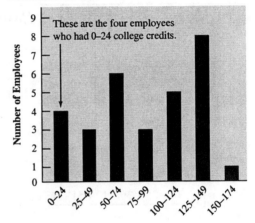

Number of College Credits Completed

30. 6–10: 17 tally marks and a class frequency of 17

32. 16–20: 10 tally marks and a class frequency of 10

34. 26–30: 7 tally marks and a class frequency of 7

36.

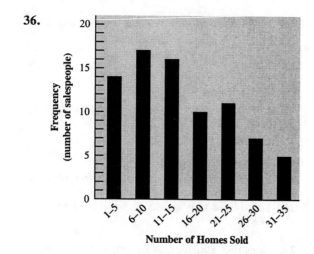

Number of Homes Sold

10.4 Mean, Median, and Mode

2. Mean $= \dfrac{\text{sum of all values}}{\text{number of values}}$

$= \dfrac{\$53 + \$77 + \$38 + \$29 + \$49 + \$48}{6}$

$= \dfrac{\$294}{6}$

$= \$49$

4. Mean $= \dfrac{32 + 26 + 30 + 19 + 51 + 46 + 38 + 39}{8}$

$= \dfrac{281}{8}$

≈ 35.1

6. Mean

$= \dfrac{27,500 + 18,250 + 17,357 + 14,298 + 33,110}{5}$

$= \dfrac{110,515}{5}$

$= 22,103$ people

8. Mean

$= \dfrac{\begin{array}{c}\$30.10 + \$42.80 + \$91.60 + \$51.20 + \\ \$88.30 + \$21.90 + \$43.70 + \$51.20\end{array}}{8}$

$= \dfrac{\$420.80}{8}$

$= \$52.60$

10.

Value	Frequency	Product
4	1	4
8	3	24
16	5	80
20	1	20
	10	128

Mean $= \dfrac{128}{10} = 12.8$

12.

Students	Frequency	Product
25	1	25
26	2	52
29	5	145
30	4	120
32	3	96
33	5	165
	20	603

Mean $= \dfrac{603}{20} = 30.15 \approx 30.2$ students

14.

Mpg	Autos	Product
15	5	75
20	6	120
24	10	240
30	14	420
32	5	160
35	6	210
40	4	160
	50	1385

Mean $= \dfrac{1385}{50}$

$= 27.7$ miles per gallon

16. Arrange the numbers in numerical order.

85, 98, 114, 122, 140

The median is the middle value.

Median = 114 or 114,000 hits

18. Number of cars in the parking lot each day:
Arrange in order.

290, 338, 420, 509, 513, 520, 523, 1283

The median is the mean of the middle scores.

$$\text{Median} = \frac{509 + 513}{2}$$
$$= 511 \text{ cars}$$

20. The mode is the value that occurs most often.
The mode is 32.

22. The mode is the value that occurs most often.
There is no mode.

24. When the same value occurs more than once, the value must be multiplied by the number of times it occurs (weighted).

A good example of using the weighted mean is when finding grade point averages. It must be used because you have several *credits* with the same *grade value.*

26. The size to order is the mode. The mode is the size most worn by customers and it would be wise to order most hats in this size.

28.

Credits	Grade	Product
3	A = 4	12
3	B = 3	9
4	B = 3	12
2	C = 2	4
3	C = 2	6
15		43

$$\text{Grade Point Average} = \frac{43}{15}$$
$$\approx 2.866$$
$$\approx 2.87$$

INDUCTIVE AND DEDUCTIVE REASONING

2. 5, 8, 11, 14, 17, ...

Note that each number after the first is greater than the one it follows.

The difference between each pair of numbers is 3 so the next number is 17 + 3 = 20.

4. 3, 9, 7, 13, 11, ...

Find the difference between each pair.

$9 - 3 = 6$
$7 - 9 = -2$
$13 - 7 = 6$
$11 - 13 = -2$

Note that to obtain the next number, either 6 or −2 is added. To obtain the next number, 6 should be added. So, the next number is $11 + 6 = 17$.

6. 1, 4, 16, 64, ...

The pattern is

$$4^0 = 1$$
$$4^1 = 4$$
$$4^2 = 16$$
$$4^3 = 64$$

The next number is $4^4 = 256$.

To obtain the next number, multiply by 4.

8. 3, 6, 12, 24, 48, ...

The numbers are increasing. To obtain the next number, 2 is multiplied by the previous number. Thus the next number is (48)(2) = 96.

10. 6, 7, 9, 12, 16, ...

The pattern is add 1, add 2, add 3, and so on.

$$6 + 1 = 7$$
$$7 + 2 = 9$$
$$9 + 3 = 12$$
$$12 + 4 = 16$$

The next number is 16 + 5 = 21.

12. Since the third shape is like the first shape, a triangle, the fourth shape must be like the second shape, a circle. Since the first two figures contain an open circle, the fourth figure must also contain a solid circle like the third figure.

14. The first three shapes are unique. The fourth shape is the reverse of the first, and the fifth is the reverse of the second. Thus, the sixth will be the reverse of the third.

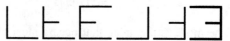

16.   All students are hard workers.
    All business majors are students.

∴ All business majors are hard workers.

The statement "All students are hard workers" is shown by a large circle that represents all people who are hard workers with a smaller circle inside that represents all students.

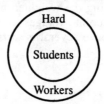

The statement "All business majors are students" is represented by adding a third circle representing business majors inside the circle representing students.

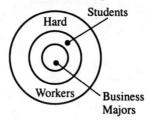

Since the circle representing business majors is completely inside the circle representing hard workers, the conclusion follows that:

    All business majors are hard workers.

18.   All boys ride bikes.

     All Americans ride bikes.

∴ All Americans are boys.

The statement "All boys ride bikes" is represented by a large circle representing bike riders and a smaller circle inside the large circle representing boys.

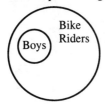

The statement "All Americans ride bikes" is represented by another circle inside the larger circle that represents Americans. (The circle for boys would overlap the one for Americans.)

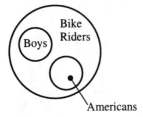

Since the circle representing Americans is not completely inside the circle representing boys, the following conclusion *does not follow* that:

All Americans are boys.

20. The 40 students in the class are represented by a large circle. The 30 students who take calculus and the 25 students who take physics are represented by circles inside the large circle, one for each subject. The circles overlap to show that 21 students take both calculus and physics.

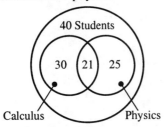

Since 21 students take calculus and physics and 30 students take calculus, (30 − 21), or 9 students take calculus but not physics. Since 25 students take physics, 34 (25 + 9) students take calculus, physics or both subjects. Therefore, (40 − 34), or 6 students take neither calculus nor physics.

22. Four cars—a Ford, a Buick, a Mercedes, and an Audi—are parked in 4 spaces.

1. The Ford is in the last space so write *Ford* in the last space of a diagram.

First	Second	Third	Last
			Ford

2. The Audi is next to the Ford, but not next to the Buick (Fact c). So write *Audi* next to Ford in the third space.

First	Second	Third	Last
		Audi	Ford

3. The Buick and Mercedes are next to each other. Since the Audi is not next to the Buick (Fact b), write *Mercedes*, in the second space and *Buick* in the first space.

First	Second	Third	Last
Buick	Mercedes	Audi	Ford

Therefore, the Buick is in the first space.